CONTENTS

Barn Owl *Tyto alba*

Editorial team
Editor • Guy Thomas
Consultant Editor • Richard West
Art Director • Heather Peters

Pricing experts
BB Stamps, Mark Bloxham, Packs &
Cards, Don Staddon, Rushstamps

This guide is produced by the team
behind Stamp Magazine.
www.stampmagazine.co.uk

Advertisement team
Manager • Jay Jones
Sales Executive • Rachel Hearn,
Sales Executive • Uty Rohrs
Production • Mike Blatchford

Publishers
IPC Media, Leon House,
233 High Street, Croydon,
Surrey CR9 1HZ.
Tel: 020 8726 8241.
Copyright: IPC Media Ltd, 2007

Distribution
Distributed to the news trade by
MarketForce. Tel: 020 7633 3300.
Distributed to the book trade by
Orca Book Services, Stanley House,
3 Fleets Lane, Poole, Dorset BH 15
3AJ. Tel 01202 665432.
Trade enquires: Chris Lynn.
Tel: 020 3148 3498.
Sales enquiries: Phil Richards.
Tel: 01299 402449.
magazinesales@ipcmedia.com

History of Britain Series

History of Britain Stamp Sheets

Designed by A G Bradbury and printed by Royal Mail.
For availability and prices please contact:

A G Bradbury 3 Link Rd, Stoneygate, Leicester   LE2 3RA
Tel: 0116 2705367   Mon-Fri: 8.30 - 1.30   **www.bfdc.co.uk**

BFDC.co.uk

Bonhams

tamps, Postcards and Cigarette Cards
onhams Stamp Department is a major
layer in the philatelic world. The
epartment's international presence,
eputation and knowledge of the market
ttracts buyers and sellers worldwide.

hams, established in 1793, embodies over 200 years of
rience and integrity. Its name is recognised worldwide
ughout all sectors of the fine art, antiques and collector's
et and it conducts over 7000 sales each year, more than
of its rivals worldwide.

name Bonhams has always represented family values and
onal commitment, a level of professionalism and service
olemented by genuinely close client relationships built up
many years.

Stamp Department

Stamp department is based at our Knightsbridge salerooms
ndon, where auctions are aimed principally at the
ctor's market. Our Stamp specialists have the combined
vledge of many years of experience in the field of philately
our experts specialise in providing advice, guidance and
ical help to philatelists around the world.

comprehensive auction schedule includes a diverse array of
We hold several major auctions each year, dealing with all
of the stamp market, ranging from complete collections
dividual rarities.

In addition to these sales we hold specialised auctions of
'Postcards and Cigarette Cards' where material ranges
from general collections to individual sets.

Enquiries
The Department
+44 (0) 20 7393 3890
stamps@bonhams.com

Illustrated:
1935 Silver Jubilee 2½d. Prussian blue.
Sold for £7,637.50 in a recent auction.

Bonhams
Montpelier Street
London SW7 1HH
+44 (0) 20 7393 3900
+44 (0) 20 7393 3905 fax
www.bonhams.com/stamps

WHY STAMPS ARE WORTH MONEY

It isn't always immediately obvious why some stamps are worth more than others. But here are the key factors in the British market

Working out how stamps become valuable isn't rocket science. Their value is largely linked to their rarity and their condition, although there are other variables too.

The Prussian Blue shade of the 1935 Silver Jubilee 2½d went on sale by mistake, creating one of Britain's great rarities

LOW NUMBERS

Some stamps are valuable today because not many survive, although there are few really scarce British stamps other than errors. More often, they are rare because comparatively few people bought them when they were in use.

Some of the Victorian era stamps had very high original face values, and only a few people could afford them. Examples include the 10/- and £1 values from the 1867-83 series, when the average pay was under £1 a week.

Recent examples are much fewer, but they do exist. For instance, the Welsh-language version of the Princess Diana presentation pack of 1998 can be classed as a modern rarity.

ERRORS

One major difference between stamps and other collectables is that mistakes can be priceless.

Printing errors include missing colours, missing or irregular perforations, inverted watermarks, inverted printings, double printings, dry printings and missing elements of artwork.

Although errors did occur prior to the reign of Elizabeth II, it was in the 1960s that their numbers exploded. More multicoloured stamps

High-value Victorian stamps such as this 1867-83 £1 can be rare because only a few people could afford to use them

were being issued at the time, so there was more chance of something going wrong.

In addition there have been a few occasions when limited numbers of stamps featuring design or colour shade errors have been sold in post offices by mistake, their rarity making them highly desirable.

Among the many Victorian stamps that are worth money are the so-called 'abnormals', printed from plates which were never put into regular use. There is also the Penny Red from plate 77, which at the time was regarded as a sub-standard printing but is now worth over £100,000.

In 2007, a 2006 Victoria Cross prestige stamp book with the first pane missing bronze and phosphor (and therefore without the Queen's head) sold at auction for over £8,000.

MARKET DEMAND

Naturally, stamps values vary with the level of demand in the market.

In recent years the British philatelic market has gone through a boom period, with higher prices paid at auctions, due to new rarities emerging, investors identifying stamps as a way to make

This 2006 Victoria Cross prestige stamp book pane, missing the Queen's head, makes the book worth over £8,000

money, and a scramble among collectors to obtain the highest quality material.

One of the key influences on this has been the online trading of stamps, both through dealers and through auction websites. Internet bidders have been forcing up the prices being paid for the most sought-after material. ∎

Printing errors can be spectacular, such as this 1965 Churchill Commemoration 4d missing black, so that the man himself fails to appear

WHERE TO BUY YOUR STAMPS

The traditional places where stamps are bought and sold still exist, but they've recently been joined by some new ones

The majority of British definitives and special issues can be purchased from any local post office for some months after their day of their issue or at least until stocks run out.

For booklets that are issued only in a certain area, regional or country stamps, presentation packs and stamp cards, you'll have to pay a visit one of the philatelic counters (or Post Shops), which are located only in the largest post offices.

You can save yourself a lot of hassle by signing up to one or other of the services provided by Royal Mail's Philatelic Bureau in Edinburgh. You can subscribe to receive all commemoratives and special issues, as singles or cylinder blocks or on first day covers, or order specific items from the monthly stock list.

For non-current stamp issues, there are many sources of material for collectors.

STARTING OFF
Many beginners get a tremendous boost to their collection by acquiring a bumper mixed packet of

Traditional stamp shops still exist, but they're less common than they once were

stamps, usually as a present.

At one time most stationers and newsagents carried extensive lines in packets of mixed stamps, from 50 to 1,000 all different, but sadly that method of retailing seems to have all but vanished. Some dealers specialise in the packet trade and can offer packets with up to 100,000 different stamps.

Once you become rather more experienced you might try a bag of kiloware, which is simply a mixture of unsorted, used stamps on paper, sold by weight. These can bulk up a collection quickly and might occasionally reveal some rarities.

SHOPS & FAIRS
There was a time when every British town had a stamp shop. Today many of these have closed. There are still many stamp dealers, but they do business by mail order or at fairs and exhibitions.

There's a monthly fair within easy reach of most collectors, and these gatherings give you the chance to shop around. To find fairs taking place near you, and dealers who specialise in your interests, check out the listings and adverts in the pages of *Stamp Magazine*.

There are five or six major stamp shows and exhibitions in the UK every year, the best known regulars being Stampex and Philatex in London. The major dealers and auction houses will be present, to sell and buy stamps.

AUCTIONS
Stamp auctions range from club sales, in which members can dispose of surplus material which will usually not be of huge value, to the great international sales, in which single lots can sell for thousands and even, rarely, millions of pounds.

Many collectors find major shows such as Stampex great places to find new material

They offer the opportunity to acquire everything from whole collections to individual rarities, and could well be the only realistic way to fill holes in really specialist collections.

You can simply peruse the sale catalogue and put in bids by post. But it is preferable to take advantage of a prior viewing of the material, so you can check its quality at first hand, and to attend the sale itself in person, so you can see who you are bidding against.

If you haven't bought at an auction before, go along to a few and observe how they are conducted before you take part in bidding. You might be surprised at the pace at which lots go under the hammer.

When bidding, make up your mind in advance how much an item is worth to you. You can pick up terrific bargains at auction, but some buyers get carried away and end up paying more than a stamp is really worth.

The advertisement pages and the monthly What's On listing in *Stamp Magazine* will tell you when auctions are coming up.

WEBSITES

The internet has made it easier than ever to buy philatelic material from around the world. Dealers and private collectors are increasingly using onine auction sites such as eBay.

The snag is that you don't get the chance to view a stamp in person. But often you do get the benefit of seeing a high-quality enlarged image on screen, and you can browse through lists at your leisure.

The well established sites offer some security for buyers. eBay's 'feedback' system gives you confidence that a seller is trustworthy, and its PayPal banking system makes transactions safe and easy. ∎

Auction websites are now an established way of buying and selling stamps

They think it's all over.

...IT IS NOW!!

and usually in less time than it took to win the Cup

...but for some it's never over

OUR CLIENTS

WORLDWIDE

have a **UNIVERSAL** range of **COLLECTING INTEREST** which allows us to offer you **COMPLETELY COST FREE** a NO OBLIGATION VALUATION on virtually ANYTHING

We are also seeking to buy, both for auction or private treaty, particularly decent GB & Commonwealth, covers & postcards, philatelic literature, coins & banknotes, broken or intact jewellery, medals and militaria.

Whether you're selling or buying our regular monthly auctions usually take just 90 minutes.

at The Bury Lodge Hotel, London Stansted Airport

for priority catalogue requests, please telephone: 01279 758854

or, if you prefer, write to us at
Dept.BSMV., Latchmore Bank Farmhouse,
Little Hallingbury, Bishop's Stortford,
Hertfordshire CM22 7PJ

email: johnfauld@aol.com
rob.myers@btinternet.com

allianceauctions.com

Around 1500 lot sales with 100s of mixed lots and collections.

Colour catalogue sent free.

Auctions at Stansted - just 2 minutes from M11, 5 minutes from airport, 40 minutes from London.

Viewing and sale at comfortable hotel.

Convenient evening sales.

Fast turnaround - monthly sales, paid six weeks after.

(and no, for everyone who spotted it, of course it's not right)

John Auld

PTS ADA APS

Incorporating
Express Stamp Auctions
founded in 1966

Alliance AUCTIONS

A to Z OF PHILATELIC TERMINOLOGY

Here's an easy-to-understand alphabetical guide to stamp collecting jargon, from simple concepts to complex printing processes

AEROGRAMME

A specially printed, ready stamped letter sheet on lightweight paper, which is intended for air mail use. It is also known as an air letter.

AIR MAIL

Any item of post that is sent to its destination by air.

ALBINO

A colourless impression that is usually produced in embossing.

ALPHABET LETTERS

The lettering printed in the corners of Queen Victoria stamps from 1840-1887 to make forgery difficult.

Each stamp in a sheet had a unique combination of letters, with those in the top row lettered AA, AB, AC, and so on, and those in the second row BA, BB, BC and so on, this pattern continuing throughout the sheet.

Originally these letters appeared in the lower corners only, but later they appeared in the top corners too, in reverse order.

FIRST DAY COVER, for the 2006 Ice Age Animals set of five stamps

ARROWS

The margins of many sheets of stamps feature arrows, intended to help post office clerks to divide the sheets into sections.

BACKSTAMP

A postmark on the back of an envelope, usually applied in transit or on arrival.

BANTAM

A stamp printed in a reduced size.

BISECT

A stamp cut in half (normally diagonally) to create two stamps, each of half the usual value. For example, 2d stamps may be bisected to meet a 1d postal rate, in times of shortage.

BLIND PERFORATION

Perforation in which the stamp paper is merely dented because the perforating machine has blunt teeth.

BLOCK

Four or more stamps still joined together.

BOOKLET

A small book containing one or more panes of stamps within a card cover. Today's GB booklets fall into two main types: definitive booklets, which usually contain standard 1st class or 2nd class stamps, and prestige stamp books, which are issued several times a year and include a mixture of definitives and commemoratives, with historical or other background information.

CACHET

A mark, other than the postmark, applied to cards and covers. This is often private or unofficial in nature, with a commemorative purpose.

CANCELLATION

The original term for the postmark applied to a stamp on an envelope or card, to prevent re-use.

CANCELLED TO ORDER (CTO)

Postmarked in bulk, usually for sale to collectors on first day covers rather than for actual use in the post.

OFFICIAL STAMP, with an IR overprint

REGIONAL STAMP, for Scotland

MALTESE CROSS, on a Penny Red

WILDING, an early QEII definitive

CHALK-SURFACED PAPER
Paper with a security coating to prevent a cancellation being cleaned off so that a stamp can be re-used.

CHANGELING
A stamp whose colour has altered through immersion in water or exposure to sunlight.

CHARITY STAMPS
Stamps issued to support a charity, usually sold with a surcharge above their postal face value.

COILS
Stamps issued in reels (usually for sale from vending machines), which can therefore be collected in strips. They may be imperforate on two opposite sides or have sideways watermarks.

COLOUR TRIALS
Proofs produced in various colours prior to the issue of a stamp, to determine the most suitable colour for it.

COMB PERFORATION
Perforation applied to three sides of a stamp at a single stroke, with the fourth side being perforated by the following stroke. This technique is aimed at providing perforations which meet perfectly at the corners.

COMPOUND PERFORATION
Perforation which has different gauges on different sides of a stamp.

CONTROL NUMBERS
Letters and numerals printed in the sheet margins of British stamps from 1881-1947 for accounting purposes. A letter indicates which part of the year the stamps were printed, and the number represents the last two digits of the year.

CORNER BLOCK
Four or more stamps still joined together from the corner of the sheet, with margins.

COVER
Envelope or wrapper with stamps affixed or pre-printed.

CYLINDER BLOCK
Four or more stamps still joined together, with the cylinder numbers showing in the margin.

CYLINDER NUMBERS
Tiny numerals printed in the sheet margin, for security reasons, denoting the cylinder from which it was printed. There is usually one number for each colour in which the stamp is printed, appearing in the respective colour.

DEFINITIVES
Stamps in general use over a period of years, as opposed to commemoratives or 'special stamps', which have a limited period on sale.

DIE
The piece of soft steel onto which the design of recess (intaglio) printed stamps has to be engraved.

DIE PROOF
A proof impression taken from the die to check that it is satisfactory.

DOCTOR BLADE
The blade used to wipe off excess ink from the cylinder in photogravure printing.

DOCTOR BLADE VARIETY
A streak of ink appearing across a printed sheet of stamps, after a build-up of dust forces the doctor blade away from the cylinder for a moment.

STAMP CARD, reproducing the enlarged image of a 1999 stamp

DUMB CANCELLATION
Postmark with no inscription or identifying mark, for example applied to naval mail in wartime for security reasons.

DUTY PLATE
Plate used to print the 'duty' (value) on stamps in conjunction with the key plate. A different duty plate is used for each different denomination in stamps sharing a common design.

EMBOSSING
A portion of a stamp design that has a relief or raised impression. This is achieved by placing the paper between male (relief) and female (recess) dies during the printing process.

ERROR
Stamp deviating from the normal in some respect, for example with missing, shifted or inverted colours or perforations, or mistakes in the design. Errors that are spotted during checks at the printing stage should be destroyed, but some slip though the net and are sold at post offices.

ESSAY
Preliminary design for a stamp, which might or might not subsequently be issued.

FAKE
A genuine stamp that has been tampered with in some way in an attempt to make it more valuable, usually by forging an overprint or removing a cancellation.

FISCAL
Stamp intended for fiscal or revenue purposes, although possibly authorised for postal use.

FIRST DAY COVER (FDC)
Souvenir envelope bearing stamps postmarked on

their first day of issue. In modern times, envelopes are designed specifically to match a set of stamps, and pictorial handstamps are available to suit the theme, both from Royal Mail and from private providers.

FLAW
A defect in printing, resulting in a constant blemish on the same stamp in every sheet.

FRANK
A mark or label that indicates that mail is transmitted free of postage. This is widely used by government departments and armed forces.

GRAPHITE LINES
Black lines incorporated into the back of some stamps between 1957 and 1959, which could be recognised by experimental electronic sorting machines.

GUM
The adhesive on the back of a stamp. On early issues this was a natural product, gum arabic, which has a shiny appearance. On later issues it was a synthetic product, polyvinyl alcohol (PVA), which is colourless but usually given a yellow tinge by printers; with dextrin added, this is known as PVAD, and has a bluish tinge.

GUTTER
The white central margin separating two panes of stamps on sheets printed by Harrison & Sons' Jumelle printing press. The machine was capable of printing in several colours and perforating in one operation, but this layout of sheets was necessary because the circumference of the printing and perforating cylinders differed.

GUTTER PAIR
Two stamps from adjoining panes, with a gutter in the middle.

IMPERFORATE
Stamps printed on sheets without perforations, and needing to be cut apart with scissors. Early Victorian stamps were imperforate before the concept of perforating them became a practical

reality. Stamps imperforate on one or more adjoining sides could be from booklets; those imperforate on opposite sides will be from coils.

IMPRIMATUR
The first sheet of stamps off the printing press, marked to indicate that it has been approved. All imprimatur sheets should have been retained by the Post Office (now Royal Mail), but some have 'escaped' into the hands of collectors.

IMPRINT
Inscription in a sheet margin giving the printer's name or logo, the date of printing and sometimes other details.

INTAGLIO PRINTING
A printing process, also known as 'recess', which requires the design of the stamp to be engraved into the printing cylinder. When the ink is applied, it fills the recesses and any excess ink is wiped away. On contact with the paper, the design is transferred as the ink leaves the recesses. Intaglio stamps can be identified from the way the ink parts of the design feel raised when you run a finger over them.

INVERT
A stamp with part of the design upside-down in relation to the rest.

BOOKLETS, including Britain's earliest

PRESENTATION PACK, of the 1978 Energy stamps

IVORY HEAD

An outline of the portrait of Queen Victoria which can be seen on the backs of certain stamps printed on blued paper.

JUBILEE LINE

A line of printer's rule reinforcing the edge of the printing plate, appearing as a bar of colour at the foot of the sheet. It is so-named because it first appeared on the 'Jubilee' issue of 1887.

KEY PLATE

A plate that provides the main part of a stamp design (usually the sovereign's head and border) where two separate printings are required, for example in a two-colour stamp. The key plate is used in conjunction with different duty plates, so the same basic design can be reproduced with different values.

KILOWARE

Any mixture of stamps sold by weight. Originally the term applied to those sold in sealed one-kilogramme bags of stamps on paper.

LINE PERFORATION

A form of perforation in which the horizontal and vertical perforations are applied by separate processes. This frequently results in ragged edges at the corners of stamps.

LITHOGRAPHIC PRINTING

A printing process in which the design appears as a number of dots, as in photogravure printing, but with the dots differing in size. The larger the dot, the deeper the colour. A lithographed stamp can be differentiated from a photogravure stamp by examining any lettering, which will appear solid.

LOCAL

A stamp (or more correctly a 'label') whose validity is restricted to a limited local area, and which cannot be used on national or international mail. For example, labels may be attached to items covering carriage from offshore islands to the mainland before entering the national postal system; onward postage must be paid by the requisite national or international stamps.

MACHIN

British definitive stamp design featuring a profile of Queen Elizabeth II's head, in use for all low-value issues since 1967. The name comes from the designer of the profile, Arnold Machin.

MALTESE CROSS

The cancellation used for the first British stamps, from 1840 to 1844. The name comes from its shape.

METER MARK

A mark applied by a meter to indicate pre-payment of postage. This usually consists of an indicium (country name and value), a date and a slogan advertising a firm or organisation.

MINIATURE SHEET

A small sheet containing a single stamp or a small group of stamps, often with broad decorative margins. Some modern stamps are issued only in a miniature sheet and in no other format.

MINT

Unused stamp with its full, original gum intact. Collectors will generally prefer 'unmounted mint', with the gum undisturbed by any mounting.

CONTROL NUMBER & JUBILEE LINE, on a George V 6d

ERROR, from 1965, with the Post Office Tower missing

OBLITERATION

Original term for the postmarking of stamps to prevent their re-use.

OFFICIAL

A stamp produced solely for the use of government departments.

OVERPRINT

An additional printing applied to a stamp after the original printing, to convert it to some other purpose, denote a surcharge or commemorate a current event.

PANE

Originally this term meant a portion of a sheet divided by gutters, but it is now also applied to a block of stamps issued in a booklet.

PERFIN

An abbreviation for 'perforated initial'. Some stamps have been perforated with the initials of firms or government departments as a security measure to prevent pilferage or improper use.

PERFORATION

Tiny circles of paper punched out by machine between stamps on a sheet, to make it easier to separate them. Different printings and varieties can sometimes be identified by a difference in the style or number of their perforations.

PHOSPHOR BANDS

Almost invisible stripes of phosphor coating applied to the face of modern stamps to facilitate electronic sorting.

PHOTOGRAVURE PRINTING

A printing process, also known as 'gravure', in which the printing cylinder consists of a large number of very small cells, each containing ink, with the depth of the cell determining how dark the colour will look. The printed stamp appears as a series of minute dots of equal size.

PLATE

Flat or curved piece of metal from which stamps are printed.

PLATE NUMBERS

The cylinder numbers of recess (intaglio) printed stamps are often referrred to as 'plate numbers'. With many Queen Victoria stamps, these were incorporated into the design of the stamp.

POSTAGE DUE

Label denoting the amount of postage to be recovered from the addressee, on unpaid or underpaid mail. Sometimes called a 'to pay' label.

POSTAGE PAID IMPRESSION (PPI)

Mark printed or handstruck on bulk postings denoting prepayment of postage.

POSTAL STATIONERY

Envelope or postcard that is sold ready-stamped to the required basic postal rate, usually as part of its design.

PRESENTATION PACK

A set of stamps mounted within a black card and contained in a folder which gives background details of the issue. The first proper example was made available with the Shakespeare Festival issue of 1964, although the 1960 prepackagings of certain definitives are now regarded as presentation packs by collectors.

PRESS SHEET

Printed sheet of miniature sheets, which is sold to collectors in its entirety rather than being cut up into separate items.

PROVISIONAL

A stamp temporarily overprinted or surcharged to meet a shortage of regular issues.

RE-ENTRY

Part of an intaglio printing plate which is re-engraved or re-entered by the transfer roller. This can usually be detected by a slight doubling of the lines.

REGIONAL

Definitive issued in deference to a specific region of the UK, and depicting appropriate regional symbols, but valid for postage throughout the nation. More recent examples for England, Wales, Scotland and Northern Ireland are known as 'country' definitives.

REPRINT

A stamp printed from the original plate, but long after the issue has ceased. This is usually distinguishable from the original by a difference on colour, paper or watermark.

RETOUCH

A repair to a letterpress (surface printing) plate or photogravure cylinder to correct a flaw.

ROULETTE

A form of separation effected using serrated instruments to produce cuts in the paper.

SELF-ADHESIVE

A stamp that is attached to a backing paper and, when peeled off, has sticky adhesive on the back that is sufficient to stick it to an envelope with no wetting agent required.

SE-TENANT

The term applied to two or more stamps of different designs printed side by side on a sheet.

SMARTSTAMPS

A modern service whereby small businesses can order their own special postal barcodes online, for a monthly or annual fee, to save them having to go to post offices to buy stamps. Businesses can include their own logos within the design.

SMILERS

A modern service whereby an individual can buy sheets of stamps with se-tenant customised labels bearing an image of his choice. Where these are supplied with labels chosen by Royal Mail, they are known as Smilers generic sheets.

SPECIAL STAMPS

Limited-lifespan stamps issued in addition to the standard definitives, often to commemorate a particular event or anniversary. In recent times Royal Mail has released 10 or 11 sets each year.

MINIATURE SHEET, accompanying the 1989 Industrial Archaeology issue

SPECIMEN

Overprint on a stamp printed for record or publicity purposes, signifying that it has no postal validity.

STAMP CARD

A postcard (also known as a PHQ card) issued by Royal Mail reproducing an enlarged image of a new stamp.

SURCHARGE

An overprint that alters the face value of a stamp.

SURFACE PRINTING

A printing process, also known as 'typography' or 'letterpress', in which the design to be printed stands proud of the surface of the cylinder.

The ink is applied only to the raised parts, so only the design is printed on contact with the paper.

TÊTE-BÊCHE

French term denoting se-tenant stamps which are upside-down in relation to each other.

TRAFFIC LIGHTS

The solid circles of colour which appear in the margins of many sheets of stamps, as a check to prove that all colours have been printed.

TRAINING LABEL

Stamp found with thick black bars on the front of it, which has probably been used at a Post Office training school. The bars render the stamp invalid for postage.

THEMATIC

A form of philately which involves collecting all relevant philatelic material surrounding a chosen theme. Among the most popular themes are elements of transport, wildlife and sport.

UNDERPRINT

A motif printed on the gummed side of a stamp, usually from a booklet, to indicate that it has been sold at a discount off face value. Typically, this is the letter 'D' or a star pattern.

USED

A stamp that has performed its postal function and has had a cancellation applied. Collectors will prefer a neat and clear cancellation, which can easily be read and doesn't obscure too much of the stamp design.

VARIETY

Any stamp which varies from the norm, in shade, paper, perforation, watermark, and so on. A variety differs from an error in that it usually applies to small corrections that are made deliberately, and affect every sheet printed.

VENDING MACHINE LABEL

Stamp of 1984-85 (also widely known as a Frama label), whose denomination was printed by a machine on insertion of a suitable value in coins.

VIGNETTE

The central pictorial portion of a stamp design.

WATERMARK

A translucent impression used as a security device in stamp printing paper, usually visible only when held up to the light.

WILDING

British definitive stamp featuring a bust of Queen Elizabeth II, in use from 1952-1967. The name comes from that of the photographer, Dorothy Wilding. ∎

CYLINDER BLOCK, with cylinder numbers in the left margin, traffic lights in the right

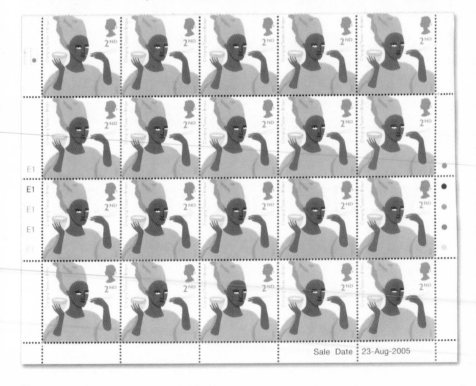

HARMERS

ESTABLISHED 1918
Philatelic Auctioneers, Experts and Valuers

Fine Great Britain at Auction for ninety years

When looking for quality look at Harmers. Where quality matters.

 Harmers, No. 11, 111 Power Road, Chiswick, London W4 5PY
Tel: 020 8747 6100   Fax: 020 8996 0649
auctions@harmers.demon.co.uk   www.harmers.com

LOOKING AFTER YOUR COLLECTION

Stamps are easy to damage, so it's vitally important to look after your investment. Here are some top tips on how to care for your collection

Most collectors spend a great deal of time and money on compiling their collection, and are justifiably proud of it. However, a few are careless about protecting it, which will allow it to deteriorate.

Follow a few basic rules and you should ensure that your stamps are well kept and remain a stunning display and a good investment.

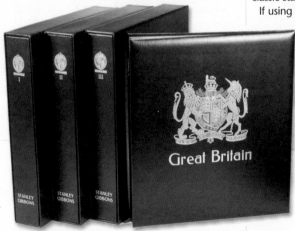

HANDLING

Always handle any philatelic material with tweezers. But make sure you use proper stamp tweezers, with blunt prongs, not those intended for other purposes such as plucking eyebrows!

If you are removing used stamps from paper, do not be in too much of a hurry. Float them on water until they slide easily off the piece, without being forced, and then dry them with care.

If mounting them using hinges, buy good quality hinges and apply as little moisture as possible to the part of the hinge that affixes to the stamp. The hinge should be placed just below the perforations, never over them.

Remember that applying hinges could adversely affect the value of a stamp, especially an unused classic stamp.

If using protective mounts, again buy good quality ones. Be very careful as you cut the mount to fit the stamp.

Remember that it is beneficial for a stamp to be removed from its mount from time to time.

A choice of dedicated GB albums is available for your collection

STORAGE

If you have stamps waiting to be arranged on exhibition sheets or mounted on album pages, the best way to keep them safe is in a stockbook, which may work as a long-term or short-term 'holding album'.

As always, look for quality when you buy a stockbook. Interleaving between the pages will protect the stamps against damage caused by contact with each other.

Keep stockbooks in an upright position, turning over the pages from time to time. Do not overfill them, as this may cause the pages to distort, and be careful as you insert or remove items; it is surprisingly easy to fold over the corner

perforations of a stamp as you slip it within the holding strips.

Remember that the top edge of poor or distorted strips could cause damage to your stamps, leaving a mark on them, so check the strips carefully.

Most collectors use stamp albums as a permanent home for their stamps. A range of dedicated album and album pages is available for GB collections, with reserved spaces not only for each different issue but often for printing, watermark and shade varieties, and so on.

When buying a stamp album, check that it meets the requirements of your collection and opt for the highest quality you can afford. Nothing looks worse than a bulging album

Always use proper philatelic tweezers when handling your stamps

caused by the leaves not being strong enough to hold the material.

Avoid over-filling albums and keep them upright, turning over the leaves from time to time to give them some air.

Covers, miniature sheets, presentation packs, booklets and blocks do not always fit easily into albums. Many collectors store them in simple boxes such as shoe boxes.

Wherever your collection is kept, avoid extremes of heat, light and humidity. Take immediate action if you have even the remotest suspicion of dampness or discoloration. ■

Is Your Precious Collection Really Safe?

10 Introduc Disc

Varying size collectables ALL in One single Archival Binder Album

Lighthouse

hawid

ARCHIVA
ACID FREE
USED BY MUSEUMS

Coins | Bank Notes

arrowfile
For all your Archival Storage requirements

Stamps | Photos

Postcards

File Box

Stock Books . Stock Cards . Magnifiers . Mounts . Tongs . Coin Storage & Accessori

PROTECT — *"My collection is now protected against dust, dirt and scratches. I no longer need c protectors or interleaves as every stamp is protected within each pocket."* Mrs Busb

ORGANISE — *"I can simply add a page to the appropriate section of my collection, something I couldn't do with ordinary stamp stock books. I can also organise and re-organise collection, without having to tackle fiddly stamp hinges."* Mr Steveson

FLEXIBLE — *"Thank you – Whatever size and shape of my stamps, I still have a matching lib which I can add to as my collection grows."* Ms Ramfield

ACCESS — *"Using Arrowfile indexes and page numbers, its takes me minutes to organise and seconds to find!"* Mrs Jarvis

Claim Your 10% Introductory Discount
visit www.arrowfile.com/BSM108
For our latest Catalogue please ring Freefone Number 0800 027 5363

HOW TO USE THIS BOOK

The prices we quote and the abbreviations we use

This guide aims to offer independent and accurate price information about all GB stamps issued between 1840 and 2007. It quotes not the inflated prices that some dealers and catalogue publishers might hope to achieve, but accurate market prices to help you pinpoint the exact worth of your collection.

The publisher of *British Stamp Market Values* is not affiliated to any dealer.

ABBREVIATIONS

The following abbreviations are used:

Des: designer
Perf: perforation
Wmk: watermark

GENERAL NOTES

■ Unused prices assume stamps are se-tenant where applicable, but used prices do not.

■ Used prices quoted are for 'fine used, with full perforations or reasonable margins as applicable, and with a light Duplex cancellation prior to 1880 or a clear, circular steel datestamp after 1880.

■ When a dash (–) appears in a price column it means that the stamp doesn't exist in that particular state, or that it is impracticable to price it.

■ Due to the proliferation of modern GB special stamps, the price for a full set may be given instead of individual prices.

THE EXPERTS WHO PROVIDED THE PRICINGS IN THIS GUIDE

PACKS & CARDS

Oaklands House, Reading Road North, Fleet, Hampshire GU51 4AB

Packs & Cards specialises in presentation packs and PHQ cards. Founded in 2000, it sells by mail order, from its website and via an eBay shop. It also supplies more unusual items such as Post Office posters (grille cards) and stamp photographs used as promotional items.

RUSHSTAMPS

PO Box 1, Lyndhurst, Hampshire SO43 7PP

Rushstamps was founded by 1958 by Allan Grant when he left school. Primarily dealing in Great Britain, it publishes a bulging catalogue which offers a very wide range of material and is available upon request.

BB STAMPS

PO Box 6277, Overton, Basingstoke, Hampshire RG25 3RN

Run by Brian Bayford, BB Stamps deals in British stamps from Queen Victoria to the Wildings.

MARK BLOXHAM

PO Box 204, Morpeth, Northumberland NE61 9AA

Mark Bloxham is a specialist in classic British stamps at the top end of the market.

DON STADDON

Stamp Magazine contributor

Don Staddon is one of the leading authorities on Machins.

The Essential Guide
To The Line Engraved 1840 To 1864
1d & 2d Stars

For each plate used, Dr Statham analyses its HISTORY, ALIGNMENT, CHARACTERISTICS, CHECK LETTERS, DESCRIPTION, DATES, QUANTITIES, IMPRIMATURS and gives detailed listings of its VARIETIES and an aid to PLATING. The impetus for this book came from the frustration in his early plating days with the information then published. The availability and access to the new information, material and original documents has enabled previous data to be checked and amended where necessary. Many THOUSANDS of NEW VARIETIES have been listed for the first time, following Dr. Statham's meticulous research and process of double-checking. It is intended that virtually EVERY VARIETY is ILLUSTRATED - all drawn by Dr. Statham.

Dr. Statham hoped that his publication would enable other collectors, both specialist and beginners alike, to derive the same pleasure that he has had over the years in collecting these issues. As the scope of the book is so large, it has been published in several parts and with the publication of Volume 18, is now complete.

Volume 1	Introduction	Volume 10	Plating Summary covering Plates..........132-177
Volume 2	The One Penny Value - Die 1 Plates............1-11	Volume 11	The One Penny Value - Plates.. 178-204, R1 to R6
Volume 3	The One Penny Value - Die 1 Plates.........12-56	Volume 12	Plating Summary covering.....178-204, R1 to R6
Volume 4	Plating Summary covering all	Volume 13	The One Penny Value - Die 2 Plates 1-21
	the red Plates from 1-56	Volume 14	Plating Summary covering plates 1-21
Volume 5	The One Penny Value - Die 1 Plates.........57-87	Volume 15	The One Penny Value Die 2 Plates 22-49
Volume 6	Plating Summary covering Plates................57-87	Volume 16	The One Penny Value Die 2 Plates 50-68
Volume 7	The One Penny Value - Die 1 Plates.......88-131	Volume 17	Plating Summary Plates.............22-68. R15-R17
Volume 8	Plating Summary covering Plates.............88-131	Volume 18	The Two Penny Value Plates 1-6
Volume 9	The One Penny Value - Die 1 Plates 132-177		Including Addenda and Corringenda to the whole series

Sets of Volumes 5&6, 7&8, 9&10, 11&12, 13&14 each in an attractive
Presentation Box available individually, £100 each. Volumes 15,16 & 17 in Presentation Box £150.
Full set of Volumes 5 to 18, each section in Presentation Box, a few only £750. Prices plus postage and packing.

We Specialise in the Line Engraved 1840 To 1864 1d & 2d SG1 to SG42

We have good stocks of IMPERFS, PERFS & PLATES, both UNPLATED and PLATED including the RARE PLATES 175, 176 and 177 IMPERF with R.P.S. certificates as well as The GARDINER-HILL Collection of the First Perforated Issue and INVERTED WMKS from the whole range.

Reflecting our COMPREHENSIVE stocks of GB, QV to KGVI They include our specialist areas mentioned above as well as:-
1) SG 43/44 1d RED PLATES with CDS postmarks
2) Queen Victoria Surface-Printed to KGVI CDS & mint
3) GREAT BRITAIN USED ABROAD

LISTS   4) INDIVIDUALLY PLATED 1d RED IMPERFS & STARS   **LISTS**

5) A RARE, UNUSUAL and DIFFICULT-TO-FIND section
ALL STAMPS ARE ILLUSTRATED

Website:
www.ericpaul.co.uk

Email: ericsyrett@ericpaulltd.fsnet.co.uk

Eric Paul Ltd.

PO BOX 44, MARPLE
CHESHIRE SK6 7EE

Tel No. 0161 427 2101
Fax No. 0161 427 6386
Postal Only

VISA

Members: P.T.S.   M.&D.P.T.A.   G.B.P.S.   A.D.P.S.

QUEEN VICTORIA

For this reign prices are given for lightly mounted unused (left) and fine used (right). The exception is for the 1840-1841 imperforate stamps, where fine used prices are subdivided into examples with four margins (centre) and three margins (right).

Take care when buying unmounted mint because there are known cases of regumming.

1d black

■ 1840, May 6. Penny Black

Engraved by Charles and Frederick Heath. Printed in recess by Perkins, Bacon, Wmk: Small crowns, Imperforate. Letters in lower corners only.

1d black	£7,500	£200	78.00
1d intense black	£8,500	£225	90.00
1d grey black	£8,000	£250	90.00
Plate 1a	£10,000	£275	90.00
Plate 1b	£7,500	£200	80.00
Plate 2	£7,500	£200	80.00
Plate 3	£9,000	£225	85.00
Plate 4	£7,500	£200	80.00
Plate 5	£7,500	£200	80.00
Plate 6	£7,500	£200	80.00
Plate 7	£8,000	£240	90.00
Plate 8	£9,000	£275	95.00
Plate 9	£9,500	£325	£125
Plate 10	£22,000	£600	£175
Plate 11	£14,000	£3,500	£750
Wmk inverted	£25,000	£1,400	£295
Bleute paper	£12,500	£375	95.00
Red Maltese cross cancellation	-	£225	90.00
Black Maltese cross cancellation	-	£200	78.00
Blue Maltese cross cancellation	-	£5,000	£1,400
Magenta Maltese cross cancellation	-	£1,950	£400
Ruby Maltese cross cancellation	-	£750	£225
Violet Maltese cross cancellation	-	£9,000	£1,750
Number in cross (1-12)	-	£6,500	£1,500
Penny Post cancellation only	-	£2,600	£600
Town datestamp only	-	£2,750	£600
1844 cancellation	-	£1,000	£175

2d blue, 1840

■ 1840, May 8. Twopenny Blue

Engraved by Charles and Frederick Heath. Printed in recess by Perkins, Bacon, Wmk: Small crowns, Imperforate. Letters in lower corners only.

2d blue	£16,000	£500	£140
2d deep full blue	£22,000	£600	£170
2d pale blue	£17,000	£550	£150
Plate 1	£16,000	£500	£140
Plate 2	£22,000	£600	£170
Wmk Inverted	£50,000	£2,500	£850
Red Maltese cross cancel (Plate 1)	-	£550	£150
Red Maltese cross cancel (Plate 2)	-	£1,000	£225
Black Maltese cross cancellation	-	£500	£140
Blue Maltese cross cancellations	-	£6,000	£1,250
Magenta Maltese cross cancellation	-	£4,000	£850
Ruby Maltese cross cancellation	-	£2,000	£500
Number in cross (1-12)	-	£6,500	£1,200
Penny Post cancellation only	-	£5,000	£1,200
Town datestamp only	-	£3,750	£800
1844 cancellation	-	£1,250	£250

1d red, 1841

■ 1841, February 10. Penny Red

Engraved by Charles and Frederick Heath. Printed in recess by Perkins, Bacon, Wmk: Small crowns, Imperforate. Letters in lower corners only.

1d red brown	£275	9.00	3.00
1d deep red brown	£550	15.00	4.00
1d orange brown	£1,200	£120	12.00
1d lake red	£3,500	£550	£100
Plate 1b	£15,000	£225	40.00
Plate 2	£8,000	£175	25.00
Plate 5	£2,950	£150	20.00
Plate 8	£2,500	90.00	20.00
Plate 9	£2,500	90.00	20.00
Plate 10	£1,750	90.00	20.00
Plate 11	£2,500	75.00	15.00
Wmk inverted	£3,000	£250	75.00
Lavender Paper	£800	£150	40.00
Red Maltese cross cancellation	-	£3,850	£875
Black Maltese cross cancellation	-	40.00	6.00
Blue Maltese cross cancellation	-	£375	75.00
Green Maltese cross cancellation	-	£6,000	£1,000
Violet Maltese cross cancellation	-	£7,000	£1,500
Number in cross (1-12)	-	95.00	22.50
Penny Post cancellation only	-	£700	£125
Black town datestamp only	-	£300	95.00

Blue town datestamp only	-	£1,200	£275
Green town datestamp only	-	£2,750	£650
Black 1844 cancellation	-	9.00	3.00
Blue 1844 cancellation	-	£100	25.00
Green 1844 cancellation	-	£1,250	£250
Red 1844 cancellation	-	£7,500	£1,750
Violet 1844 cancellation	-	£2,500	£600
B blank error	-	£25,000	£7,000

2d blue, 1841

■ 1841, March 13. Twopenny Blue

Engraved by Charles and Frederick Heath. Printed in recess by Perkins, Bacon, Wmk: Small crowns, Imperforate. Letters in lower corners only. White lines added to design.

2d blue	£3,000	50.00	12.00
2d pale blue	£3,200	55.00	12.00
2d deep full blue	£4,000	70.00	15.00
2d violet (lavender paper)	£16,500	£950	£175
Plate 3	£3,000	60.00	12.00
Plate 4	£3,500	50.00	12.00
Wmk inverted	£7,500	£400	£125
Black Maltese cross cancellation	-	£150	22.50
Blue Maltese cross cancellation	-	£2,250	£400
Number in cross (1-12)	-	£250	60.00
Black town datestamp only	-	£1,000	£275
Blue town datestamp only	-	£2,500	£700
Black 1844 cancellation	-	50.00	12.00
Blue 1844 cancellation	-	£475	£100
Green 1844 cancellation	-	£2,750	£750
Red 1844 cancellation	-	£17,500	£3,500

■ 1854

As above but perf: 16

1d red-brown (February 1854)	£195	12.00
2d blue (March 1, 1854)	£2,100	60.00

■ 1855

As above but perf: 14.

1d red-brown (January 1855)	£450	45.00
2d blue (March 4, 1855)	£6,000	£160

■ 1855

As above but wmk. Large crown and perf: 16

1d red-brown (May 15, 1855)	£700	65.00
2d blue (July 20, 1855)	£7,000	£230

■ 1855

As above but perf: 14

1d red-brown (August 18, 1855)	£160	8.00
2d blue (July 20, 1855)	£1,600	30.00

■ 1858-1870

As above with wmk: 'half penny' extending over three stamps (½d) or Large Crowns (1d, 1½d, 2d). Perf: 14 but letters in all four corners. These plates have the number included in the design of the stamps.

½d rose-red

½d rose-red (October 1, 1870)	75.00	10.00
Plate 1	£180	50.00
Plate 3	£120	25.00
Plate 4	£100	18.00
Plate 5	75.00	10.00
Plate 6	80.00	10.00
Plate 8	£225	60.00
Plate 9	£3,250	£550
Plate 10	85.00	10.00
Plate 11	80.00	10.00
Plate 12	80.00	10.00
Plate 13	80.00	10.00
Plate 14	80.00	10.00
Plate 15	£115	24.00
Plate 19	£140	28.00
Plate 20	£200	50.00

1d rose-red

1d rose-red (April 1, 1864)	12.00	1.50
Plate 71	22.00	2.00
Plate 72	27.00	2.50
Plate 73	24.00	2.00
Plate 74	25.00	1.50
Plate 76	25.00	1.50
Plate 77	-	-
Plate 78	45.00	1.50
Plate 79	22.00	1.50
Plate 80	30.00	1.50
Plate 81	35.00	1.50
Plate 82	85.00	2.75
Plate 83	£110	6.00
Plate 84	40.00	1.60
Plate 85	27.00	1.60
Plate 86	35.00	2.75
Plate 87	22.00	1.50
Plate 88	£150	7.00
Plate 89	25.00	1.50

GB AT SANDAFAYRE

WE OFFER **THOUSANDS OF ITEMS AND COLLECTIONS EVERY WEEK**
IN OUR EXCITING **MAIL-SALE CATALOGUES** AND ON OUR WEBSITE.

There's something for everyone with lots priced from £15 to £15,000.

We've got it all, whatever your interest, including GB, Commonwealth, USA, Latin America,
Old and 'New' Europe and the many lands of Asia. Whether it's single items, starter collections
or medal winners, sorter cartons or entire estates you'll find it at Sandafayre.

Send the coupon today for your **FREE** introductory mail-sale
catalogues or access our online sales at: **www.sandafayre.com**

SANDAFAYRE
THE WORLD'S MOST EXCITING STAMP SALES

SANDAFAYRE LTD, KNUTSFORD, WA16 8XN, UK Tel: +44 (0)1565 653214 Fax: +44 (0)1565 651637

EASE SEND ME MY **FREE** INTRODUCTORY **SANDAFAYRE** CATALOGUES

me:

dress:

tcode: E-mail:

collecting interests are:

(BMV)

ANDAFAYRE'S   • See lots that only match your interests • No unwanted catalogues
LLECTORS REGISTER   • **FREE** to register and use • Just email your details to stampregister@sandafayre.com

PHILANGLES

international postage stamp
& postal history auctioneers

ESTABLISHED 1990

AUCTIONEERS OF QUALITY POSTAGE STAMPS
POSTAL HISTORY AND COLLECTIONS OF THE WORLD

Our monthly sales always includes interesting and unusual Great Britain
single stamps, collections, accumulations, postal history and all other
aspects to suit all requirements.

Unusual

Superb

Interesting

www.philangles.co.uk

Request your auction catalogue or view our latest sale online.

SELLING?

Contact Simon Carson for professional advice on buying and selling
postage stamps (singles, collections, and estates).
Valuations carried out for probate.

PHILANGLES

Carson House, 44 Legh Street
Warrington, Cheshire, WA1 1UJ

Telephone: 01925 231151
Facsimile: 01925 232204
E-MAIL: philangles@btinternet.com
Website: www.philangles.co.uk

Plate			Plate		
Plate 90	25.00	1.50	Plate 152	40.00	4.00
Plate 91	35.00	4.50	Plate 153	90.00	7.00
Plate 92	21.00	1.50	Plate 154	30.00	1.50
Plate 93	30.00	1.50	Plate 155	30.00	1.75
Plate 94	28.00	4.00	Plate 156	35.00	1.50
Plate 95	25.00	1.50	Plate 157	30.00	1.50
Plate 96	28.00	1.50	Plate 158	23.00	1.50
Plate 97	25.00	2.50	Plate 159	23.00	1.50
Plate 98	30.00	4.50	Plate 160	23.00	1.50
Plate 99	35.00	4.00	Plate 161	40.00	5.00
Plate 100	40.00	1.50	Plate 162	30.00	5.00
Plate 101	40.00	7.50	Plate 163	30.00	2.00
Plate 102	28.00	1.50	Plate 164	30.00	2.00
Plate 103	30.00	2.75	Plate 165	35.00	1.50
Plate 104	60.00	4.00	Plate 166	35.00	4.50
Plate 105	55.00	5.50	Plate 167	35.00	1.50
Plate 106	35.00	1.50	Plate 168	30.00	6.00
Plate 107	40.00	5.00	Plate 169	30.00	6.00
Plate 108	60.00	1.75	Plate 170	21.00	1.50
Plate 109	65.00	2.50	Plate 171	12.00	1.50
Plate 110	40.00	7.50	Plate 172	23.00	1.50
Plate 111	36.00	1.75	Plate 173	48.00	6.50
Plate 112	50.00	1.70	Plate 174	23.00	1.50
Plate 113	30.00	9.00	Plate 175	40.00	2.50
Plate 114	£240	9.00	Plate 176	40.00	1.75
Plate 115	85.00	1.75	Plate 177	32.00	1.50
Plate 116	60.00	7.50	Plate 178	40.00	2.50
Plate 117	28.00	1.50	Plate 179	30.00	1.75
Plate 118	30.00	1.50	Plate 180	40.00	4.00
Plate 119	28.00	1.50	Plate 181	36.00	1.50
Plate 120	12.00	1.50	Plate 182	75.00	4.00
Plate 121	25.00	8.00	Plate 183	35.00	2.00
Plate 122	12.00	1.50	Plate 184	23.00	1.75
Plate 123	25.00	1.50	Plate 185	30.00	2.00
Plate 124	22.00	1.50	Plate 186	35.00	1.75
Plate 125	25.00	1.50	Plate 187	30.00	1.50
Plate 127	35.00	1.75	Plate 188	50.00	7.50
Plate 129	25.00	6.50	Plate 189	50.00	5.50
Plate 130	35.00	1.75	Plate 190	30.00	4.50
Plate 131	45.00	12.00	Plate 191	23.00	5.50
Plate 132	£125	18.00	Plate 192	30.00	1.50
Plate 133	£105	7.50	Plate 193	23.00	1.50
Plate 134	12.00	1.50	Plate 194	30.00	6.50
Plate 135	70.00	22.00	Plate 195	30.00	6.50
Plate 136	65.00	17.00	Plate 196	30.00	4.00
Plate 137	22.00	1.75	Plate 197	35.00	7.00
Plate 138	14.00	1.50	Plate 198	32.00	4.50
Plate 139	40.00	12.50	Plate 199	35.00	4.50
Plate 140	14.00	1.50	Plate 200	40.00	2.00
Plate 141	£100	7.00	Plate 201	23.00	4.00
Plate 142	50.00	22.00	Plate 202	40.00	6.50
Plate 143	40.00	12.00	Plate 203	23.00	13.00
Plate 144	75.00	16.00	Plate 204	35.00	1.75
Plate 145	23.00	1.75	Plate 205	35.00	2.25
Plate 146	25.00	4.50	Plate 206	35.00	7.00
Plate 147	30.00	2.00	Plate 207	40.00	7.00
Plate 148	25.00	2.00	Plate 208	35.00	12.50
Plate 149	25.00	4.50	Plate 209	30.00	8.00
Plate 150	12.00	1.50	Plate 210	45.00	10.00
Plate 151	40.00	7.50	Plate 211	50.00	18.00

Plate 212	40.00	10.00
Plate 213	40.00	10.00
Plate 214	45.00	15.00
Plate 215	45.00	15.00
Plate 216	50.00	15.00
Plate 217	50.00	6.00
Plate 218	45.00	7.00
Plate 219	80.00	58.00
Plate 220	32.00	6.00
Plate 221	50.00	15.00
Plate 222	60.00	30.00
Plate 223	75.00	50.00
Plate 224	£110	45.00
Plate 225	£1,800	£550

1½d red-rose

1½d red-rose (October 1, 1870)	£250	25.00
Plate 1*	£450	48.00
Plate 3	£275	32.00

(* plate 1 does not appear in the stamp design)

2d blue (July 1858)	£250	8.00
Plate 7	£925	40.00
Plate 8	£850	25.00
Plate 9	£250	8.00
Plate 12	£1,500	£100
Plate 13	£260	15.00
Plate 14	£340	16.00
Plate 15	£320	16.00

10d brown

■ 1847-1854. Embossed issue.

Die engraved at the Royal Mint by William Wyon. Printed using the embossed process at Somerset House. Wmk: VR (6d), unwatermarked (10d, 1/-). Imperforate.

6d lilac (March 1, 1854)	£7,000	£525
10d brown (November 6, 1848)	£5,500	£775
1/- green (September 11, 1847)	£7,000	£550

(* The above are priced cut square; examples cut to shape are worth considerably less.)

4d carmine

■ 1855-1857

Surface-printed by De La Rue. Perf: 14.

4d carmine (Wmk: Small Garter)		
(July 31, 1855)	£6,500	£275
4d carmine (Wmk: Medium Garter)		
(February 25, 1856)	£5,000	£325
4d carmine (Wmk: Large Garter)		
(January 1857)	£1050	55.00

6d lilac

■ 1856

As above but wmk: Emblems.

6d lilac (October 21, 1856)	£775	68.00
1/- green (November 1, 1856)	£1,200	£160

9d bistre

■ 1862-1864

As above but wmk: Large Garter (4d), Emblems (3d, 6d, 9d, 1/-).

3d carmine (May 1, 1862)	£1,200	£225
4d red (January 15, 1862)	£875	55.00
6d lilac (December 1, 1862)	£1,050	50.00
9d bistre (January 15, 1862)	£2,750	£280
1/- green (December 1, 1862)	£1,700	£150

(* The 1/- exists with either a number 1 or a number 2 in the border)

MALCOLM SPREI – M&S STAMPS

2 Savoy Court, Strand, London WC2R 0EZ

Tel: 020 7379 9264   **GREAT BRITAIN**   *Fax: 020 7379 9263*

GREAT BRITAIN

REQUEST YOUR FREE
MONTHLY LIST

SG14wi

SG76 mint

SG166 misperf

SG143imprimatur

SG 127 unused

SG063

SG257
unmounted

SG277
unmounted

SPEC
N1plate proof

SEE US AT STAMPEX STAND 41
OR VISIT US AT OUR NEW OFFICES

SG316 unmounted

SG351 variety

SG 411

SPEC NCom6t

www.malcolmsprei.co.uk

| Elstree | Stamps |

Fine quality GREAT BRITAIN from 1840

www.elstreestamps.com

PO Box 52 Borehamwood WD6 3QB UK
Tel/Fax +44 (0)20 83875673
Email: info@elstreestamps.com

GREAT BRITAIN

QV line engraved specialist has available thousands of 1ᵈ Imperfs;
Stars Plates in stock for reconstructions and for collectors
of varieties and cancellations

Also Postal History 'on Piece' Material and Covers

WANTS lists please to:

**HUGH PALMER, 80 Potash Road, Billericay,
Essex CM11 1HH**

hughpalmer@supanet.com

K & C Philatelics

Great Britain Queen Victoria (1840-1901)
Stamps, Varieties, Cancels, covers
and Pre-Stamp Material. Extensive range
of quality items to suit all pockets

Wants lists welcomed and serviced.
PO Box 5003, Danbury CM3 4JU
Tel: 01245 223120. Fax/Ans: 01245 224608

Visit our website at
www.kcphilatelics.co.uk

GREAT BRITAIN
1840 - 1971

FREE MONTHLY LISTS OF OVER 200
INDIVIDUAL CAREFULLY SELECTED ITEMS.
MANY STAMPS ARE ILLUSTRATED.

FINE QUALITY & INDIVIDUAL PRICES
WRITE FOR YOUR FREE PRICE LIST.

Stephen J Sayer

PO Box No 61 Keynsham
BRISTOL BS31 3YA
Tel/Fax: 01225 356 208
Email: stephen@gbstamps4u.com
www.gbstamps4u.com

10d brown

1865-1867

Designs as above, but with large corner letters (all values). The designs of the 3d and 4d values are as the 1862 issue. Wmk: Larger Garter (4d), Emblems (3d, 6d, 9d, 10d, 1/-).

3d carmine (March 1, 1865) (plate 4)	£1000	£125
4d vermilion (July 4, 1865)	£400	40.00
Plate 7	£440	65.00
Plate 8	£400	40.00
Plate 9	£400	40.00
Plate 10	£475	85.00
Plate 11	£400	40.00
Plate 12	£400	40.00
Plate 13	£400	40.00
Plate 14	£440	60.00
6d lilac (April 1, 1865)	£650	55.00
Plate 5	£650	55.00
Plate 6	£1,800	£100
9d bistre (December 1, 1865) (plate 4*)	£2,000	£360
10d brown (November 11, 1867) (plate 1)	-	£30,000
1/- green (February 1, 1865) (plate 4)	£1,100	£125

(* Copies of the 9d from an Imprimatur sheet of plate 5 are known to exist.)

2/- blue
(other designs as previous issue)

1867-1880

Wmk: Flowering rose.

3d red (July 12, 1867)	£375	35.00
Plate 4	£675	£125
Plate 5	£375	35.00
Plate 6	£400	35.00
Plate 7	£500	35.00
Plate 8	£400	35.00
Plate 9	£400	35.00
Plate 10	£550	75.00
6d lilac (June 21, 1867)	£400	55.00
Plate 8	£400	55.00
Plate 9	£400	55.00
Plate 10	-	£25,000
9d bistre (October 3, 1867) (plate 4)	£1,300	£200
10d brown (July 1, 1867)	£1,900	£225
Plate 1	£1,900	£200

Plate 2	£25,000	£10,000
1/- green (July 13, 1867)	£480	25.00
Plate 4	£675	40.00
Plate 5	£500	25.00
Plate 6	£700	25.00
Plate 7	£750	45.00
2/- blue (July 1, 1867) (plate 1)	£2,100	£140
2/- brown (February 27, 1880) (plate 1)	£15,000	£2,250

6d grey

1872-1873

Wmk: Flowering Rose.

6d brown (April 12, 1872)	£450	35.00
Plate 11	£450	35.00
Plate 12	£1,700	£160
6d grey (April 24, 1873) (plate 12)	£1100	£130

£1 brown

1867-1868

Wmk: Maltese Cross. Perf: 15 x 15.

5/- red (July 1, 1867)		
Plate 1	£3,850	£450
Plate 2	£5,000	£550
10/- grey-green (September 26, 1878)		
Plate 1	£45,000	£1,900
£1 brown (September 26, 1878)		
Plate 1	£60,000	£3,000

1882-1883

Wmk: Large Anchor. Perf: 14.

5/- red (November 25, 1882)		
Plate 4	£19,000	£1,950
10/- grey-green (February 1883)		
Plate 1	£85,000	£3,000
£1 brown (December 1882)		
Plate 1	£100,000	£6,000
£5 orange (March 21, 1882)		
Plate 1	£9,000	£3,500

■ 1873-1880

A) Wmk: Small Anchor
2½d mauve (July 1, 1875)

Plate 1	£385	55.00
Plate 2	£385	55.00
Plate 3	£600	80.00

B) Wmk: Orb
2½d mauve (May 16, 1876)

Plate 3	£750	75.00
Plate 4	£350	35.00
Plate 5	£350	35.00
Plate 6	£350	35.00
Plate 7	£350	35.00
Plate 8	£350	35.00
Plate 9	£350	35.00
Plate 10	£375	40.00
Plate 11	£350	35.00
Plate 12	£350	35.00
Plate 13	£350	35.00
Plate 14	£350	35.00
Plate 15	£350	35.00
Plate 16	£350	35.00
Plate 17	£1050	£190

2½d blue (February 5, 1880)

Plate 17	£325	40.00
Plate 18	£350	22.50
Plate 19	£325	22.50
Plate 20	£350	22.50

C) Wmk: Flowering Rose.
3d red (July 5, 1873)

Plate 11	£300	30.00
Plate 112	£325	30.00
Plate 114	£375	30.00
Plate 115	£300	30.00
Plate 116	£300	30.00
Plate 117	£325	30.00
Plate 118	£325	30.00
Plate 119	£300	30.00
Plate 120	£300	55.00

6d buff (March 15, 1873)

Plate 13	-	£17,000

6d grey (March 31, 1874)

Plate 113	£300	40.00
Plate 114	£300	40.00
Plate 115	£300	40.00
Plate 116	£300	40.00
Plate 117	£525	90.00

1/- green (September 1, 1873)

Plate 18	£500	80.00
Plate 19	£500	80.00
Plate 110	£500	90.00
Plate 111	£500	80.00
Plate 112	£475	65.00
Plate 113	£475	65.00
Plate 114	-	£24,000

1/- brown (October 14, 1880)

Plate 13	£2,400	£400

D) Wmk: Large Garter.
4d vermilion (March 1, 1867)

Plate 15	£1,400	£300
Plate 16	-	£24,000

4d green (March 12, 1877)

Plate 15	£825	£180
Plate 16	£775	£170
Plate 17	-	£14,000

4d brown (August 15, 1880)

Plate 17	£1,250	£325

8d orange (September 11, 1876)

Plate 1	£900	£175

3d (red) on 3d lilac

■ 1880-1883
Wmk: Imperial Crown.
2½d blue (March 23, 1881)

	£325	14.00
Plate 21	£350	18.00
Plate 22	£325	18.00
Plate 23	£325	14.00

3d red (February 1881)

Plate 20	£500	90.00
Plate 21	£380	55.00

3d (in red) on 3d lilac (January 1, 1883)

Plate 21	£400	80.00

4d brown (December 9, 1880)

	£300	38.00
Plate 17	£300	38.00
Plate 18	£300	38.00

6d grey (January 1, 1881)

	£310	45.00
Plate 17	£350	45.00
Plate 18	£310	45.00

6d (in red) on 6d lilac (January 1, 1883)

Plate 18	£425	80.00

1/- brown (May 29, 1881)

Plate 13	£525	90.00
Plate 14	£425	90.00

5d indigo

■ 1880-1881
Wmk: Imperial Crown.

½d green (October 14, 1880)	35.00	6.00
1d brown (January 1, 1880)	18.00	3.00
1½d red-brown (October 14, 1880)	£140	30.00
2d red (December 8, 1880)	£180	60.00
5d indigo (March 15, 1881)	£550	65.00

Warwick & Warwick

AUCTIONEERS AND VALUERS
www.warwickandwarwick.com

SELLING YOUR STAMP COLLECTION?

Warwick and Warwick have an expanding requirement for world collections, single country collections, single items, covers, proof material and specialised collections, with G.B. material being particularly in demand. Our customer base is increasing dramatically and we need an ever-larger supply of quality material to keep pace with demand. The market has never been stronger and if you are considering the sale of your collection, now is the time to act.

FREE VALUATIONS
We will provide a free, professional valuation of your collection, without obligation on your part to proceed. Either we will make you a fair, binding private treaty offer, or we will recommend inclusion of your property in our next public auction.

FREE TRANSPORTATION
We can arrange insured transportation of your collection to our Warwick offices completely free of charge. If you decline our offer, we ask you to cover the return carriage costs only.

FREE VISITS
Visits by our valuers are possible anywhere in the country or abroad, usually within 48 hours, in order to value larger collections. Please phone for details.

VALUATION DAYS
We are staging a series of valuation days across the country. Please visit our website or telephone for further details.

EXCELLENT PRICES
Because of the strength of our customer base we are in a position to offer prices that we feel sure will exceed your expectations.

ACT NOW
Telephone or e-mail Ian Hunter today with details of your property.

GET THE EXPERTS ON YOUR SIDE!

Warwick & Warwick Ltd.
Chalon House, Scar Bank, Millers Road, Warwick CV34 5DB England
Tel: (01926) 499031 • Fax: (01926) 491906
Email: ian.hunter@warwickandwarwick.com
www.warwickandwarwick.com

Great Britain 1839–1951

A selection of exceptional items sold in recent years

Free Quarterly and Specialised Lists featuring all aspects of British Philately from 1839 to 1951 are available on request.

We are keen to help you find the items you are looking for and supply fine quality material, with emphasis on the unusual. Our stock includes issued stamps, proofs, essays, imprimaturs, specialised shades, covers.

We are also interested in **buying** fine single items and specialised collections and are happy to provide valuations and estate advice.

Andrew G Lajer
The Old Post Office, Davis Way, Hurst
Berkshire RG10 0TR, United Kingdom
T: +44 (0)1189 344151 F: +44 (0)1189 344947
E: andrew.lajer@btinternet.com
www.andrewglajer.co.uk

Andrew Claridge
PO Box 1999, White Notley, Witham
Essex CM8 1XN, United Kingdom
T: +44 (0)1376 584412 F: +44 (0)1376 585388
E: andrew.claridge@btinternet.com

1d lilac

■ 1881
Wmk: Imperial Crown.
A) 14 white dots in each corner

1d lilac (July 12, 1881)	£150	15.00

B)16 white dots in each corner

1d lilac (December 12, 1881)	1.75	0.75

5/- red

■ 1883-1884
Wmk: Large Anchor.

2/6 lilac (July 2, 1883)	£350	70.00
5/- red (April 1, 1884)	£700	£110
10/- blue (April 1, 1884)	£1,300	£275

£1 green, 1891

■ 1884-1891
A) Wmk: Imperial Crowns.

£1 brown (April 1, 1884)	£22,000	£1,850
£1 green (January 27, 1891)	£4,000	£550

B) Wmk: Orbs.

£1 brown (February 1, 1888)	£60,000	£2,800

6d green

■ 1883-84, 'Lilac & Green issue'
Wmk: Imperial Crown (sideways on 2d, 2½d, 6d, 9d)

½d blue (April 1, 1884)	14.00	3.50
1½d lilac (April 1, 1884)	80.00	23.00
2d lilac (April 1, 1884)	£140	40.00
2½d lilac (April 1, 1884)	57.50	5.00
3d lilac (April 1, 1884)	£135	38.00
4d green (April 1, 1884)	£325	£100
5d green (April 1, 1884)	£325	£100
6d green (April 1, 1884)	£300	£110
9d green (August 1, 1883)	£725	£300
1/- green (April 1, 1884)	£775	£150

9d violet, blue

■ 1887, January 1. 'Jubilee issue'
Wmk: Imperial Crown.
A) Wmk upright.

½d orange	1.20	0.50
½d green (April 17, 1900)	1.40	0.60
1½d purple, green	10.00	2.00
2d green, red	18.00	8.00
2½d purple (blue paper)	14.00	0.75
3d purple (yellow paper)	18.00	1.50
4d green, brown	22.00	7.00
4½d green, red	7.00	25.00
5d purple, blue	26.00	5.00
6d purple (red paper)	20.00	5.00
9d violet, blue	45.00	25.00
10d purple, red	40.00	24.00
1/- green	£150	40.00
1/- green, red (July 11, 1900)	45.00	70.00
Set	£400	£200

B) Wmk inverted

½d orange	25.00	20.00
½d green	25.00	25.00
1½d purple, green	£600	£250
2d purple, red	£525	£325
2½d purple (blue)	£850	£550
4d green, brown	£500	£275
5d purple	£9,500	£525
6d purple (red)	£1,700	£600
9d violet, blue	£1,800	£675
10d purple, red	£2,600	£650
1/- green	£700	£350
1/- green, red	£750	£675

DO YOU COLLECT GREAT BRITAIN STAMPS?

Our printed monthly retail list covers
all issues from 1840 to date
(with many new issues offered at face value!)

**JUST COMPLETE THE COUPON BELOW TO
RECEIVE YOUR FREE COPY - NO STAMP REQUIRED
- OR VISIT OUR USER FRIENDLY WEBSITE**
www.gbstamps.co.uk

GREAT BRITAIN COLLECTORS ON THE INTERNET

The world's largest selection of Great Britain stamps is just one
click away. Our profusely illustated private treaty catalogues are
issued twice monthly and contain a wide selection of better
singles, rarities, proofs, colour trials, high values, multiples,
Cinderella material and much more other specialist material
seldom offered elsewhere. Up to £500,000 of fine GB material
can be viewed on-line at

www.gbstamps.co.uk

YOU CAN ORDER BY MAIL, PHONE, FAX OR ON-LINE 24 HOURS A DAY, 7 DAYS A WEEK. CREDIT CARDS ACCEPTED.

Please tick boxes of interest:
- ☐ Pre stamp/postal history
- ☐ QV Surface printed
- ☐ King Edward VII
- ☐ Essays/proofs/colour trials
- ☐ Specialised shades
- ☐ QV Line engraved
- ☐ QV High values
- ☐ King George V
- ☐ General Great Britain
- ☐ Cinderella

Arthur Ryan & Co.
OF RICHMOND

FREEPOST, Dept. SM, RICHMOND, SURREY TW9 1DY

Please send me a **FREE** copy of your Retail List

NAME ....

ADDRESS ....

....

.... POST CODE ....

OR TELEPHONE: 020 8940 7777   FAX: 020 8940 7755

For this reign most stamps are priced in three columns: unmounted mint (left), mounted mint (centre) and fine used (right). The exception is booklet panes, priced at mounted mint only.

To help you distinguish the work of the three printers, note that the De La Rue printings are generally cleaner, with good centering and clean perforations, whereas the Harrison & Sons and Somerset House printings are coarser, with poor centering and ragged perforations.

A vast range of shades exists on all printings. Full details of these are beyond the scope of this publication.

½d yellow-green   5/- red

■ **1902, January 1**
Designs as Queen Victoria 1887 issues and 1883-84 high values.

A) Surface printed by De La Rue. Wmk. Imperial Crown (½d to 1/-), Large Anchor (2/6, 5/-, 10/-), Three Imperial Crowns (£1). Perf: 14.

½d blue-green	2.00	1.00	0.70
½d yellow-green	2.00	1.00	0.70
Wmk inverted	20.00	12.00	12.00
1d scarlet	1.75	1.00	0.50
Wmk inverted	7.00	5.00	6.00
1½d purple, green	60.00	30.00	10.00
on chalky paper	60.00	30.00	10.00
2d green, red (Mar 25, 1902)	70.00	30.00	10.00
on chalky paper	60.00	28.00	12.00
2½d blue	25.00	12.00	3.00
3d purple (yellow paper)	70.00	30.00	7.00
on chalky paper	60.00	30.00	10.00
4d green, brown	95.00	40.00	18.00
on chalky paper	65.00	30.00	15.00
4d orange (Nov 1, 1909)	32.00	15.00	10.00
5d purple blue (May 14, 1902)	90.00	40.00	15.00
on chalky paper	85.00	45.00	15.00
Wmk inverted	£4,500	£3,000	£1,750
6d purple	60.00	28.00	14.00
on chalky paper	60.00	30.00	14.00
7d grey	10.00	7.00	16.00
9d purple, blue	£170	70.00	40.00
on chalky paper	£155	60.00	40.00
10d purple, red (Jul 3, 1902)	£210	60.00	40.00
on chalky paper	£175	55.00	40.00

1/- green, red (Mar 24, 1902)	£165	60.00	20.00
on chalky paper	£165	60.00	24.00
2/6 lilac (Apr 5, 1902)	£450	£200	75.00
on chalky paper	£450	£300	90.00
Wmk inverted	£3,500	£2,750	£1,750
5/- red (Apr 5, 1902)	£600	£280	£120
10/- blue (Apr 5, 1902)	£1,500	£525	£350
£1 green (Jun 16, 1902)	£2,200	£1,200	£600

Booklet panes	*Wmk Upright*	*Inverted*
Pane of five se-tenant		
with label showing St Andrew's Cross	£400	£400
Pane of six ½d	55.00	90.00
Pane of six 1d	40.00	70.00

B) As above but printed by Harrison.

½d yellow-green (May 3, 1911)	3.50	2.00	1.30
Wmk inverted	25.00	15.00	12.00
1d red (May 3, 1911)	10.00	6.00	8.00
Wmk inverted	28.00	15.00	10.00
2½d blue (Jul 10, 1911)	£100	45.00	18.00
Wmk inverted	£1,150	£750	£450
3d purple (Sep 12, 1911)			
yellow paper	£140	80.00	£140
4d orange (Jul 13, 1911)	£130	60.00	45.00

Booklet panes	*Wmk Upright*	*Inverted*
Pane of five ½d se-tenant with label		
showing St Andrew's Cross	£700	£700
Pane of six ½d	80.00	£110
Pane of six 1d	70.00	90.00

C) As above but printed by Somerset House.

1½d purple, green (Jul 13, 1911)	50.00	25.00	12.00
2d green, red (Mar 11, 1912)	46.00	24.00	11.00
5d purple, blue (Aug 7, 1911)	50.00	28.00	11.00
6d purple (Oct 31, 1911)	50.00	26.00	14.00
chalky paper	50.00	28.00	60.00
7d grey (Aug 1, 1912)	20.00	12.00	15.00
9d purple, blue (Jul 24, 1911)	£105	65.00	40.00
10d purple, red (Oct 9, 1911)	£140	75.00	45.00
1/- green, red (Jul 17, 1911)	£115	58.00	25.00
Wmk inverted	£250	£150	-
2/6 purple (Sep 27, 1911)	£450	£190	85.00
5/- red (Feb 29, 1912)	£600	£280	£120
10/- (Jan 14, 1912)	£1,500	£600	£400
£1 green (Sep 3, 1911)	£2,100	£1,200	£700

D) As above, but printed by Harrison with perf: 15x14.

½d green (Oct 30, 1911)	50.00	30.00	30.00
1d red (Oct 5, 1911)	32.00	16.00	8.50
2½d blue (Oct 14, 1911)	45.00	21.00	7.00
3d purple (Sep 22, 1911)			
yellow paper	55.00	30.00	13.00
4d orange (Nov 22, 1911)	48.00	26.00	10.00

■ **1910**
A 2d value with a new design printed in Tyrian plum was prepared for use but the death of the King prevented its release. Copies are known unused and one example used.

KING GEORGE V

For this reign the stamps are priced in three columns: unmounted mint (left), mounted unused (centre) and fine used (right).

Many stamps are found in a wide variety of shades. Full details of these are beyond the scope of this guide.

½d green

■ 1911-1912

Des: Bertram Mackennal and G.W. Eve. Portrait based on photograph by Downey. Die engraved by J. A. C. Harrison. Printed in typography by Harrison. Perf: 15x14.

A) Wmk: Imperial Crown

½d green (Jun 22, 1911)	7.50	3.50	2.00
Wmk inverted	15.00	7.50	3.50
1d red (Jun 22, 1911)	6.50	3.00	1.50
Wmk inverted	12.50	7.00	3.00

(* These stamps also exist with Wmk sideways and printed in error with perf: 14.)

Booklet panes	Wmk Upright	Inverted
Pane of six ½d	80.00	£120
Pane of six 1d	75.00	£110

B) Wmk: Crown with script GVR (Royal Cypher). Issued August 1912 in booklets.

½d green	70.00	30.00	28.00
Wmk inverted	70.00	30.00	28.00
1d green	35.00	16.00	18.00
Wmk inverted	35.00	16.00	18.00

Booklet panes	Wmk Upright	Inverted
Pane of six ½d	£500	£500
Pane of six 1d	£250	£240

■ 1912

As above except that the King's hair is lighter on the ½d and the lion is shaded on the 1d.

A) Wmk: Imperial Crown

½d green (Jan 1, 1912)	8.50	4.50	1.00
Wmk inverted	£1,000	£800	£450
1d red (Jan 1, 1912)	5.00	2.00	0.80
Wmk inverted	£450	£350	£250

B) Wmk: Crown with script GVR (Royal Cypher).

½d green (Aug 1912)	8.00	4.00	1.25
Wmk inverted	£225	£140	60.00
1d red (Aug 1912)	7.00	3.50	1.00
Wmk inverted	22.00	14.00	12.00

C) Wmk: Multiple Royal Cypher (Crown and script GVR).

½d green (Oct 1912)	12.00	7.00	9.00
Wmk inverted	15.00	12.00	12.50
Wmk sideways	-	-	£2,750
1d red (Oct 1912)	15.00	9.00	4.50
Wmk inverted	20.00	15.00	16.00
Wmk sideways	£220	£150	£160

1d red

■ 1912-1913

Designed and engraved as before. Printed in typography by Harrison (all values except 6d) and at Somerset House (½d, 1d, 1½d, 2d, 2½d, 3d, 4d, 5d, 6d, 7d, 8d, 9d, 10d, 1/-)

A) Wmk: Crown and script GVR (Royal Cypher)
i) Wmk upright

½d green (Jan 1913)	1.00	0.40	0.40
Wmk inverted	4.00	2.25	1.10
1d red (Oct 1919)	1.00	0.40	0.40
Wmk inverted	4.00	2.25	0.90
1½d brown (Oct 1912)	3.50	2.00	0.80
Wmk inverted	8.00	4.00	1.60
2d orange (Aug 1912)	3.50	1.75	0.60
Wmk inverted	20.00	10.00	8.50
2½d blue (Oct 1912)	16.00	8.00	2.25
Wmk inverted	90.00	45.00	45.00
3d violet (Oct 1912)	8.00	3.75	1.00
Wmk inverted	£120	65.00	65.00
4d green (Jan 1913)	16.00	7.00	1.50
Wmk inverted	40.00	25.00	25.00
5d brown (Jun 1913)	20.00	8.00	4.00
Wmk inverted	£700	£400	£400
6d purple (Aug 1913)			
chalky paper	18.00	8.00	2.00
Wmk inverted	65.00	35.00	35.00
7d green (Aug 1913)	28.00	11.00	7.50
Wmk inverted	65.00	40.00	40.00
8d black (Aug 1913)			
yellow paper	42.00	20.00	11.00
Wmk inverted	£180	110.00	110.00
9d black (Jun 1913)	20.00	10.00	3.75
Wmk inverted	£160	100.00	100.00
9d green (Sep 1922)	£200	75.00	24.00

Wmk inverted	£1,000	£700	£625
10d blue (Aug 1913)	32.00	15.00	18.00
Wmk inverted	£3,500	£2,000	£1,400
1/- brown (Aug 1913)	28.00	13.00	1.80
Wmk inverted	£240	£150	£140

Booklet panes	Wmk Upright	Inverted
Pane of six ½d	35.00	45.00
Pane of six 1d	35.00	45.00
Pane of six 1½d	60.00	75.00
Pane of four 1½d with two advert labels	£750	£750
Pane of six 2d	80.00	£130

B) Wmk: Multiple Royal Cypher (Crown and Script GVR).

½d green (Aug 1913)	£160	£100	95.00
Wmk inverted	£500	£350	£350
1d red (Aug 1913)	£350	£225	£180
Wmk inverted	£800	£600	£600

1924-1926

As above, but printed by typography by Waterlow (all values except 6d), Harrison (all values) or Somerset House (1½d, 6d), Wmk: Multiple Crown and block GVR.

½d green (Feb 1924)	0.60	0.30	0.20
Wmk inverted	5.00	2.50	1.00
Wmk sideways	11.00	5.50	4.50
1d red (Feb 1924)	0.85	0.35	0.20
Wmk inverted	5.00	2.50	1.25
Wmk sideways	26.00	15.00	16.00
1½d brown (Feb 1924)	0.90	0.40	0.20
Wmk inverted	2.50	1.25	1.00
Wmk sideways	14.00	7.00	4.50
2d orange (Sept1924)	2.00	0.85	0.70
Wmk inverted	40.00	25.0	18.00
Wmk sideways	£175	60.00	65.00
2½d blue (Oct 1924)	7.50	4.00	1.10
Wmk inverted	65.00	45.00	30.00
3d violet (Oct 1924)	11.00	5.00	1.00
Wmk inverted	65.00	45.00	30.00
4d green (Nov 1924)	18.00	7.00	1.40
Wmk inverted	£160	85.00	60.00
5d brown (Nov 1924)	30.00	12.00	2.00
Wmk inverted	£110	70.00	55.00
6d purple (Sep 1924)	3.80	1.50	0.50
chalky paper	15.00	9.00	1.75
ordinary paper, Wmk inverted	65.00	48.00	35.00
chalky paper, Wmk inverted	70.00	50.00	40.00
9d green (Dec 1924)	20.00	7.00	2.50
Wmk inverted	£105	75.00	70.00
10d blue (Nov 1923)	65.00	28.00	22.00
Wmk inverted	£2,650	£1,950	£950
1/- brown (Oct 1924)	35.00	16.00	1.40
Wmk inverted	£550	£400	£260

Booklet panes	Wmk Upright	Inverted
Pane of six ½d	35.00	45.00
Pane of six 1d	35.00	45.00
Pane of six 1½d	60.00	75.00
Pane of four 1½d with two advert labels	£125	£125

(* A wide range of advertising labels exists)

4d green

1934-1936

As above but printed in photogravure by Harrison. Designs differ in the shading behind the portrait. Wmk: Multiple Crown and block GVR, Perf: 15 x 14.

½d green (Nov 19, 1934)	0.25	0.10	0.15
Wmk inverted	15.00	7.00	3.00
Wmk sideways	9.00	6.00	3.00
1d red (Sep 24, 1934)	0.25	0.20	0.15
Wmk inverted	15.00	7.00	2.50
Wmk sideways	22.00	11.00	14.00
1½d brown (Aug 20, 1934)	0.20	0.15	0.10
Wmk inverted	2.50	1.25	0.60
Wmk sideways	10.00	6.00	2.50
2d orange (Jan 21, 1935)	0.60	0.35	0.40
Wmk sideways	£175	70.00	65.00
2½d blue (Mar 18, 1935)	1.40	0.90	0.75
3d violet (Mar 18, 1935)	1.80	1.00	0.75
4d green (Dec 2, 1935)	2.50	1.40	0.75
5d brown (Feb 17, 1936)	9.00	5.00	2.50
9d deep green (Dec 2, 1935)	16.00	7.00	2.25
10d blue (Feb 24, 1936)	25.00	11.00	9.00
1/- brown (Feb 24, 1936)	32.00	12.00	0.75

Booklet panes	Wmk Upright	Inverted
Pane of six ½d	60.00	£100
Pane of six 1d	60.00	£150
Pane of six 1½d	20.00	25.00
Pane of four 1½d with two advert labels	75.00	75.00

Seahorses (all values)

1913-1934. High values. 'Seahorses'

Des: Bertram Mackennal. Dies engraved by J.A.C. Harrison. Wmk: single crown with script GVR (Royal Cypher) Perf: 11x12

A) Printed in recess by Waterlow. Released in July 1913.

2/6 brown	£500	£175	£100

5/- red	£800	£325	£175
10/- blue	£1,500	£700	£300
£1 green	£4,000	£2,250	£110

B) Printed in recess by De La Rue. Released in December 1915.

2/6 brown	£450	£200	£100
5/- red	£700	£280	£190
10/- blue	£3,000	£1,500	£500

C) Printed in recess by Bradbury, Wilkinson. Released in December 1918.

2/6 brown	£225	75.00	32.00
5/- red	£325	£150	45.00
10/- blue	£600	£300	£100

(* To distinguish between the above, note that the De La Rue printings have a yellow gum, while the Waterlow design is about 22mm high and that of Bradbury, Wilkinson 23mm high.)

D) Printed in recess by Waterlow by die re-engraved so that the background to the portrait consists of horizontal and diagonal lines. Released in October 1934.

2/6 brown	£130	60.00	12.00
5/- red	£350	£120	45.00
10/- blue	£500	£300	50.00

1d, 1½d.
(inscribed '1924'
and later '1925')

▪ 1924-1925. British Empire Exhibition

Des: H. Nelson. Printed in recess by Waterlow. Wmk: Multiple Crown and block GVR. Perf: 14.

Set	18.00	8.00	8.00
Inscribed '1925'	45.00	30.00	30.00
First Day Cover	-	-	£375
Inscribed '1925'	46.00	-	£1,500

£1

▪ 1929, May 10. Postal Union Congress

Des: J. Farleigh (½d, 2½d), E. Linzell (1d, 1½d), H. Nelson (£1). Printed in typography by Waterlow (½d to 2½d) or in recess by Bradbury, Wilkinson (£1). Wmk: Multiple Crown and block GRV (½d to 2½d), Large Crown and script GVR (£1). Perf: 15x14 (½d to 2½d), 12 (£1).

½d green	1.50	0.50	0.45
Wmk inverted	20.00	11.00	8.00
Wmk sideways	70.00	25.00	25.00
1d red	2.50	1.50	1.00
Wmk inverted	25.00	13.00	14.00
Wmk sideways	90.00	60.00	60.00
1½d brown	2.00	1.25	0.80
Wmk inverted	12.00	6.00	4.50
Wmk sideways	65.00	20.00	20.00
2½d blue	16.00	7.00	5.00
Wmk inverted	£3,000	£2,000	£750
Set	20.00	9.00	6.75
First Day Cover	-	-	£450
£1 black	£800	£480	£480
First Day Cover	-	-	£6,500

Booklet panes		Wmk Upright	Inverted
Pane of six ½d		40.00	£120
Pane of six 1d		45.00	£200
Pane of six 1½d		30.00	90.00
Pane of four 1½d with two advert labels	£250		£280

2½d

▪ 1935, May 7. Silver Jubilee

Des: B. Freedman. Printed in photogravure by Harrison Wmk: Multiple Crown and block GVR. Perf: 15x14

½d green	0.80	0.40	0.30
Wmk inverted	11.00	6.00	6.00
1d red	1.40	0.70	0.70
Wmk inverted	11.00	6.00	6.00
1½d brown	1.25	0.50	0.40
Wmk inverted	2.00	1.00	0.90
2½d blue	3.00	2.00	4.00
2½d Prussian blue	£10,000	£8,000	£9,000
Set (excluding Prussian blue)	6.00	3.25	4.75
First Day Cover	-	-	80.00
Pictorial cover	-	-	£800

Booklet panes	Wmk Upright	Inverted
Pane of four ½d	30.00	60.00
Pane of four 1d	30.00	60.00
Pane of four 1½d	15.00	20.00

AGL **Great Britain** 1839–1951

Only the best.

Andrew G Lajer
The Old Post Office, Davis Way, Hurst
Berkshire RG10 0TR, United Kingdom
T: +44 (0)1189 344151 F: +44 (0)1189 344947
E: andrew.lajer@btinternet.co
www.andrewglajer.co.uk

Andrew Claridge
PO Box 1999, White Notley, Witham
Essex CM8 1XN, United Kingdom
T: +44 (0)1376 584412 F: +44 (0)1376 585388
E: andrew.claridge@btinternet.com

FOR FINE G.B. FROM 1840 - TO DATE SEND FOR OUR LATEST FREE LIST

SG 5h
Superb

SG 132
v.f.u.

SG 115wi
Very fine mint

SG 310
Superb mint

X869a
Superb u/m

We buy and sell fine G.B. from 1840 and can offer you a good selection of scarcer items from stock. Our stock of u/m Machins is one of the finest in the world. We maintain stocks of singles, cylinder blocks, booklets, panes, coils, errors & varieties etc. Our long established Machin New Issue Service will keep you up to date.

WANTS LISTS ARE WELCOMED, PHOTOCOPIES SENT OF ITEMS OF INTEREST

See you at
Stampex
19th-22nd
Sept '07 &
27th Feb -
1st March '08

MIKE HOLT

Dealer in fine G.B. 1840-2008 - Est. 1974, Specialists in Machins

Visit our web-site
www.mike-holt.com

DEPT BSMV, PO BOX 177, STOURBRIDGE, WEST MIDLANDS DY8 3DE
Tel: (01384) 443317 Fax: (01384) 440877 Email:sales@mikeholt.com

---

Great Britain illustrated Price List 1840 - 1940

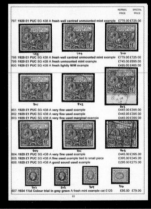

Phone or write for your free copy of our latest 40 page list

Or visit **www.british-stamps.co.uk**

Swan Stamps 21 Torwood Street Torquay TQ1 1ED

Telephone 01803 290619 email steve@british-stamps.co.uk

KING EDWARD VIII

For this reign stamps are priced in two columns: unmounted mint (left) and fine used (right). The exception is booklet panes, which are priced only for unmounted mint with good perforations.

Mounted unused stamps can normally be obtained for about 50% of the quoted unmounted prices.

½d green

■ 1936

Printed by Photogravure by Harrison. Wmk: Multiple Crown and E8R. Perf: 15x14.

½d green (September, 1, 1936)	0.10	0.10
Wmk inverted	6.00	2.50
1d red (September 14, 1936)	0.20	0.20
Wmk inverted	5.00	2.25
1½d brown (September 1, 1936)	0.20	0.10
Wmk inverted	0.75	0.80
2½d blue (September 1, 1936)	0.20	0.30
Set	0.50	0.50

Booklet panes	Wmk Upright	Inverted
Pane of six ½d	15.00	42.00
Pane of six 1d	15.00	42.00
Pane of two 1½d	10.00	10.00
Pane of four 1½d with two advert labels	55.00	55.00
Pane of six 1½d	8.00	14.00

Stamp Magazine is Britain's best for GB collectors

Available from newsagents, or visit www.stampmagazine.co.uk

GREAT BRITAIN 1840 TO DATE

To browse one of the biggest and easiest to use GB websites on the net please visit:

www.british-stamps.com

You will find 1000's of items pictured ranging from basic commemorative sets and single stamps to rare Victorian issues. Also shown are FDC's, Packs and Cards plus Machins, Regionals and Booklets etc etc. There is even a Postal History section with both sides of the cover shown! The site features a secure server so you can "order online" if you wish. Items are added almost daily.

For my Commonwealth stock visit: **www.commonwealth-stamps.com**
For my Foreign stock visit: **www.foreign-stamps.com**
For my USA stock visit: **www.usa-stamps.com** (online autumn 07)

Personal callers are welcome at my shop, details below:

SG 131 light mounted mint

ROWAN S. BAKER
The Covent Garden Stamp Shop
28 Bedfordbury, Covent Garden, London WC2N 4RB
Open Monday-Friday 10.30am-6.00pm Saturday 10.30am-3.00pm

Tele: 020 7379 1448
Fax: 020 7836 3100
email: rowanbaker@btopenworld.com
www.british-stamps.com

30 years in full time dealing

◆ *Lighthouse*®

FOR ALL YOUR COLLECTING NEEDS

HINGELESS ALBUMS

STOCKBOOKS

BINDERS

HAWID MOUNTS

MAGNIFIERS

UV LAMPS

STOCK CARDS

FDC ALBUMS

UNIVERSAL SHEETS

POSTCARD ALBUMS

ACCESSORIES

NEW 2008 BROCHURE AVAILABLE NOW!

Buy online at
www.duncannon.co.uk

hawid®

T: 01737 244222   F: 01737 224743

THE DUNCANNON PARTNERSHIP

4 BEAUFORT ROAD, REIGATE, RH2 9DJ

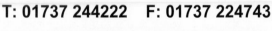

KING GEORGE VI

For this reign, prices are priced in two columns: unmounted mint (left) and fine used (right). The exception is booklet panes, which are priced only for unmounted mint with good perforations.

1½d

■ **1937, May 13. Coronation**
Des: E. Dulac. Printed in photogravure by Harrison. Wmk: Multiple Crown and GVIR. Perf: 15x14

1½d	0.25	0.15
First Day Cover		3.00
Pictorial cover		20.00

½d, 1d, 1½d, 2d, 2½d, 3d

4d, 5d, 6d

7d, 8d, 9d, 10d, 11d, 1/-

■ **1937-47 Definitives**
Des: E. Dulac and E. Gill (½d to 6d), E. Dulac (7d to 1/-). Printed in photogravure by Harrison. Wmk: Multiple Crown and GVIR. Perf: 15x14

A) Original colours

½d green (May 10, 1937)	0.15	0.10
Wmk inverted	7.00	0.50
Wmk sideways	0.25	0.30
1d red (May 10, 1937)	0.15	0.10
Wmk inverted	30.00	2.50
Wmk sideways	15.00	5.00
1½d red-brown (July 30, 1937)	0.15	0.15
Wmk inverted	9.00	1.00
Wmk sideways	1.00	0.50
2d orange (January 31, 1938)	0.50	0.35
Wmk inverted	36.00	2.50
Wmk sideways	36.00	20.00
2½d blue (May 10, 1937)	0.25	1.00
Wmk inverted	32.00	3.00
Wmk sideways	50.00	25.00
3d violet (January 31, 1938)	1.50	0.60

4d green (November 21, 1938)	1.75	0.20
5d brown (November 21, 1938)	2.00	0.30
6d purple (January 30, 1939)	1.00	0.15
7d emerald (February 27, 1939)	3.50	0.50
8d carmine (February 27, 1939)	5.00	0.50
9d deep green (May 1, 1939)	4.00	0.50
10d blue (May 1, 1939)	3.00	0.50
11d brown-purple (December 29, 1947)	1.75	1.00
1/- brown (May 1, 1939)	4.00	0.15
Set	24.00	4.00

Booklet panes	Wmk Upright	Inverted
Pane of two ½d	10.00	10.00
Pane of six ½d	15.00	25.00
Pane of two 1d	10.00	50.00
Pane of six 1d	15.00	£150
Pane of two 1½d	5.00	10.00
Pane of four 1½d with two advert labels (*)	£110	£110
Pane of six 1½d	20.00	25.00
Pane of six 2d	50.00	£200
Pane of six 2½d	50.00	£195
		Wmk Sideways
Pane of four ½d		45.00
Pane of four 1d		70.00

(* 15 different combinations of advertising labels exist. Prices quoted are for the cheapest; scarcer panes can fetch up to twice as much)

B) As above, but with paler colours

½d pale green (September 1, 1941)	0.15	0.10
Wmk inverted	3.00	0.40
1d pale red (August 11, 1941)	0.20	0.10
Wmk sideways	3.00	3.00
1½d pale red-brown (September 28, 1942)	0.50	0.35
2d pale orange (October 6, 1941)	0.50	0.25
Wmk inverted	3.00	0.40
Wmk sideways	10.00	8.00
2½d pale blue (July 21, 1941)	0.15	0.10
Wmk inverted	1.00	0.50
Wmk sideways	7.00	6.00
3d pale violet (November 3, 1941)	1.00	0.25
Set	1.50	1.00

Booklet panes	Wmk Upright	Inverted
Pane of two ½d	9.00	-
Pane of six ½d	10.00	25.00
Pane of two 1d	9.00	-
Pane of two 1½d	9.00	-
Pane of six 2d	7.50	30.00
Pane of six 2½d pale blue	4.00	15.00

C) As above, but with colours changed

½d orange (May 3, 1951)	0.10	0.20
Wmk inverted	0.20	0.30
1d blue (May 3, 1951)	0.10	0.10
Wmk inverted	2.25	1.00
Wmk sideways	0.20	0.40
1½d green (May 3, 1951)	0.25	0.20
Wmk inverted	2.75	2.00
Wmk sideways	1.25	1.50

2d red-brown (May 3, 1951)	0.25	0.25
Wmk inverted	4.00	3.50
Wmk sideways	0.75	0.75
2½d red (May 3, 1951)	0.15	0.15
Wmk inverted	1.00	0.50
Wmk sideways	0.60	0.85
4d blue (October 2, 1950)	1.00	0.65
Set	1.50	1.10

Booklet panes	Wmk Upright	Inverted
Pane of two ½d	9.00	-
Pane of four ½d	7.00	9.00
Pane of six ½d	5.00	6.00
Pane of two 1d	9.00	-
Pane of three 1d with three labels reading 'MINIMUM INLAND PRINTED PAPER RATE 1½d'	25.00	25.00
Pane of three 1d with three labels reading 'SHORTHAND IN ONE WEEK'	35.00	35.00
Pane of four 1d	6.00	7.00
Pane of six 1d	5.00	20.00
Pane of two 1½d	5.00	-
Pane of four 1½d	6.00	14.00
Pane of six 1½d	8.50	22.00
Pane of six 2d	17.00	60.00
Pane of six 2½d	3.50	6.50

2/6, 5/-   10/-, £1

■ 1939-1948. High Values

Des: E. Dulac (2/6, 5/-), G. R. Bellew (10/-, £1). Printed in recess by Waterlow. Wmk: Single Crown and GVIR. Perf: 14

2/6 brown (September 4, 1939)	45.00	5.00
2/6 green (March 9, 1942)	9.00	0.50
5/- red (August 21, 1939)	18.00	1.25
10/- dark blue (October 30, 1939)	£220	17.00
10/- ultramarine (November 30, 1942)	30.00	3.50
£1 brown (October 1, 1948)	18.00	12.00
Set	£280	40.00

½d green, 1d red, 1½d brown, 2d orange, 2½d blue, 3d violet

■ 1940, May 6. Centenary of First Adhesive Postage Stamp

Des: H. L. Palmer. Printed in photogravure by Harrison. Wmk: Multiple Crown and GVIR. Perf: 14½ x 14

Set	4.00	3.50
First Day Cover		7.50
Pictorial cover		35.00

2½d blue, 3d violet

■ 1946, June 11. Victory

Des: H. L. Palmer (2½d), Reynolds Stone (3d). Printed in photogravure by Harrison. Wmk: Multiple Crown and GVIR. Perf: 15x14

Set	0.20	0.25
First Day Cover		9.00
Pictorial cover		45.00

2½d, £1

■ 1948, April 26. Royal Silver Wedding

Des: G.T. Knipe and Joan Hassall (from photographs by Dorothy Wilding Studios). Printed in photogravure by Harrison. Wmk: Multiple Crown and GVIR. Perf: 15x14 (2½d), 14 x 15 (£1).

Set	27.00	25.00
First Day Cover		50.00
Pictorial cover		£400

■ 1948, May 10. Liberation of the Channel Islands

Although this set was placed on sale at eight post offices in Great Britain, it is listed under Regional Issues

Globe surrounded by a Laurel Wreath (2½d)
Globe with Olympic Rings (3d)
Olympic Rings (6d)
Victory and Olympic Rings (1/-)

■ 1948, July 29. Olympic Games

Des: P. Metcalfe, A. Games, S. Scott and E. Dulac. Printed in photogravure by Harrison. Wmk: Multiple Crown and GVIR. Perf: 15x14

Set	2.50	1.20
First Day Cover		8.00
Pictorial cover		35.00

Two Hemispheres (2½d)
UPU Monument (3d)
Globe and Compass (6d)
Globe and Posthorn (1/-)

■ **1949, October 10.**
75th Anniversary of the Universal Postal Union
Des: Mary Adshed (2½d), P. Metcalfe (3d). H. Fleury (6d),
G. R. Bellew (1/-). Printed in photogravure by Harrison. Wmk:
Multiple Crown and GVIR. Perf: 15x14.

Set	1.50	1.25
First Day Cover		9.50
Pictorial cover		47.00

H.M.S. Victory (2/6)
White Cliffs of Dover (5/-)
St. George and the Dragon (10/-)
Royal Coat of Arms (£1)

■ **1951, May 3. High Values**
Des: Mary Adshead (2/6, 5/-), P. Metcalfe (10/-, £1).
Printed in recess by Waterlow. Wmk: Single Crown and GVIR.
Perf: 11x12.

Set	50.00	15.00

2½d red, 4d blue

■ **1951, May 3. Festival of Britain**
Des: E. Dulac (2½d), A. Games (4d). Printed in photogravure by
Harrison. Wmk: Multiple Crown and GVIR. Perf: 15x14.

Set	0.35	0.40
First Day Cover		3.00
Pictorial cover		17.00

PRESENTATION PACKS

Britain's largest stocks of GB Presentation packs. Commemoratives, Definitives, Greetings, Forerunners,
Welsh, Souvenir, POM Post Office missed packs (Set of 16 packs – special offer £95 post free)

FREE 32 PAGE COLOUR LIST

Also includes GB PHQ cards, maxicards, miniature sheets, stamp posters and stamp press photos

PTS **PACKS & CARDS**

Oaklands House (M03), Reading Road North, Fleet, Hampshire, GU51 4AB. UK.
Tel: **01252 360530** Fax: **01252 620519**

PacksAndCards.com

**ALL RISKS COVER
for ALL COLLECTABLES**
Stamps, Postcards, Coins, Diecast Models,
Dolls Houses etc
£5,000 Cover from £21pa * for stamps & Postcards
£4,000 Cover from £25pa * for all other collectables
*plus Government Insurance Premium Tax
**PUBLIC LIABILITY COVER FOR SOCIETIES
DEALERS POLICY AVAILABLE
STAMP INSURANCE SERVICES**
Dept 03SV C G I Services Limited
29 Bowhay Lane, Exeter EX4 1PE
tel: **01392 433 949** fax: **01392 427 632**
www.stampinsurance.co.uk
Authorised and Registered by the Financial Services Authority

**Stamp Magazine
is Britain's
best for GB
collectors**

STAMP MAGAZINE

Near perfect?
Why this close-up on the Bahamas' first
issue is the loveliest Chalon head of all

Every issue includes:
■ Five pages of GB news
■ Full details of latest issues
■ The best first day covers

**Available from newsagents, or
visit www.stampmagazine.co.uk**

QUEEN ELIZABETH II PRE-DECIMALS

In this section, prices are priced in two columns: unmounted mint (left) and fine used (right). The exception is booklet panes, which are priced only for unmounted mint with good perforations.

Except where otherwise stated, all the stamps have the same technical details: Printed in photogravure by Harrison. Perf: 15x14 (definitives), 15x14 (special issues with a horizontal design) or 14x15 (special issues with a vertical design).

½d, 1d, 1½d, 2d

2½d, 3d

4d, 4½d

5d, 6d, 7d

8d, 9d, 10d, 11d

1/-, 1/6

1/3

■ 1952-1968. Wilding Definitives

Des: Miss E. Mark (½d, 1d, 1½d, 2d). M.C. Farrar-Bell (2½d, 3d, 4d, 4½d), G. Knipe (5d, 6d, 7d), Miss M. Adshead (8d, 9d, 10d, 11d), E. Dulac (1/-, 1/3, 1/6): portrait by Dorothy Wilding Studios.
On the 2½d value the top line of the diadem was initially broken (Type I), but this was later corrected (Type II).

A) Wmk: Multiple Tudor Crown E2R ('Tudor Crown').

½d orange (August 31, 1953)	0.10	0.10
Wmk inverted	0.15	0.40
1d blue (August 31, 1953)	0.15	0.10
Wmk inverted	4.50	2.50
1½d green (December 5, 1952)	0.10	0.10
Wmk inverted	0.35	0.30
Wmk sideways	0.35	0.30
2d deep brown (August 31, 1953)	0.20	0.15
Wmk inverted	20.00	12.00
Wmk sideways	0.75	0.50
2½d carmine (type 1) (December 5, 1952)	0.15	0.10
Wmk inverted (type 2)	0.40	0.30
Wmk sideways (type 1)	3.50	4.00
3d violet (January 18, 1954)	1.00	0.20
4d blue (November 2, 1953)	1.00	0.70
5d brown (July 6, 1953)	4.00	2.50
6d purple (January 18, 1954)	3.00	0.75
7d pale green (January 18, 1954)	8.00	2.00
8d magenta (July 6, 1953)	5.00	0.75
9d myrtle-green (February 8, 1954)	14.00	1.50
10d blue (February 8, 1954)	12.00	1.50
11d brown-red (February 8, 1954)	30.00	10.00
1/- bistre (July 6, 1953)	1.00	0.50
1/3 deep-green (November 2, 1953)	3.00	1.50
1/6 grey-blue (November 2, 1953)	12.00	1.25
Set	60.00	20.00
Wmk inverted	18.00	14.00
Wmk sideways	4.50	4.50
First Day Cover		£140
Pictorial cover		£600

Booklet panes	Wmk Upright	Inverted
Pane of two ½d	2.00	-
Pane of four ½d	4.00	4.00
Pane of six ½d	2.00	4.00
Pane of two 1d	2.00	-
Pane of four 1d	3.00	25.00
Pane of three 1d with three labels reading: MINIMUM INLAND PRINTED PAPER RATE 1½d	£300	£300
Pane of three 1d with three labels reading: PLEASE POST EARLY IN THE DAY	40.00	40.00
Pane of three 1d with three labels reading: PACK YOUR PARCELS SECURELY/ADDRESS YOUR LETTERS CORRECTLY/POST EARLY IN THE DAY	40.00	40.00
Pane of six 1d	8.00	30.00
Pane of two 1½d	2.00	-
Pane of four 1½d	4.00	4.00
Pane of six 1½d	2.00	4.00
Pane of six 2d	27.00	£160
Pane of six 2½d	3.50	3.50

B) As before but Wmk: Multiple St. Edward's Crown E2R ('Edward's Crown').

½d (August 1955)	0.15	0.10
Wmk inverted	0.20	0.20
1d (September 19, 1955)	0.20	0.10
Wmk inverted	0.50	0.50

1½d (August 1955)	0.15	0.10
Wmk inverted	0.30	0.20
Wmk sideways	0.20	0.25
2d deep brown (September 6, 1955)	0.25	0.30
Wmk inverted	7.00	5.00
Wmk sideways	0.50	0.50
2d brown (October 17, 1956)	0.25	0.10
Wmk inverted	5.00	4.00
Wmk sideways	5.00	3.00
2½d (type 1) (September 28, 1955)	0.25	0.15
Wmk inverted	0.75	1.00
Wmk sideways	0.75	1.00
2½d (type 2) (September 1955)	0.30	0.60
Wmk inverted	0.30	0.30
3d (July 17, 1956)	0.25	0.20
Wmk inverted	1.75	1.50
Wmk sideways	12.00	7.50
4d (November 14, 1955)	1.50	2.00
5d (September 21, 1955)	5.00	3.00
6d purple (December 20, 1955)	3.50	1.00
6d deep purple (May 8, 1958)	3.00	1.00
7d (April 23, 1956)	30.00	7.00
8d (December 21, 1955)	4.00	1.25
9d (December 15, 1955)	12.00	2.00
10d (September 22, 1955)	10.00	2.00
11d (October 28, 1955)	0.50	1.25
1/- (November 3, 1955)	6.50	0.50
1/3 (March 27, 1956)	14.00	1.00
1/6 (March 27, 1956)	20.00	0.75
Set	100.00	25.00
Wmk inverted	14.00	7.00
Wmk sideways	14.00	9.00

Booklet panes	Wmk Upright	Inverted
Pane of two ½d	3.00	-
Pane of four ½d	4.00	4.00
Pane of six ½d	2.00	3.50
Pane of two 1d	3.50	-
Pane of three 1d with three labels reading: PACK YOUR PARCELS SECURELY/ADDRESS YOUR LETTERS CORRECTLY/POST EARLY IN THE DAY	30.00	35.00
Pane of four 1d	4.00	4.00
Pane of six 1d	2.50	3.00
Pane of two 1½d	3.50	-
Pane of four 1½d	4.00	4.00
Pane of six 1½d	2.00	2.00
Pane of six 2d deep brown	13.00	65.00
Pane of six 2d brown	8.00	22.50
Pane of six 2½d	3.00	3.00
Pane of four 3d	10.00	15.00
Pane of six 3d	6.00	20.00

C) As before but Wmk: Multiple St. Edward's Crown ('Multiple Crowns').

½d (November 25, 1958)	0.10	0.10
chalky paper (July 15, 1963)	2.00	2.50
Wmk inverted	0.30	0.10
chalky paper and Wmk inverted	1.50	2.00
Wmk sideways	0.25	0.15

1d (November 1958)	0.10	0.10
Wmk inverted	0.20	0.20
Wmk sideways	0.60	0.35
1½d (December 1958)	0.15	0.15
Wmk inverted	1.00	0.40
Wmk sideways	4.50	3.50
2d brown (December 4, 1958)	0.10	0.10
Wmk inverted	75.00	40.00
Wmk sideways	0.50	0.40
2½d (type 1) (October 4, 1961)	0.10	0.40
Wmk sideways	0.20	0.25
2½d (type 2) (November 1958)	0.35	0.20
chalky paper (July 15, 1963)	0.30	0.25
Wmk inverted	3.50	0.90
chalky paper & Wmk inverted	0.30	0.25
Wmk sideways	0.40	0.50
3d (November 1958)	0.15	0.10
Wmk inverted	0.25	0.20
Wmk sideways	0.25	0.15
4d blue (October 29, 1958)	0.50	0.25
4d deep blue (April 28, 1965)	0.20	0.12
Wmk inverted	0.35	0.20
Wmk sideways	0.35	0.15
4½d red-brown (February 9, 1959)	0.12	0.12
5d (November 10, 1958)	0.20	0.10
6d deep purple (December 23, 1958)	0.25	0.10
7d (November 26, 1958)	0.50	0.20
8d (February 24, 1960)	0.35	0.10
9d (March 24, 1959)	0.35	0.20
10d (November 18, 1958)	0.75	0.25
1/- (October 30, 1958	0.35	0.25
1/3 (June 17, 1959)	0.35	0.15
1/6 (December 16, 1958)	3.00	0.15
Set	5.00	1.50
Wmk inverted	80.00	42.00
Wmk sideways	5.50	4.00

Booklet panes	Wmk Upright	Inverted
Pane of three ½d and one 2½d (chalky paper)	8.00	8.00
Pane of four ½d	2.50	2.50
Pane of six ½d	1.25	2.00
Pane of four 1d	2.50	2.50
Pane of six 1d	1.50	2.50
Pane of four 1½d	2.50	2.50
Pane of six 1½d	5.00	6.00
Pane of six 2d	40.00	£500
Pane of four 2½d (chalky paper)	1.00	1.00
Pane of six 2½d	3.00	15.00
Pane of four 3d	2.00	2.00
Pane of six 3d	1.50	1.50
Pane of six 4d deep blue	1.50	1.50

	Wmk Sideways
Pane of two ½d se-tenant with two 2½d (type 2)	1.00
Pane of four ½d	2.00
Pane of two 1d se-tenant with two 3d to left	5.00
Pane of two 1d se-tenant with two 3d to right	5.00
Pane of four 1d	3.00
Pane of four 1½d	25.00
Pane of four 3d	2.00
Pane of four 4d	2.00

<table>
</table>

ii) Wmk: Multiple St. Edwards Crown.		
2d brown	4.00	3.00
2½d (type2)	10.00	10.00
3d	14.00	7.50
4d blue	8.00	5.00
4½d	25.00	20.00
Set	50.00	40.00
First Day Cover		75.00

■ Graphite Lined Issues

As before but each stamp has two black lines on the back, except for the 2d which has just one line on the right as viewed from the back.

A) Wmk: Multiple St. Edward's Crown E2R upright. Released on November 19, 1957.

½d	0.20	0.20
1d	0.20	0.20
1½d	1.25	0.50
2d brown	1.00	1.25
2½d (type 2)	4.50	3.50
3d	0.75	0.50
Set	6.75	5.50
First Day Cover		75.00

B) Wmk: Multiple St. Edward's Crown.

½d (June 15, 1959)	5.00	5.00
Wmk inverted	1.00	1.25
1d (December 18, 1958)	1.00	1.00
Wmk inverted	1.00	0.75
1½d (August 4, 1959)	60.00	50.00
Wmk inverted	20.00	20.00
2d (December 4, 1958)	4.75	2.50
2½d (type 2) (June 9, 1959)	6.00	6.00
Wmk inverted	35.00	30.00
3d (November 24, 1958)	0.60	0.45
Wmk inverted	0.55	0.40
4d (April 29, 1959)	3.25	3.25
4½d (June 3, 1959)	3.50	2.25
Set	70.00	55.00
Wmk inverted	60.00	50.00

Booklet panes	*Wmk Upright*	*Inverted*
Pane of six **½d**	20.00	12.00
Pane of six **1d**	7.50	7.00
Pane of six **1½d**	£500	£125
Pane of six **2½d**	30.00	£300
Pane of six **3d**	4.00	4.00

■ Phosphor Graphite Issue

As before but in addition to the graphite lines on the back, each stamp has two bands of phosphor on the front, except for the 2d which has just one band to the left.

A) Wmk: Multiple St. Edward's Crown E2R. Released on November 18, 1959.

½d	3.00	3.00
1d	9.00	9.00
1½d	2.50	3.00
2d brown	95.00	90.00

■ Phosphor Issue

As before but without graphite lines. Each stamp has two bands of phosphor on the front except where stated. Released on June 22, 1960 except where stated. Wmk: Multiple St. Edward's Crown.

½d	0.15	0.15
Wmk inverted	1.00	1.00
Wmk sideways	5.00	7.50
1d	0.10	0.10
Wmk inverted	0.35	0.30
Wmk sideways	0.40	0.50
1½d	0.12	0.20
Wmk inverted	5.00	5.00
Wmk sideways	5.00	7.50
2d brown (one band)	14.00	12.00
2d brown (October 4, 1961)	0.20	0.10
Wmk sideways	0.30	0.25
2½d (type 2)	0.20	0.20
Wmk inverted	£135	£120
2½d (type 2 – one band)	1.50	0.50
Wmk inverted	24.00	17.00
2½d (type 1 – one band)	30.00	25.00
3d	0.50	0.35
Wmk inverted	0.80	0.50
Wmk sideways	1.25	0.55
3d (April 29, 1965) (one band at left)	0.30	0.40
Wmk inverted	40.00	42.00
Wmk sideways	4.00	4.00
3d (one band at right)	0.30	0.40
Wmk inverted	6.00	6.50
Wmk sideways	4.00	4.00
Se-tenant pair	0.60	1.50
Se-tenant pair with Wmk inverted	47.00	49.00
Se-tenant pair with Wmk sideways	8.00	10.00
3d (December 8, 1966) (one band in centre)	0.25	0.25
Wmk inverted	3.00	3.50
Wmk sideways	0.40	0.50
4d blue	2.75	3.25
4d deep blue (April 28, 1965)	0.15	0.25
Wmk inverted	0.25	0.20
Wmk sideways	0.35	0.25
4½d (September 13, 1961)	0.15	0.25
5d (June 9, 1967)	0.20	0.25
6d deep purple (June 27, 1960)	0.20	-
7d (February 15, 1967)	0.20	0.25
8d (June 28, 1967)	0.20	0.25
9d (December 29, 1966)	0.50	0.25
10d (December 30, 1966)	0.50	0.40
1/- (June 28, 1967)	0.40	0.20
1/3	1.00	1.00
1/6 (December 12, 1966)	2.00	2.00

Set (one of each value)	4.50	5.00
Wmk inverted	£180	£170
Wmk sideways	15.00	18.00

Booklet panes	Wmk Upright	Inverted
Pane of six ½d	3.00	4.00
Pane of six 1d	2.00	2.00
Pane of six 1½d	8.00	30.00
Pane of six 2½d (type 2 with two bands)	80.00	£1,100
Pane of six 2½d (type 2 with one band)	22.00	£140
Pane of six 3d (two bands)	5.00	5.00
Pane of six 3d (one band at left or right)	20.00	90.00
Pane of six 3d (one centre band)	4.00	15.00
Pane of six 4d	2.00	3.00
		Wmk sideways
Pane of four ½d		35.00
Pane of two 1d se-tenant with two 3d (two bands)		3.00
Pane of two 1d se-tenant with two 3d (one band, left)		11.00
Pane of two 1d se-tenant with two 3d (one band, right)		11.00
Pane of four 1d		5.00
Pane of four 1½d		35.00
Pane of four 3d (two bands)		5.00
Pane of four 4d		1.00

Carrickfergus Castle (2/6)
Caernarvon Castle (5/-)
Edinburgh Castle (10/-)
Windsor Castle (£1)

■ 1955-1968. Castle High Values
Printed in recess. Perf: 11x12

A) Wmk: Multiple St. Edward's Crown E2R upright.
i) Printed by Waterlow.

2/6 brown (September 23, 1955)	14.00	2.00
5/- carmine (September 23, 1955)	30.00	3.00
10/- blue (September 1, 1955)	60.00	10.00
£1 black (September 1, 1955)	85.00	20.00
Set	£160	30.00
First Day Cover		£300
Pictorial cover		£850

ii) Printed by De La Rue.

2/6 (July 17, 1958)	25.00	3.50
5/- (April 30, 1958)	50.00	8.00
10/- (April 25, 1958)	£150	14.00
£1 (April 28, 1958)	£200	30.00
Set	£375	47.00

(* The top perforation tooth of each side of the stamps from the De La Rue printing is narrower than that found on the Waterlow printing.)

B) Wmk: St. Edward's Crown upright. Colours as before.
i) Printed by De La Rue.

2/6 (July 22, 1958)	12.00	0.50
5/- (June 15, 1959)	50.00	1.00
10/- (July 21, 1959)	40.00	2.75
£1 (June 23, 1959)	80.00	12.00
Set	£150	15.00

ii) Printed by Bradbury, Wilkinson.

2/6 (July 1, 1963)	0.50	0.15
5/- (September 3, 1963)	2.00	0.40
10/- (October 16, 1963)	3.50	2.50
£1 (November 14, 1963)	9.50	3.00
Set	13.50	7.00

iii) Printed by Bradbury, Wilkinson on chalky paper.

2/6 (May 30, 1968)	0.50	0.75

(* The Queen's diadem is more detailed on the Bradbury, Wilkinson printing than on the De La Rue printing.)

C) No Wmk. Printed by Bradbury, Wilkinson.

2/6 (July 1, 1968)	0.30	0.40
5/- (April 10, 1968)	1.50	0.75
10/- (April 10, 1968)	6.00	4.00
£1 (December 4, 1967)	7.00	4.50
Set	10.50	10.50

Four different designs (2½d, 4d, 1/3, 1/6)

■ 1953, June 3. Coronation
Des: E.G. Fuller (2½d), M. Goaman (4d), E. Dulac (1/3), M.C. Farrar-Bell (1/6). Wmk: Multiple Tudor Crown E2R.

Set	7.50	4.00
First Day Cover		27.00

Scout Badge (2½d)
Flying Birds (4d)
Globe within compass (1/3)

■ 1957, August 1. World Scout Jubilee Jamboree
Des: Mary Adshead (2½d), Pat Keely (4d), W. H. Brown (1/3).
Wmk: Multiple St Edward's Crown E2R.

Set	2.75	2.25
First Day Cover		15.00

(* These stamps were issued in coils as well as normal sheets.)

4d

■ 1957, September 12. Inter-Parliamentary Union Conference
Wmk: Multiple St. Edward's Crown E2R.

4d	0.50	0.50
First Day Cover		75.00

Welsh Dragon (3d)
Games emblem (6d)
Welsh Dragon (1/3)

■ 1958, July 18. British Empire & Commonwealth Games
Des: Reynolds Stone (3d), W.H. Brown (6d), Pat Keely (1/3). Wmk: Multiple St. Edward's Crown E2R.

Set	1.25	1.00
First Day Cover		60.00

1660 Postboy (3d)
1660 Posthorn (1/3)

■ 1960, July 7. Anniversary of General Letter Office
Des: Reynolds Stone (3d), Faith Jacques (1/3). Wmk: Multiple St. Edward's Crown.

Set	1.75	1.75
First Day Cover		30.00

Europa emblem (6d, 1/6)

■ 1960, September 19. Europa (First Anniversary)
Des: P. Rahikainen and Reynolds Stone. Wmk: Multiple St. Edward's Crown.

Set	7.50	3.00
First Day Cover		22.00

Thrift plant (2½d)
Squirrel and stylised tree (3d)
Thrift plant (1/6)

■ 1961, August 28. Post Office Savings Bank Centenary
Des: P. Gauld (2½d), M. Goaman (3d, 1/6). Wmk: Multiple St. Edward's Crown.
A) Printed on a Timson machine.

Set	1.25	1.00
First Day Cover		35.00

B) Printed on a Thrissell machine: 2½d, 3d only

Pair	1.50	1.50

(* The portrait on the 2½d is greyer from the Thrissell machine, and that on the 3d is much clearer on the Timson printing.)

CEPT emblem (2d)
Doves and emblem (4d)
Doves and emblem (10d)

■ 1961, September 18. CEPT Conference
Des: M. Goaman and T. Kurperschoek. Wmk: Multiple St. Edward's Crown.

Set	0.25	0.25
First Day Cover		2.75

Roof of Westminster Hall (6d)
Palace of Westminster (1/3)

■ **1961, September 23. Commonwealth Parliamentary Conference**
Des: Faith Jacques. Wmk: Multiple St. Edward's Crown.

Set	1.00	1.25
First Day Cover		18.00

Boxes bearing arrows (2½d)
Arrows over the British Isles (3d)
Joining arrows (1/3)

■ **1962, November 14. National Productivity Year**
Des: D. Gentleman. Wmk: Multiple St. Edward's Crown, inverted on 2½d and 3d values.
A) Non-phosphor issue: 2½d, 3d, 1/3

Set	1.25	1.00
First Day Cover		20.00

B) Phosphor issue: 2½d (one band); 3d, 1/3 (three bands.)

Set	14.00	10.00
First Day Cover		90.00

Ears of Wheat (2½d)
Three Children (1/3)

■ **1963, March 21. Freedom from Hunger.**
Des: M. Goaman. Wmk: Multiple St. Edward's Crown, inverted on both values.
Ai) Non-phosphor issue: 2½d, 1/3.

Set	1.25	1.25
First Day Cover		15.00

B) Phosphor issue: 2½d (one band), 1/3 (three bands).

Set	13.00	10.00
First Day Cover		22.00

1863 Paris Postal Conference Centenary (6d)˙

■ **1963, May 7. Paris Postal Conference Centenary**
Des: Reynolds Stone. Wmk: Multiple St. Edward's Crown, inverted.
A) Non-phosphor issue.

6d	30	25
First Day Cover		8.00

B) Phosphor issue (three bands).

6d	3.50	3.00
First Day Cover		18.00

Bee on flowers (3d)
Selection of wildlife (4½d)

■ **1963, May 16. National Nature Week**
Des: S. Scott (3d), M. Goaman (4½d). Wmk: Multiple St. Edward's Crown.
A) Non-phosphor issue.

Set	0.15	0.20
First Day Cover		12.00

B) Phosphor issue (three bands).

Set	1.75	1.75
First Day Cover		20.00

Helicopter over boat (2½d)
Lifeboat (4d)
Lifeboatmen (1/6)

■ **1963, May 31. International Lifeboat Conference**
Des: D. Gentlemen. Wmk: Multiple St. Edward's Crown.
A) Non-phosphor issue.

Set	1.50	1.50
First Day Cover		20.00

B) Phosphor issue: 2½d (one band), 4d, 1/6 (three bands).

Set	25.00	15.00
First Day Cover		35.00

Red Cross (3d, 1/3, 1/6 with different borders)

■ 1963, August 15. Red Cross Centenary Congress

Des: H. Bartram. Wmk: Multiple St. Edward's Crown.
A) Non-phosphor issue.

Set	3.00	3.00
First Day Cover		20.00

B) Phosphor issue (three bands).

Set	35.00	25.00
First Day Cover		50.00

Cable over globe (1/6)

■ 1963, December 3. Opening of COMPAC Cable

Des: P. Gauld. Wmk: Multiple St. Edward's Crown.
A) Non-phosphor issue.

1/6	1.50	1.25
First Day Cover		14.00

B) Phosphor issue (three bands).

1/6	7.50	6.50
First Day Cover		20.00

Puck and Bottom (3d)
Feste (6d)
Romeo and Juliet (1/3)
Henry V (1/6)
Hamlet (2/6)

■ 1964, April 23. Shakespeare Festival

Des: D. Gentleman (3d to 1/6); C. and R. Ironside (2/6). Printed
in recess by Bradbury, Wilkinson (2/6). Perf: 11x12 (2/6). Wmk:
Multiple St. Edward's Crown.
A) Non-phosphor issue: 3d, 6d, 1/3, 1/6, 2/6

Set	2.50	2.50
First Day Cover		5.00

B) Phosphor issue (three bands): 3d, 6d, 1/3, 1/6

Set	6.00	6.00
First Day Cover		8.00

Flats, Richmond Park (2½d)
Shipbuilding, Belfast (4d)
Forest Park, Snowdonia (8d)
Nuclear Reactor, Dounreay (1/6)

■ 1964, July 1. International Geographical Congress

Des: D. Bailey. Wmk: Multiple St. Edward's Crown.
A) Non-phosphor issue: 2½d, 4d, 8d, 1/6

Set	2.25	2.25
First Day Cover		12.00

B) Phosphor issue: 2½d (one band), 4d, 8d, 1/6 (three bands).

Set	15.00	11.00
First Day Cover		19.00

Spring Gentian (3d)
Dog Rose (6d)
Honeysuckle (9d)
Fringed Water Lily (1/3)

■ 1964, August 5. International Botanical Congress

Des: Michael and Sylvia Goaman. Wmk: Multiple St. Edward's
Crown.
A) Non-phosphor issue.

Set	2.50	2.50
First Day Cover		12.00

B) Phosphor issue (three bands).

Set	15.00	11.00
First Day Cover		19.00

Forth Road Bridge (3d)
Forth Road and Railway Bridges (6d)

■ 1964, September 4. Opening of the Forth Road Bridge

Des: A. Restall. Wmk: Multiple St. Edward's Crown.
A) Non-phosphor issue.

Set	0.25	0.30
First Day Cover		3.50

B) Phosphor issue (three bands).

Set	2.50	2.75
First Day Cover		8.00

Sir Winston Churchill (4d, 1/3 with slightly different designs)

1965, July 8. Churchill Commemoration

Des: D. Gentleman and Rosaline Dease. Wmk: Multiple St. Edward's Crown.
A) Non-phosphor issue.

Set	0.30	0.30
First Day Cover		2.00

B) Phosphor issue (three bands).

Set	1.50	1.50
First Day Cover		3.00

C) Printed on a Timson machine

4d	0.10	0.10

* The Timson printing shows far more details on the portrait of Churchill.

Seal of Simon de Montfort (6d)
Parliament Buildings (2/6)

1965, July 19. 700th Anniversary of Simon de Montfort's Parliament

Des: S.R. Black (6d), Professor R. Guyatt (2/6). Wmk: Multiple St. Edward's Crown.
A) Non-phosphor issue: 6d, 2/6

Set	0.65	0.65
First Day Cover		8.00

B) Phosphor issue (three bands): 6d only

6d	0.50	0.60
First Day Cover		15.00

Salvation Army Band (3d)
Three Salvation Army members (1/6)

1965, August 9. Centenary of Salvation Army

Des: M.C. Farrar-Bell (3d), G. Trenaman (1/6). Wmk: Multiple St. Edward's Crown.
A) Non-phosphor issue.

Set	0.55	0.60
First Day Cover		11.00

B) Phosphor issue: 3d (one band), 1/6 (three bands).

Set	1.35	1.25
First Day Cover		14.00

Carbolic Spray (4d)
Joseph Lister (1/-)

1965, September 1. Centenary of Joseph Lister's Discovery of Antiseptic Surgery

Des: P. Gauld (4d), F. Ariss (1/-). Wmk: Multiple St. Edward's Crown.
A) Non-phosphor issue.

Set	0.50	0.60
First Day Cover		6.00

B) Phosphor issue (three bands).

Set	1.50	1.50
First Day Cover		8.00

Trinidad Carnival Dancers (6d)
Canadian Folk Dancers (1/6)

1965, September 1. Commonwealth Arts Festival

Des: D. Gentleman and Rosalind Dease. Wmk: Multiple St. Edward's Crown.
A) Non-phosphor issue.

Set	0.50	0.60
First Day Cover		8.00

B) Phosphor issue (three bands).

Set	1.80	1.75
First Day Cover		10.00

Spitfires (4d)
Pilot in hurricane (4d)
Overlapping wings (4d)
Spitfires attacking Heinkel bomber (4d)
Spitfire attacking Stuka bomber (4d)
Tail wing of Dornier bomber (4d)
Anti-aircraft Artillery (9d)
St Paul's Cathedral (1/3)

■ 1965, September 13. 25th Anniversary of the Battle of Britain

Des: D. Gentleman and Rosalind Dease (4d, 1/3), A. Restall (9d). Wmk: Multiple St. Edward's Crown. Six 4d values se-tenant.
A) Non-phosphor issue.

Set	4.50	5.00
First Day Cover		12.00

B) Phosphor issue (three bands).

Set	8.00	8.50
First Day Cover		13.00

Post Office Tower (3d)
Post Office Tower and Nash Terrace (1/3)

■ 1965, October 8. Opening of the Post Office Tower

Des: C. Abbott. Wmk: Multiple St. Edward's Crown.
A) Non-phosphor issue.

Set	0.25	0.30
First Day Cover		3.00

B) Phosphor issue: 3d (one band), 1/3 (three bands).

Set	0.40	0.50
First Day Cover		5.00

UN emblem (3d)
ICY emblem (1/6)

■ 1965, October 25. 20th Anniversary of United Nations and International Co-operation Year

Des: J. Matthews. Wmk: Multiple St. Edward's Crown.
A) Non-phosphor issue.

Set	0.50	0.60
First Day Cover		6.00

B) Phosphor issue: 3d (one band), 1/6 (three bands).

Set	1.50	1.50
First Day Cover		7.00

Telecommunications (9d)
Radio Waves (1/6)

■ 1965, November 15. International Telecommunication Union Centenary

Des: A. Restall. Wmk: Multiple St. Edward's Crown.
A) Non-phosphor issue.

Set	0.50	0.60
First Day Cover		7.00

B) Phosphor issue (three bands).

Set	2.75	2.75
First Day Cover		9.00

Robert Burns (4d)
Robert Burns (portrait by Nasmyth) (1/3)

■ 1966, January 25. Robert Burns

Des: G.F. Huntly. Wmk: Multiple St. Edward's Crown.
A) Non-phosphor issue.

Set	0.30	0.40
First Day Cover		1.50

B) Phosphor issue (three bands).

Set	1.00	1.00
First Day Cover		2.75

Westminster Abbey (3d)
Roof of Westminster Abbey (2/6)

■ 1966, February 28. 900th Anniversary of Westminster Abbey

Des: Sheila Robinson (3d), Bradbury Wilkinson (2/6). Printed in recess by Bradbury Wilkinson (2/6). Wmk: Multiple St. Edward's Crown. Perf: 11 x 12 (2/6)
A) Non-phosphor issue: 3d, 2/6

Set	0.50	0.50
First Day Cover		2.75

B) Phosphor issue: 3d only (one band).

3d	0.15	0.20
First Day Cover		8.00

Sussex Downs (4d)
Antrim, Northern Ireland (6d)
Harlech Castle (1/3)
The Cairngorms (1/6)

■ 1966, May 2. Landscapes

Des: L. Rosoman. Wmk: Multiple St. Edward's Crown.
A) Non-phosphor issue.

Set	0.50	0.60
First Day Cover		3.50

B) Phosphor issue (three bands).

Set	0.50	0.70
First Day Cover		4.00

Two footballers (4d)
Four footballers (6d)
Saving the ball (1/3)

■ 1966, June 1. World Cup

Des: D. Gentleman (4d), W. Kempster (6d), D. Caplan (1/3). Wmk: Multiple St. Edward's Crown.
A) Non-phosphor issue: 4d, 6d, 1/3

Set	0.40	0.40
First Day Cover		9.00

B) Phosphor issue: 4d (two bands), 6d, 1/3 (three bands).

Set	0.30	0.40
First Day Cover		10.00

Black-headed Gull (4d)
Blue Tit (4d)
Robin (4d)
Blackbird (4d)

■ 1966, August 8. British Birds

Des: J. Norris Wood. Wmk: Multiple St. Edward's Crown. All four values in se-tenant blocks.
A) Non-phosphor issue.

Se-tenant block of four	0.40	0.50
First Day Cover		4.00

B) Phosphor issue (three bands).

Se-tenant block of four	0.40	0.50
First Day Cover		4.00

Two footballers and legend 'ENGLAND WINNERS' (4d)

■ 1966, August 18. England's World Cup Victory

As June 1 issue, but with inscription 'ENGLAND WINNERS'. Non-phosphor only.

4d	0.20	0.25
First Day Cover		7.50

Jodrell Bank Radio Telescope (4d)
Jaguar 'E' type and Mini cars (6d)
Hovercraft (1/3)
Windscale Nuclear Reactor (1/6)

■ 1966, September 19. British Technology
Des: D. and A. Gillespie (4d, 6d), A. Restall (1/3, 1/6). Wmk:
Multiple St. Edward's Crown.
A) Non-phosphor issue.

Set	0.40	0.45
First Day Cover		1.75

B) Phosphor issue (three bands).

Set	0.45	0.50
First Day Cover		2.00

Scenes from the Bayeux Tapestry (4d, six different designs)
Norman Ship (6d)
Norman horseman attacking Harold's troops (1/3)

■ 1966, October 14. 900th Anniversary of the Battle of Hastings
Des: D. Gentleman. Wmk: Multiple St. Edward's Crown,
sideways on 1/3 value. Six 4d values se-tenant.
A) Non-phosphor issue.

Set	1.00	1.25
First Day Cover		2.25

B) Phosphor issue: 4d, 6d (three bands), 1/3 (four bands).

Set	1.00	1.25
First Day Cover		2.75

King of the Orient (3d)
Snowman (1/6)

■ 1966, December 1. Christmas
Des: Miss T. Shemza (3d), J. Berry (1/6), both aged six. Wmk:
Multiple St. Edward's Crown, upright on both values.
A) Non-phosphor issue.

Set	0.15	0.20
First Day Cover		1.00

B) Phosphor issue: 3d (one band), 1/6 (two bands).

Set	0.15	0.20
First Day Cover		0.90

(* Phosphor 3d can be found with band at left or right).

Loading freight on a ship (9d)
Loading freight on an aeroplane (1/6)

■ 1967, February 20. European Free Trade Association
Des: C. Abbott. Wmk: Multiple St. Edward's Crown.
A) Non-phosphor issue.

Set	0.15	0.20
First Day Cover		0.75

B) Phosphor issue (three bands).

Set	0.15	0.20
First Day Cover		0.80

Hawthorn and Bramble (4d)
Bindweed and Viper's Bugloss (4d)
Daisy, Buttercup and Coltsfoot (4d)
Bluebell, Anemone and Red Campion (4d)
Dog Violet (9d)
Primrose (1/9)

■ 1967, April 24. British Flowers
Des: Keeble Martin (4d), Mary Grierson (9d, 1/9). Wmk:
Multiple St. Edward's Crown. Four 4d values se-tenant.
A) Non-phosphor issue.

Set	0.60	0.75
First Day Cover		1.50

B) Phosphor issue (three bands).

Set	0.35	0.50
First Day Cover		1.50

'Master Lambton' by Lawrence (4d)
'Mares and Foals in a Landscape' by Stubbs (9d)
'Children coming Out of School' by Lowry (1/6)

1967, July 10. British Paintings
No Wmk.

Set	0.20	0.20
First Day Cover		1.50

Gipsy Moth IV (1/9)

1967, July 24. Sir Francis Chichester's Single-Handed Voyage Around the World
Des: Michael and Sylvia Goaman. No Wmk. Three phosphor bands.

1/9	0.10	0.10
First Day Cover		0.50

Radar screen (4d)
Penicillin Mould (1/-)
Jet Engine (1/6)
Television Equipment (1/9)

1967, September 19. British Discoveries
Des: C. Abbott (4d, 1/-), Negus and Sharland (1/6,1/9). Wmk: Multiple St. Edward's Crown. Three phosphor bands on the 4d.

Set	0.25	0.30
First Day Cover		0.75

'The Adoration of the Shepherds' by the School of Seville (3d)
'Madonna and Child' by Murillo (4d)
'The Adoration of the Shepherds' by Louis Le Nan (1/6)

1967. Christmas
No Wmk. 3d has one central phosphor band.
3d released on November 27, 4d on October 18, 1/6 on November 27.

Set	0.15	0.20
First Day Cover		0.75

Tarr Steps (4d)
Aberfeldy Bridge (9d)
Menai Bridge (1/6)
M4 Viaduct (1/9)

1968, April 29. British Bridges
Des: J. Matthews (4d, 1/9), A. Restall (9d), L. Rosoman (1/6). No Wmk.

Set	0.25	0.30
First Day Cover		0.75

Trades Union Congress (4d)
Votes for Women (9d)
Royal Air Force: Sopwith Camel (1/-)
James Cook Signature and 'Endeavour' (1/9)

1968, May 29. Anniversaries
Des: D. Gentleman (4d), C. Abbott (others). No Wmk.

Set	0.25	0.30
First Day Cover		2.25

'Queen Elizabeth I' by an unknown artist (4d)
'Pinkie' by Lawrence (1/-)
'Ruins of St Mary le Port' by Piper (1/6)
'The Hay Wain' by Constable (1/9)

■ 1968, August 12. British Painters.
No Wmk.

Set	0.25	0.30
First Day Cover		0.60

Boy and Girl and Rocking Horse (4d)
Girl and Doll's House (9d)
Boy and Train Set (1/6)

■ 1968, November 25. Christmas
Des: Rosalind Dease. No Wmk.
A) Printed on a Rembrandt machine: 4d, 9d, 1/6

Set	0.20	0.20
First Day Cover		0.50

B) Printed on a Thrissell machine: 4d only.

4d	0.15	0.20

(* The Thrissell printing can be distinguished by the boy's pullover having a more mottled appearance.)

'Queen Elizabeth 2' (5d)
Elizabethan Galleon (9d)
East Indiaman (9d)
'Cutty Sark' (9d)
SS 'Great Britain' (1/-)
RMS 'Mauretania' (1/-)

■ 1969, January 15. British Ships
Des: D. Gentleman. No Wmk. Three 9d values in se-tenant strip.
Two 1/- values in se-tenant pair.

Set	0.75	1.00
First Day Cover		1.75

'Concorde' over Great Britain and France (4d)
Silhouettes of 'Concorde' (9d)
Nose and Tail of 'Concorde' (1/6)

■ 1969, March 3. Flight of Concorde
Des: Michael and Sylvia Goaman (4d), D. Gentleman (9d, 1/6).
No Wmk.

Set	0.75	0.50
First Day Cover		1.75

First Transatlantic Flight: Vickers 'Vimy', Alcock & Brown (5d)
Europa/CEPT (9d)
International Labour Organisation: hand holding wrench (1/-)
NATO: Flags (1/6)
First England-Australia Flight: Vickers 'Vimy', route on globe (1/9)

■ 1969, April 2. Anniversaries
Des: P. Sharland (5d, 1/-, 1/6), Michael and Sylvia Goaman (9d, 1/9).
No Wmk.

Set	0.50	0.60
First Day Cover		1.10

Durham Cathedral (5d)
York Minster (5d)
St Giles' Cathedral, Edinburgh (5d)
Canterbury Cathedral (5d)
St Paul's Cathedral (9d)
Liverpool Metropolitan Cathedral (1/6)

■ 1969, May 28. British Cathedrals
Des: P. Gauld. No Wmk. Four 5d values se-tenant.

Set	0.60	0.75
First Day Cover		1.20

The King's Gate, Caernarvon Castle (5d)
The Eagle Tower, Caernarvon Castle (5d)
Queen Eleanor's Gate, Caernarvon Castle (5d)
Celtic Cross, Margam Abbey (9d)
Prince of Wales (1/-)

■ **1969, July 1. Investiture of the Prince of Wales**
Des: D. Gentleman. No Wmk. Three 5d values se-tenant.

Set	0.30	0.50
First Day Cover		0.90

Gandhi and Flag of India (1/6)

■ **1969, August 13. Gandhi Centenary Year**
Des: Biman Mullick.

1/6	0.15	0.15
First Day Cover		0.50

National Giro symbol (5d)
Telephone Dials (9d)
Pulse Code Modulation (1/-)
Automatic Sorting (1/6)

■ **1969, October 1. Post Office Technology**
Des: D. Gentleman. Printed in litho by De La Rue. No Wmk.
Perf: 13½x14.

Set	0.25	0.30
First Day Cover		0.60

The Herald Angel (4d)
The Three Shepherds (5d)
The Three Kings (1/6)

■ **1969, November 26. Christmas**
Des: F. Wegner. No Wmk.

Set	0.15	0.20
First Day Cover		0.50

Fife Harling (5d)
Cotswold Limestone (9d)
Welsh Stucco (1/-)
Ulster Thatch (1/6)

■ **1970, February 11. Rural Architecture**
Des: D. Gentleman (5d, 9d), Sheila Robinson (1/-, 1/6). No Wmk.

Set	0.30	0.40
First Day Cover		0.65

Signing the Declaration of Arbroath (5d)
Florence Nightingale and Patients (9d)
Signing the International Co-operative Alliance (1/-)
Sailing of the 'Mayflower' (1/6)
Royal Astronomical Society: Sir William and Sir John Herschel
with Francis Bailey (1/9)

■ **1970, April 1. Anniversaries**
Des: F. Wegner (5d, 9d, 1/6), Marjorie Seynor (1/-, 1/9).
No Wmk.

Set	0.35	0.40
First Day Cover		1.00

Mr Pickwick and Sam (5d)
Mr and Mrs Micawber (5d)
David Copperfield and Betsey Trotwood (5d)
Oliver Twist asking for more (5d)
Grasmere (1/6)

■ 1970, June 3. Literary Anniversaries
Des: Rosalind Dease. No Wmk. Four 5d vaues se-tenant.

Set	0.50	0.60
First Day Cover		1.00

Runners (5d)
Swimmers (1/6)
Cyclists (1/9)

■ 1970, July 15. British Commonwealth Games
Des: A. Restall. Printed in litho by De La Rue. No Wmk. Perf: 13½x14.

Set	0.50	0.45
First Day Cover		0.60

Penny Black (line engraved) (5d)
1/- Green (embossed) (9d)
4d Carmine (surface printed) (1/6)

■ 1970, September 18. Philympia 1970 International Stamp Exhibition
Des: D. Gentleman. No Wmk.

Set	0.30	0.40
First Day Cover		0.75

The Angel appearing to the Shepherds (4d)
Mary, Joseph and Jesus (5d)
The Wise Men bringing gifts (1/6)

■ 1970, November 25. Christmas
Des: Sally Stiff (based on the De Lisle Psalter). No Wmk.

Set	0.25	0.25
First Day Cover		0.50

Stamp Magazine is Britain's best for GB collectors

Every issue includes:
■ Five pages of GB news
■ Full details of latest issues
■ The best first day covers
■ Newly discovered errors

STAMP MAGAZINE

Near perfect?

Available from newsagents, or visit www.stampmagazine.co.uk

TEL: 01736 751910
FAX: 01736 751911
WEB: WWW.PRINZ.CO.UK EM: INFO@PRINZ.CO.UK
PRINZ PUBLICATIONS UK LTD,
HAYLE INDUSTRIAL PARK, HAYLE, CORNWALL. TR27 5JR

NUMBER ONE FOR ALL YOUR STAMP ACCESSORY NEEDS!

ALBUMS
CATALOGUES
MOUNTS
HINGES
STOCKBOOKS
MAGNIFIERS
TWEEZERS
WATERMARK DETECTORS
UV LIGHTS
PLUS MORE...

WE ARE ALSO

LINDNER

AGENTS

CALL TODAY FOR OUR LATEST BROCHURES!

VERATRINDER

LONDON'S OLDEST STAMP ACCESSORY STORE

WE HAVE ONE OF THE LARGEST SELECTIONS OF PHILATELIC
LITERATURE IN EUROPE COVERING ALMOST ALL COUNTRIES AND
SPECIALITIES. PLEASE CONTACT US FOR THE LATEST BOOK LISTS.

WE STOCK ALL OF THE TOP BRANDS INCLUDING;
STANLEY GIBBONS, DAVO, LIGHHOUSE, HAWID,
SHOWGARD, SHAUBEK, LINDNER, PRINZ, PRANGNELL
RAPKIN, BARRINGTON, FRANK GODDEN & KABE.

OUR RANGE OF ACCESSORIES INCLUDE:
STAMP ALBUMS, STOCKBOOKS,
FDC ALBUMS, POSTCARD ALBUMS,
HINGES, STOCKCARDS, MAGNIFIERS,
TESTING EQUIPMENT, MINISHEET FILES,
TWEEZERS, CUTTERS, CLEAR BAGS &
WALLETS, DRYING BOOKS...ETC

WWW.VERATRINDER.COM
TEL: 0207 257 9940 / FAX: 0207 836 0873
38 BEDFORD STREET, THE STRAND, LONDON, WC2E 9EU, UK

PRE-DECIMAL MACHIN DEFINITIVES

In this section, prices are given for lightly mounted unused (left) and fine used (right). Exceptions are made where used prices are not applicable, for example booklet panes and gum varieties.

The Machin head of Queen Elizabeth II is so-called because it is from a sculpture by Arnold Machin. All designs in the series are similar, but small differences can be found in the head itself and in its setting in the design.

There are also varieties in the number and positioning of phosphor bands.

4d sepia

■ 1967-1969. Definitives

Des: A. Machin. Printed in photogravure by Harrisons. No wmk.
Head 1 with two phosphor bands except where stated

A) Gum Arabic.

3d violet (August 8, 1967) (one band)	0.30	-
4d sepia (June 5, 1967)	0.50	-
head 2	£2,000	-
4d red (one band)	20.00	-
9d green (August 8, 1967)	0.50	-
1/- pale violet (June 5, 1967)	0.35	-
1/- deep violet	2.00	-
1/6 green, deep blue (August 8, 1967)	0.70	-
1/9 orange, black (June 5, 1967)	1.25	-
First Day Cover (4d, 1/-, 1/9)		1.50
First Day Cover (3d, 9d, 1/6)		1.40

Se-tenant coil stamps.
Released on August 27, 1969

1d olive (head 2, one band)	0.50	-
2d brown (head 2, one band)	0.35	0.30
3d violet (head 2, one band)	0.50	-
4d red (head 2, one band)	0.50	-
Se-tenant coil of two 2d, one 1d, one 3d and one 4d	1.25	2.50

Booklet panes

Pane of six 4d sepia (head 1)	17.50	-
Pane of six 4d red (head 1)	£120	-

B) PVA gum.

½d orange (February 5, 1968)	0.40	0.10
1d olive (February 5, 1968)	0.40	0.10
head 2	0.25	0.10
head 2 (one centre band)	0.60	0.50
2d brown (February 5, 1968)	0.40	0.10
setting 2	0.40	0.20
3d violet (one centre band)	0.40	0.10
head 2 (one centre band)	3.00	0.10
3d violet	0.40	0.10
head 2	0.45	0.10
4d sepia (shades)	0.40	0.10
head 2	0.40	0.10
4d sepia (one centre band)	0.40	0.10
head 2 (one centre band)	0.40	0.10
4d red (January 6, 1969) (one centre band)	0.40	0.10
head 2 (one centre band)	0.30	0.10
head 2 (one band at left)	1.25	1.00
head 2 (one band at right)	2.25	3.00
5d blue (July 1, 1968)	0.40	0.10
head 2	0.40	0.10
head 2 (two bands on 'all over' phosphor)	£250	-
6d purple (February 5, 1968)	0.40	0.10
head 2	12.00	4.00
7d green (July 1, 1968) (head 2)	0.50	0.30
8d red (July 1, 1968)	0.40	0.25
8d light-blue (January 6, 1969) (head 2)	0.75	0.40
9d green	0.45	0.20
10d brown (July 1, 1968)	0.75	0.40
1/- deep violet	0.50	0.20
1/6 green, deep blue	0.80	0.50
'all-over' phosphor	1.60	0.30
1/9 orange, black	1.75	0.30
Set (one of each value)	3.00	3.00
First Day Cover (½d, 1d, 2d, 6d)		2.00
First Day Cover (5d, 7d, 8d, 10d)		2.00
First Day Cover (4d red, 8d light blue)		2.00

Booklet panes of four

Four 4d sepia (head 2, two bands)	1.00	-
Four 4d sepia (head 2, one centre band)	2.00	-
Four 4d red (head 2, one centre band)	1.00	-
Two 1d left of two 3d (head 2, two bands)	2.50	-
Two 1d right of two 3d (head 2, two bands)	2.50	-
Two 4d sepia (head 2, one centre band) with two labels reading '£4,315 FOR YOU AT AGE 55' and 'SEE OTHER PAGES'	1.00	-
Two 4d red (head 2, one centre band) with two labels reading '£4,315 FOR YOU AT AGE 55' and 'SEE OTHER PAGES'	2.50	-

Booklet panes of six

Six 1d olive (head 2, two bands)	1.25	-
Six 3d violet (head one, centre band)	15.00	-
Six 4d sepia (head 1, two bands)	1.00	-
Six 4d sepia (head 1, one centre band)	1.40	-

x **4d** red (head 1, one centre band)	1.50	-
x **4d** red (head 2, one centre band)	1.25	-
x **5d** blue (head 2, two bands)	1.00	-
our **1d** olive (one centre band) with two **4d** sepia (head 2, one centre band)	3.00	-
our **1d** olive (two bands) with two **4d** red (head 2, one left band)	4.00	-

ooklet panes of 15 (all head 2)
ix **1d** olive (two bands) with three **4d** red
one band at left), three **4d** (one band at right)
nd three **5d** blue, attached to recipe label   10.00
ifteen **4d** red (one centre band) attached
o a label headed 'Stuffed Cucumber'   3.00
ifteen **4d** red (one centre band) attached
o a label headed 'Method'   3.00
ifteen **5d** blue (two bands) attached
o a recipe label   3.00
* These panes come from the £1 Stamps For Cooks booklet
nd can be found with just four holes in the binding margin,
vhere stapled together, or with a larger number of equally
paced holes, where stitched.)

5/- brown-red

■ **1969, March 5. High values**
Des: A. Machin. Printed in recess by Bradbury, Wilkinson. Perf: 12.

2/6 brown	0.60	0.50
5/- brown-red	2.50	1.00
10/- deep blue	8.00	7.00
£1 black	5.00	2.00
Set	10.00	7.00
First Day Cover		20.00

<u>GENUINE GB CHARITY!</u> Fed up with sifting through GB charity mixture that appears to have been picked through, that is old and unexciting?

We now receive GB Charity sent to us direct from the donator bypassing the charity and any other dealer. You could be sorting through GB stamps that have been collected by offices, schools, banks last week and could find absolutely anything including foreign stamps.

GREAT Britain charity mix from some of the leading charities in the UK
MODERN: How can we prove this, well it comes in on a daily basis so you <u>will</u> receive charity that has arrived over the last few days!
MIXTURE: Received still in their sealed envelopes direct from the donator to us so therefore unopened and unpicked by any charity or dealer.

Tried and tested and extremely popular as our customers have the expressed the excitement of sorting through GB Charity that nobody has been through before!

5kg Box £55.00   **9kg Box £95.00**

Bonus! All GB boxes will have latest Miniature sheets and full sets 'fine used' on the box as postage. Rarely seen commercially used these days and very popular with our customers. We look after your interests! Overseas customers must pay full postage.

Remember these have not been sorted by the charity or any dealer. Direct from donator to you!

<u>GB COMMEMS NO XMAS.</u> A wide ranging on paper mixture with recent issues and high values. **1/2lb £11.00, 1lb £20.00.**
<u>GB HIGH VALUE DEFINS</u> On Paper. Excellent variety, a clean modern mixture. **1/2lb £11.00, 1lb £20.00.**
<u>GB REGIONALS</u> (On Paper). A wealth of variet from all four regions, find those elusive band/perf varieties very cheaply. Over 7000 - 8000 stamps/2lb **1lb £8.00, 2lbs £15.00.**
<u>*Exclusive!*</u> GREAT BRITAIN Queen Victoria - King George VI. We have been very fortunate to buy up the entire stock of the original Wallace Bros in London which has been stored for many years and are guaranteed unpicked. Mostly on paper and will contain a good variety of cancellations, watermarks and especially **Perfins**. Mostly KGVI low value charity also includes other regions. A few odd foreign stamps have slipped in plus the usual Postage Dues. **1/4lb £25, 1/2lb £48.00, 1lb £90.00.**

WE ACCEPT: CHEQUES, POSTAL ORDERS, SWITCH, VISA, ACCESS, MASTERCARD, AMERICAN EXPRESS
- advise expiry date and security code. We always offer a full refund.

COURT PHILATELICS
Dept BSMV, PO Box 6198, Leighton Buzzard, Beds LU7 9XT.
TEL: 01296 662420   FAX: 01296 668328   E-MAIL: courtphilatelics@aol.com

MACHINS

DECIMAL MACHIN DEFINITIVES

In this section, prices are given for lightly mounted unused (left) and fine used (right). Exceptions are made where used prices are not applicable, for example in the case of booklet panes and gum varieties.

All stamps have fluorescent coated paper unless otherwise stated

Gum

These stamps can be found with three different gums:

Gum Arabic is either colourless or yellow in appearance and is very shiny.

Polyvinyl alcohol gum (PVA) is likewise colourless but has a matt appearance.

Polyvinyl alcohol with dextrin gum (PVAD) is also matt, but has a blueish or greenish tinge.

In recent years self-adhesive definitives have become more common.

Phosphor

As with the earlier non-decimal definitives and special issues, the phosphor at first was applied in the form of 'bands'.

When you hold a stamp up to the light and look along the surface, the paper itself appears shiny while the bands have a dull appearance.

Most stamps have two phosphor bands, on the two vertical edges; others have just one, which can be central or down the left or right vertical edge.

The width of the phosphor bands can vary, as can the size of the printing screen used to apply them, but these differences are beyond the scope of this publication.

In recent times, booklet panes, where stamps of the second-class rate (requiring a single phosphor band) have been printed adjacent to other stamps (needing two phosphor bands), have been found with the phosphor printed as bars rather than bands. Whereas bands extend across the perforations to the next stamp, these bars stop at the edge of the stamp design.

The term *all over phosphor* means that the phosphor was printed over the entire surface of the stamp, rather than in the form of bands. In some cases it was printed onto the paper before the stamp design was printed; in other cases it was printed above the stamp design. You can positively identify all-over phosphor from certain marginal stamps, where the phosphor will be seen to end in the sheet margin.

The term *no phosphor* is usually applied to stamps discovered with the phosphor omitted in error; such errors are outside the scope of this publication. However, two values have been printed without phosphor in the normal course of events: the 50p and 75p, both with PVAD gum.

Paper

At first these stamps were printed on what is now known as *original coated paper*, which gives a dull violet reaction when the front of the stamp is viewed ultra-violet light.

This was replaced by *fluorescent coated paper*, which gives a bright reaction under ultra-violet light, and then by *phosphor-coated paper*, which adds the after-glow of phosphor.

With phosphor coated paper, the phosphor is included with the coating of the surface of the paper. This makes the stamp appear uniformly shiny. Note that most stamps intended to have phosphor bands have been found with the phosphor omitted, which also produces a uniformly shiny surface, so those with phosphor coated paper can only be positively identified by their reaction under ultra-violet light.

The appearance of stamps with phosphor coated paper can vary considerably, due to differences in their drying time after printing. The differences range from dull to very shiny. A dull appearance is known as *Phosphor Coated Paper I* (PCPI), and a highly glazed appearance as *Phosphor Coated Paper II* (PCPII).

Some stamps have been found with the fluorescent brightener omitted (with phosphor coated paper). These still give the phosphor afterglow, but the paper gives a dull violet reaction similar to that found with original coated paper.

Attempts to standardise the paper have produced what is known as *Advanced Coated Paper* (ACP), which has been used for a number of National and Country definitives. The visual difference between ACP and PCPI is slight, but the former gives a brighter reaction under ultra-violet light.

Printers and processes

Many of the Machin decimal definitives have been printed in photogravure by Harrisons. But some of the work has been undertaken by John Waddington, House of Questa, Walsall, Enschedé and De La Rue. For a time lithography was used, but Royal Mail then decided that it preferred photogravure.

In 1979 the 10p definitive was printed on a Chambon press at Harrisons which produced sheets of 200 stamps, comprising two panes of 100 stamps separated by a horizontal gutter. Stamps from this printing have either two phosphor bands on top of phosphor coated paper or two phosphor bands on top of fluorescent coated paper.

Value position and portrait types

Changes can be noted in the position of the value in relation to the Queen's portrait, and the position of the portrait in relation to the base of the stamp.

Booklet panes

At first booklets were held together by stitching, so that a number of small holes can be found in the binding margin on the left hand side of panes. Later, the panes were stuck into booklet covers by the binding margins; in many such cases, panes can be found with the binding margin to the left or to the right.

In the case of stitched booklets, the booklet panes are recorded separately. Where the panes are stuck into the covers most collectors prefer these as complete booklets, so the separate panes are not recorded.

Many of the early decimal booklet panes included labels se-tenant with the stamps in the pane, adjacent to the binding margin. At first these panes were perforated between the labels and the margin, but later they were not.

In 1987, as an experiment to counter complaints about the poor guillotining of panes, two booklet panes were produced with imperforate sides. These produce stamps with either the left or right-hand edge imperforate.

A further experiment of 1987 was to introduce booklets with 'bar codes' on the back cover, and with a window in the front cover, so that the stamp content could be ascertained. The anes in these booklets have a margin surrounding the stamps, and as such are listed separately.

Coils

There are two types of coils from which stamps may be found. Some coils contain just one value, with the stamps joined either horizontally or vertically. Today, these usually comprise the basic 1st or 2nd class letter rate stamps, and are prepared for use by businesses. They are not separately listed, but where the source of a particular stamp is given as 'coils', this refers to the single value version.

Other coils contain a mixture of values joined as a se-tenant strip. These have been produced for sale through vending machines, although two cases are known of coils specially produced for a commercial mailing shot. These are referred to here as 'se-tenant coils', and they are also separately listed.

Cartons

In an experiment staged in Scotland in 1976-78, 1st and 2nd-class definitives (including Country stamps) were sold in cartons from vending machines. Sold at 30p or 60p, they contained either 6½p and 8½p, or 7p and 9p stamps.

LOW VALUES 1971-93

Designed by Arnold Machin. Printed in photogravure by Harrisons, no Wmk, Perf: 15x14, except where stated.

1p with portrait above bottom margin and traditional perf

1p with portrait closer to bottom margin and elliptical perf

½p turquoise, February 15, 1971

A) gum Arabic, two phos bands

i. original coated paper	0.40	-	se-tenant coils
ii. original coated paper with silicone	40.00	-	se-tenant coils
iii. fluorescent coated paper	0.30	-	sheets
iv. fluorescent coated paper with silicone	0.40	-	se-tenant coils

B) PVA gum, two phos bands

i. original coated paper	0.30	-	sheets, se-tenant coils, booklets
ii. fluorescent coated paper	0.50	-	sheets, booklets
C) PVA gum, one band at left	45.00	22.00	£1 Wedgwood booklet
D) PVAD gum, two phos bands	0.25	0.20	sheets, se-tenant coils, booklets
E) PVAD gum, one centre band	0.30	0.20	se-tenant coils, booklets

F) PVAD gum, phos-coated paper

i. PCPI	0.25	0.20	sheets, se-tenant coils
ii. PCPII	0.35	0.45	sheets
iii. fluorescent brightener omitted (poor gum)	50.00	17.50	se-tenant coils
iv. fluorescent brightener omitted (good perfs and gum)	£800	-	se-tenant coils

1p purple, February 15, 1971

A) gum Arabic, two phos bands

i. original coated paper	0.40	-	se-tenant coils
ii. original coated paper with silicone	40.00	-	se-tenant coils
iii. fluorescent coated paper	0.60	-	coils
iv. fluorescent coated paper with silicone	0.60	-	se-tenant coils

B) PVA gum, two phos bands

i. original coated paper	0.40	-	sheets
ii. fluorescent coated paper	1.25	-	sheets, booklets

C) PVAD gum, two phos bands

i. value low	0.45	0.20	10p booklets

ii. value in intermediate position	0.45	0.30	10p se-tenant coils, 50p booklets,
iii. value high	0.45	0.20	sheets, 5p se-tenant coils
D) PVAD gum, one centre phos band			
i. portrait above bottom margin	0.30	0.20	se-tenant coils
ii. portrait closer to bottom margin	0.30	0.20	se-tenant coils, 10p, 50p booklets,
E) PVAD gum, all over phos	0.30	0.20	sheets
F) PCPI, phos-coated paper			
i. PCPI, portrait above bottom margin	0.30	0.20	sheets
ii. PCPI, portrait closer to bottom margin	0.30	0.20	sheets, se-tenant coils
iii. PCPII	0.40	0.25	sheets
iv. ACP	0.30	0.25	sheets
G) PVAD gum, one phos band at left	1.30	1.00	50p booklet
H) PVAD gum, one phos band at right	2.00	2.25	£5 P&O booklet

■ 1½p black, February 15, 1971

A) PVA gum, two phos bands			
i. original coated paper	0.30	-	sheets, booklets
ii. fluorescent coated paper	0.90	-	sheets, booklets
B) PVAD gum, two phos bands	0.50	0.25	sheets, booklets

■ 2p green, February 15, 1971

A) gum Arabic, two phos bands			
i. original coated paper	2.25	-	se-tenant coils
ii. original coated paper with silicone	150.00	-	se-tenant coils
iii. fluorescent coated paper with silicone	2.00	-	se-tenant coils
B) PVA gum, two phos bands			
i. original coated paper	0.25	-	sheets, booklets
ii. fluorescent coated paper	1.25	-	sheets, booklets
C) PVAD gum, two phos bands			
i. portrait above bottom margin	0.30	0.20	sheets, se-tenant coils, booklets
ii. portrait close to bottom margin	0.80	0.40	booklets
D) PVAD gum, all over phos	0.30	0.20	sheets
E) PVAD gum, phos-coated paper			
i. PCPI	0.30	0.20	sheets
ii. PCPII	0.35	0.20	sheets
F) PVAD gum, phos-coated paper, litho by Questa, perf 13½x14	0.25	0.25	sheets
G) PVAD gum, phos-coated paper, litho by Questa, perf 15x14	0.30	0.25	sheets
H) PVAD, phos-coated paper, ACP, litho by Questa, perf 15x14	0.35	0.25	sheets

■ 2p deep green, February 23, 1988

A) PVAD gum, phos paper	0.60	0.35	sheets, booklets
B) PVAD gum phos paper, litho by Walsall	0.80	0.75	booklets

■ 2½p pink, February 15, 1971

A) gum arabic, one centre phos band	0.30	-	sheets, coils
B) PVA gum, one centre phos band			
i. original coated paper	0.30	0.20	sheets, coils, booklets,
ii. fluorescent coated paper	0.60	0.25	sheets, booklets
C) PVA gum, one phos band at left			
i. original coated paper	5.00	1.00	50p booklets,
ii. fluorescent coated paper	2.00	1.20	50p, £1 Wedgwood booklets
D) PVA gum, one phos band at right	3.00	2.00	£1 Wedgwood booklet
E) PVAD gum, two phos bands	0.40	0.25	sheets
F) PVAD gum, one centre phos band	0.30	0.20	sheets

■ 2½p rose, January 14, 1981

A) PVAD gum, phos-coated paper			
i. PCPI	0.50	0.20	sheets, se-tenant coils
ii. PCPII	0.30	0.20	sheets,
iii. fluorescent brightener omitted	35.00	35.00	se-tenant coils

) PVAD gum, two phos bands   0.40   0.30   50p booklets

3p blue, February 15, 1971
.) gum Arabic, two phos bands

original coated paper	45.00	-	coils
fluorescent coated paper	0.50	-	sheets, coils
) gum arabic, one centre phos band	1.50	-	sheets
:) PVA gum, two phos bands			
original coated paper	0.30	0.20	sheets, coils, booklets
. fluorescent coated paper	0.60	0.25	sheets, booklets
i. phos-coated paper	£1,2000	-	only two examples known
)) PVA gum, one centre phos band	0.60	-	sheets, booklets
) PVAD gum, one centre phos band	0.30	0.20	sheets, coils, booklets

3p pink, October 22, 1980
A) PVAD gum, phos-coated paper

PCPI	0.30	0.25	sheets, se-tenant coils
. PCPII	0.35	0.25	
i. fluorescent brightener omitted	4.50	4.00	se-tenant coils
v. ACP	0.30	0.20	sheets, £4 Royal Mint booklet
) PVAD gum, two phos bands	0.30	0.25	50p, £4 SG booklets

3½p olive green, February 15, 1971
A) PVA gum, two phos bands

original coated paper	0.40	0.25	sheets
. fluorescent coated paper	1.50	-	sheets, 35p booklets
B) PVAD gum, two phos bands			
original coated paper	£150	50.00	sheets
. fluorescent coated paper	0.40	0.30	sheets, coils, 35p, 50p booklets
C) PVAD gum, one centre phos band	0.35	0.25	sheets, coils, 35p, 85p booklets

3½p light red-brown, March 30, 1983
A) PVA gum, two phos bands

PCPI	0.50	0.40	sheets,
. ACP	1.20	1.00	sheets, £4 Royal Mint booklet
B) PVAD gum, one centre phos band	1.30	1.10	50p booklets

4p bistre, February 15, 1971

A) gum arabic, two phos bands	0.30	-	sheets
B) PVA gum, two phos bands			
original coated paper	0.30	0.25	sheets
i. fluorescent coated paper	3.00	-	sheets
C) PVAD gum, two phos bands	0.30	0.20	sheets

4p blue, January 30, 1980

A) PVA gum, two phos bands, litho by Waddingtons	0.30	0.20	sheets
B) PVAD gum, phos-coated paper, litho by Waddingtons	0.30	0.20	sheets
C) PVAD gum, phos-coated paper, litho by Questa, perf 15x14	0.50	0.45	sheets
D) PVAD gum, two phos bands	1.25	0.75	50p booklets
E) PVAD gum, phos-coated paper			
. PCPI	0.35	0.30	se-tenant coils
i. fluorescent brightener omitted (perfect gum)	£400	35.00	se-tenant coils
ii. PCPI, value high	0.35	0.30	se-tenant coils
F) PVAD gum, one centre phos band	0.75	0.70	50p booklets
G) PVAD gum, one phos band at left	1.50	1.25	£5 booklet
H) PVAD gum, one phos band at right	1.50	1.25	£5 booklet

4p bright blue, July 26, 1988

A) PVAD gum, phos paper, litho by Questa	0.45	0.50	sheets
A) PVAD gum, phos paper	0.30	0.25	sheets and coils

■ 4½p grey-blue, October 24, 1973

A) PVAD gum, two phos bands	1.00	0.40	sheets, coils, 45p, 85p booklets
B) PVAD gum, two phos bands on all-over phos	0.65	-	sheets

■ 5p violet, February 15, 1971

A) PVA gum, two phos bands			
i. original coated paper	0.30	0.25	sheets
ii. fluorescent coated paper	3.00	-	sheets
B) PVAD gum, two phos bands	0.50	0.25	sheets
C) PVAD gum, phos-coated paper			
i. PCPI	0.35	0.25	sheets
ii. PCPI, value high	0.50	0.35	sheets
D) PVAD gum, phos-coated paper, litho by Questa	0.30	0.25	sheets
E) PVA gum, phos-coated paper, litho by Questa	0.50	0.25	sheets

■ 5p red-brown, January 27. 1982

A) PVAD gum, phos-coated paper, litho by Questa, perf 13½x14	0.40	0.30	sheets
B) PVAD gum, phos-coated paper, litho by Questa, perf 15x14	0.50	0.40	sheets
C) PVAD gum, ACP, litho by Questa, perf 15x14	0.45	0.40	sheets
D) PVAD gum, one centre phos band	1.80	1.20	50p booklet

■ 5½p deep purple, October 24, 1973

A) PVAD gum, two phos bands	0.75	0.60	sheets
B) PVAD gum, one centre phos band	0.50	0.35	sheets

■ 6p light green, February 15, 1971

A) gum arabic, two phos bands	1.50	-	sheets
B) PVA gum, two phos bands			
i. original coated paper	0.35	-	sheets, se-tenant coils
ii. fluorescent coated paper	20.00	-	sheets
C) PVAD gum, two phos bands	0.30	0.25	sheets, se-tenant coils, 10p booklet

■ 6p olive, September 10, 1991

A) PVAD gum, phos paper	0.30	0.30	sheets

■ 6½p green-blue, September 7, 1974

A) PVA gum, two phos bands	25.00	-	sheets
B) PVAD gum, two phos bands	0.75	0.30	sheets
C) PVAD gum, one centre phos band			
i. portrait above bottom margin	0.40	0.25	sheets
ii. portrait close to bottom margin	0.30	0.25	sheets, coils, 65p booklets
D) PVAD gum, one phos band at left	0.70	0.70	50p booklets
E) PVAD gum, one phos band at right	1.00	0.80	50p booklets

■ 7p red-brown, January 15, 1975

A) PVAD gum, two phos bands	0.50	0.25	sheets
B) PVAD gum, one centre phos band			
i. portrait above bottom margin	0.35	0.25	sheets, coils
ii. portrait close to bottom margin	0.40	0.25	sheets, coils, se-tenants coils, booklets
C) PVAD gum, one phos band at left	0.50	0.45	50p booklets
D) PVAD gum, one phos band at right	1.00	0.70	50p booklets

■ 7p brick-red, October 29, 1985

A) PVAD gum, phos-coated paper	1.50	1.30	sheets

■ 7½p brown, February 15, 1971

A) PVA gum, two phos bands			
i. original coated paper	0.40	0.25	sheets
ii. fluorescent coated paper	3.00	-	sheets

B) PVAD gum, two phos bands   0.30   0.25   sheets

■ 8p red, October 24, 1973

A) PVAD gum, two phos bands	0.40	0.25	sheets
B) PVAD gum, one centre phos band, printed by Harrisons			
i. portrait high, value low	0.35	0.25	sheets
ii. portrait low, value high	0.50	0.30	sheets, coils, booklets
C) PVAD gum, one centre phos band, printed by Enschedé	0.35	0.25	sheets
D) PVAD gum, one phos band at left	0.50	0.30	50p booklets
E) PVAD gum, one phos band at right	0.50	0.30	50p booklets

■ 8½p line green, September 24, 1975

A) PVAD gum, two phos bands			
i. value high	0.40	0.25	sheets, coils, 85p booklets
ii. value low	0.45	0.35	50p booklets
B) PVAD gum, phos-coated paper	0.55	0.40	sheets

■ 9p orange and black, February 15, 1971

A) PVA gum, two phos bands			
i. original coated paper	2.00	1.00	sheets
ii. fluorescent coated paper	2.75	-	sheets
B) PVAD gum, two phos bands	1.00	0.70	sheets

■ 9p violet, February 25, 1976

A) PVAD gum, two phos bands	0.45	0.25	sheets, coils, 50p, 90p, £1.60 booklets

■ 9½p purple, February 25, 1976

A) PVAD gum, two phos bands	0.35	0.30	sheets

■ 10p yellow and orange, August 11, 1971

A) PVA gum, two phos bands	0.50	-	sheets
B) PVAD gum, two phos bands	0.75	0.35	sheets

■ 10p orange, February 25, 1976

A) PVA gum, two phos bands			
i. base of value above edge of bust	0.30	0.20	sheets, £1.80 booklets
ii. base of value at edge of bust	0.35	0.25	50p booklets
iii. re-drawn (narrower) value	15.00	12.50	£4 Heritage booklet
B) PVAD gum, all-over phos	0.60	0.30	sheets, £1 booklets
C) PVAD gum, phosphor coated paper, PCPI	0.50	0.25	sheets
D) PVAD gum, ACP	0.40	0.25	sheets
E) PVAD gum, one centre phos band	0.35	0.20	sheets, £1, £2.20, £3 booklets
F) PVAD gum, one phos band at left	0.60	0.50	50p, £3 booklets
G) PVAD gum, one phos band at right	0.60	0.50	50p booklets
H) PVAD gum, two phos bands, PCPI, Chambon press	0.50	-	sheets
gutter pair	1.25	-	sheets
I) PVAD gum, two phos bands, fluoresc-coated paper, Chambon	0.45	0.35	sheets
gutter pair	1.00	1.50	sheets
J) PVAD gum, one centre phos band, PCPI	1.00	-	sheets

■ 10½p yellow, February 25, 1976

A) PVAD gum, two phos bands	0.40	0.35	sheets

■ 10½p blue, Aril 26, 1978

A) PVAD gum, two phos bands	0.50	0.50	sheets

■ 11p orange-pink, February 25, 1976

A) PVAD gum, two phos bands	0.50	0.30	sheets
B) PVAD gum, phos-coated paper PCPI	0.60	0.50	sheets

▪ 11½p sepia, August 15, 1979

A) PVAD gum, phos-coated paper
PCPI	0.60	0.30	sheets

▪ 11½p mushroom, January 14, 1981

A) PVAD gum, one centre phos band	0.60	0.30	sheets, coils, £1.15, £2.55 booklets
B) PVAD gum, one phos band at left	0.50	0.30	50p, £1.30 booklets
C) PVAD gum, one phos band at right	0.50	0.30	50p, £1.30 booklets

▪ 12p yellow-green, January 30, 1980

A) PVAD gum, phos-coated paper
i. PCPI	0.50	0.25	sheets, coils, £1.20 booklet
ii. PCPII	1.50	0.40	sheets
B) PVAD gum, two phos bands	0.50	0.35	50p, £2.20, £3 booklets

▪ 12p emerald-green, October 29, 1985

A) PVAD gum, one centre phos band	0.50	0.25	sheets, 50p, £1.20, £5 booklets
B) PVAD gum, one centre phos band, blue star on gummed side	0.50	-	sheets
C) PVAD gum, one centre phos band in ACP-type phos	0.50	0.30	sheets
D) PVAD gum, one phos band at left	0.60	0.50	£1.50, £5 booklets
E) PVAD gum, one phos band at right	0.60	0.50	£1.50, £5 booklets

▪ 12½p light green, January 27, 1982

A) PVAD gum, one centre phos band	0.50	0.25	sheets, coils, 50p, £1.25, £4 SG booklets
B) PVAD gum, one centre phos band, PCPI	5.00	-	sheets
C) PVAD gum, one phos band at left	0.60	0.50	50p, £1.43, £1.46, £4 booklets
D) PVAD gum, one phos band at right	0.60	0.50	50p, £1.43, £1.46, £4 booklets
E) PVAD gum, one centre phos band, blue star on gummed side	0.50	0.50	£2.50 booklet
F) PVAD gum, one centre band, simple blue star on gummed side	0.60	0.40	£2.20 booklet

▪ 13p olive, August 15, 1979

A) PVAD gum, phos-coated paper, PCPI	0.50	0.30	sheets

▪ 13p light brown, August 28, 1984

A) PVAD gum, one centre phosband	0.50	0.25	sheets, 50p, £1.30, £5 booklets
B) PVAD gum, one centre phosband, blue star on gummed side	0.60	-	£1.20 booklet
C) PVAD gum, one centre phos band in ACP-type phos	0.60	0.30	sheets
D) PVAD gum, one phos band at left	0.65	0.35	50p, £1.54, £4 Heritage, £5 booklets
E) PVAD gum, one phos band at right	0.65	0.35	£1, £1.54, £4 Heritage, £5 booklets
F) PVAD gum, one centre phos band, litho by Questa	0.60	0.50	booklets
G) PVAD gum, one phos band at left, litho by Questa	1.00	0.70	booklets
H) PVAD gum, one phos band at right, litho by Questa	1.00	0.70	booklets

▪ 13½p red-brown, January 30, 1980

A) PVAD gum, phosphor coated paper, PCPI	0.60	0.35	sheets

▪ 14p grey-blue, January 14, 1981

A) PVAD gum, phos-coated paper
i. PCPI	0.45	0.30	sheets, coils, £1.40 booklets
ii. PCPII	0.60	0.30	sheets, coils £1.40 booklets
iii. fluorescent brightener omitted	2.50	-	£1.40 booklets
B) PVAD gum, two phos bands	0.80	0.50	50p, £1.30, £2.55 booklets

▪ 14p deep blue, August 23, 1988

A) PVAD gum, one centre phos band	0.45	0.25	sheets, booklets
B) PVAD gum, one phos band at right	2.25	2.30	booklets
C) PVAD gum, one centre phos band, litho by Questa	1.50	1.50	booklets
D) PVAD gum, one phos band at right, litho by Walsall	2.15	2.25	booklets

15p blue, August 15, 1979
A) PVAD gum, phos-coated paper

PCPI	0.50	0.30	sheets
i. PCPII	0.55	0.55	sheets

15½p pale purple, January 14, 1981
A) PVAD gum, phosphor coated paper

. PCPI	0.60	0.25	sheets, coils, £1.55 booklets
i. PCPI	0.60	0.25	sheets
ii. fluorescent brightener omitted	15.00	-	sheets
v. advanced coated paper	3.00	3.00	£1.55 booklets
3) PVAD gum, two phos bands	0.60	0.40	£1.43, £4 SG booklets
C) PVAD gum, two phos bands, blue star on gummed side	0.65	0.55	£2.50 booklets

16p light mushroom, March 30, 1983

A) PVAD gum, phos-coated paper, PCPI	0.60	0.35	sheets, £1.60, £4 Royal Mint booklets
3) PVAD gum, PCPI and D on gummed side	0.70	0.70	£1.45 booklet
C) PVAD gum, ACP	0.60	0.50	sheets
D) PVAD gum, two phos bands	1.20	1.00	£1.46 booklet

16½p light brown, January 27 1982
A) PVAD gum, phos-coated paper

. PCPI	0.75	0.50	sheets
i. PCPII	3.50	2.00	sheets

17p sage green, January 30, 1980
A) PVAD gum, phos-coated paper

. PCPI	0.70	0.70	sheets
i. PCPII	3.00	2.00	sheets
ii. fluorescent brightener omitted	2.00	-	sheets

17p steel blue, March 30, 1983

A) PVAD gum, PCPI	0.70	0.40	sheets, £1.70, £4 Heritage booklets
B) PVAD gum, PCPI, D on gummed side	1.00	-	£1.55 booklet
C) PVAD gum, ACP	0.60	0.40	sheets, £1.70, £5 booklets
D) PVAD gum, two phos bands	0.70	0.30	50p, £1.50, £1.54, £4 Heritage, £5 booklets
E) PVAD gum, two phos bands, stars on gummed side	0.70	-	50p booklet

17p deep blue, September 4, 1990

A) PVAD gum, one centre phos band	0.75	0.35	sheets
B) PVAD gum, one phos band at left	0.80	0.80	booklets
C) PVAD gum, one phos band at right	1.50	1.60	booklets
D) PVAD gum, one centre phos band, litho by Questa	0.80	0.75	booklets

17½p light brown, January 30, 1979
A) PVAD gum, phos-coated paper

. PCPI	0.75	0.40	sheets
i. PCPII	1.75	1.75	sheets

18p violet, January 14, 1981
A) PVAD gum, phos-coated paper

. PCPI	0.65	0.40	sheets
ii. PCPII	0.70	0.40	sheets

18p grey-green, August 28, 1984

A) PVAD gum, ACP	0.65	0.30	sheets
B) PVAD gum, two phos bands	0.80	0.40	50p, £1 booklets
C) PVAD gum, phos-coated paper	0.90	0.70	£1.80 booklet

D) PVAD gum, phos paper, litho by Questa	0.80	0.75	booklets
E) PVAD gum, two phos bands, litho by Questa	3.75	4.00	booklets

■ 18p bright green, September 10, 1991

A) PVAD gum, one centre phos band	0.50	0.30	sheets
B) PVAD gum, one centre phos band, litho by Questa	0.90	0.95	booklets
C) PVAD gum, one phos band at left, litho by Questa	1.30	1.35	booklets
D) PVAD gum, one phos band at right, litho by Questa	1.00	1.05	booklets

■ 19p orange-red, August 23, 1988

A) PVAD gum, phos paper	0.50	0.30	sheets, booklets
B) PVAD gum, phos paper, litho by Questa	1.40	1.50	booklets
C) PVAD gum, two phos bands, litho by Walsall	1.50	1.60	booklets

■ 19½p, January 27, 1982

A) PVAD gum, phosphor coated paper, PCPI	1.75	1.25	sheets

■ 20p dull purple, February 25, 1976

A) PVA gum, two phos bands, litho by Waddingtons	0.80	0.70	sheets
B) PVAD gum, phos-coated paper, litho by Waddingtons	1.00	0.80	sheets
dull purple and sepia	2.00	1.40	sheets
C) PVAD gum, phos-coated paper, litho by Questa, perf 15x14	1.00	0.90	sheets
D) PVAD gum, two phos bands	0.70	0.30	sheets
E) PVAD gum, phos-coated paper			
i. PCPI	0.75	0.50	sheets
ii. PCPII	0.75	0.60	sheets

■ 20p turquoise, August 23, 1988

A) PVAD gum, phos paper	0.50	0.35	sheets

■ 20p brownish-black, September 26, 1989

A) PVAD gum, phos paper	0.50	0.35	sheets, booklets
B) PVAD gum, two phos bands	1.50	1.50	sheets

■ 20½p bright blue, March 30, 1983

A) PVAD gum, phos-coated paper, PCPI	1.25	1.10	sheets

■ 22p deep blue, October 22, 1980

A) PVAD gum, phos-coated paper			
i. PCPI	0.70	0.50	sheets
ii. PCPII	0.70	0.50	sheets
B) PVAD gum, experimental coated paper	2.75	2.75	sheets

■ 22p yellow-green, August 28, 1984

A) PVAD gum, ACP	0.60	0.45	sheets
B) PVAD gum, two phos bands, litho by Questa	4.50	4.50	booklets

■ 22p orange-red, September 4, 1990

A) PVAD gum, two phos bands	0.80	0.90	sheets
B) PVAD gum, phos paper	0.60	0.70	sheets
C) PVAD gum, phos paper, litho by Questa	0.80	0.75	booklets

■ 23p rose, March 30, 1983

A) PVAD gum, phos-coated paper, PCPI	1.20	1.00	sheets

■ 23p bright green, August 23, 1988

A) PVAD gum, phos paper	0.75	0.75	sheets

■ 24p light purple, August 28, 1984

A) PVAD gum, ACP	1.40	1.10	sheets

■ 24p red, September 26, 1989

A) PVAD gum, phos paper	1.10	1.15	sheets

■ 24p chestnut, September 10, 1991

A) PVAD gum, phos paper	0.80	0.75	sheets
B) PVAD gum, phos paper, litho by Questa	0.70	0.70	booklets
C) PVAD gum, two phos bands, litho by Questa	1.10	1.10	booklets
D) PVAD gum, phos paper, litho by Walsall	0.90	0.90	booklets

■ 25p purple, January 14, 1981

A) PVAD gum, phos-coated paper			
i. PCPI	2.00	1.95	sheets
ii. PCPII	1.50	0.75	sheets

■ 25p red, February 6, 1986

A) PVAD gum, two phos bands	4.25	4.25	sheets

■ 26p red, January 27, 1982

A) PVAD gum, phos-coated paper, PCPI	0.75	0.50	sheets
B) PVAD gum, ACP	0.75	0.50	sheets
C) PVAD gum, two phos bands	6.00	5.50	£5 P&O booklet
D) PVAD gum, two phos bands, narrow value	3.50	3.00	£1.04 booklet

■ 26p drab, September 4, 1990

A) PVAD gum, phos paper	1.00	1.05	sheets

■ 27p chestnut, August 23, 1988

A) PVAD gum, phos paper	0.90	0.95	sheets, booklets

■ 27p violet, September 4, 1990

A) PVAD gum, phos paper	1.00	1.05	sheets

■ 28p blue, March 30, 1983

A) PVAD gum, phos-coated paper, PCPI	0.90	0.90	sheets
B) PVAD gum, ACP	1.10	1.10	sheets

■ 28p ochre, August 23, 1988

A) PVAD gum, phos paper	0.95	0.95	sheets

■ 28p blue-grey, September 10, 1991

A) PVAD gum , phos paper	0.80	0.75	sheets

■ 29p sepia, January 27, 1982

A) PVAD gum, phos-coated paper			
i. PCPI	2.50	2.25	sheets
ii. PCPII	5.00	3.50	sheets

■ 29p mauve, September 26, 1989

A) PVAD gum, phos paper	1.50	1.50	sheets
B) PVAD gum, two phos bands, litho by Walsall	3.40	2.50	booklets
C) PVAD gum, phos paper, litho by Walsall	3.25	2.75	booklets

■ 30p olive, September 26, 1989

A) PVAD gum, phos paper	1.00	0.80	sheets

■ 31p purple, March 30, 1983

A) PVAD gum, phos-coated paper, PCPI	1.20	1.25	sheets
B) PVAD gum, ACP	1.10	0.75	sheets
C) PVAD gum, two phos bands	7.50	7.50	£5 British Rail Booklet

■ 31p ultramarine, September 4, 1990

A) PVAD gum, phos paper	1.00	1.00	sheets
B) PVAD gum, phosphor paper, litho by Walsall	1.20	1.10	booklets

■ 32p green-blue, August 23, 1988

A) PVAD gum, phos paper	1.00	1.00	sheets

■ 33p emerald, September 4, 1990

A) PVAD gum, phos paper	0.90	0.90	sheets
B) PVAD gum, phos paper, litho by Questa	1.50	1.40	booklets
C) PVAD gum, two phos bands, litho by Questa	1.00	1.00	booklets
D) PVAD gum, phos paper, litho by Walsall	1.00	1.00	booklets

■ 34p sepia, August 28, 1984

A) PVAD gum, phos-coated paper	1.00	1.00	sheets
B) PVAD gum, two phos bands	6.00	5.50	£5 Times booklet
C) PVAD gum, ACP	1.25	1.25	sheets
D) PVAD gum, two phos bands, litho by Questa	4.50	4.40	booklets

■ 34p blue-grey, September 26, 1989

A) PVAD gum, phos paper	1.00	1.00	sheets

■ 34p mauve, September 10, 1991

A) PVAD gum, phos paper	1.10	1.10	sheets

■ 35p sepia, August 23, 1988

A) PVAD gum, phos paper	1.20	1.25	sheets

■ 35p yellow, September 10, 1991

A) PVAD gum, phos paper	0.95	0.95	sheets

■ 37p rosine, September 26, 1989

A) PVAD gum, phos paper	1.40	1.30	sheets

■ 39p mauve, September 10, 1991

A) PVAD gum, phos paper	1.15	1.15	sheets
B) PVAD gum, two phos bands, litho by Questa	2.00	1.90	booklets
C) PVAD gum, phos paper, litho by Walsall	1.10	1.10	booklets

■ 50p dull brown, February 2, 1977

A) PVAD gum, two phos bands	1.50	0.50	sheets
B) PVAD gum, no phos	1.50	0.70	sheets

■ 50p ochre, March 13, 1990

A) PVAD gum, phos paper	1.50	1.25	sheets
B) PVAD gum, two phos bands	3.00	3.00	sheets

■ 75p deep grey, January 30, 1980

A) PVAD gum, no phos, litho by Questa, perf 13½x14	3.00	70	sheets
B) PVA gum, no phos, litho by Questa, perf 15x14	3.00	90	sheets
C) PVAD gum, no phos, litho by Questa, perf 15x14	3.75	-	sheets
D) PVA gum, no phos, litho by Questa: perf 15x14 on paper supplied by Coated Paper Ltd	3.00	-	sheets

■ 75p grey and black, February 23, 1988

A) PVAD gum, litho by Questa	8.00	7.50	sheets

■ 75p grey and black, July 26, 1988

A) PVAD gum, no phosphor	1.75	1.25	sheets

Congratulations!

You've purchased this catalogue – where do you go to find stamps at these prices or lower?

In fact – wouldn't YOU PREFER to decide how much stamps are worth?

offers you an unique service – they re-offer each unsold stamp lot at ever increasing price reductions until ...

... SOLD OR GIVEN AWAY FOR JUST 1p!

and they tell you how many times each lot has been unsold! Could this be one of the reasons why over

1000 collectors regularly bid in each c.10,000 lot quarterly produced auction +

- UPA offers collectors and dealers a level playing field – no pre-auction viewing service – so no hidden advantages for anybody
- Each lot guaranteed – return within 14 days of receipt for full refund if fails to please
- No buyer's premium – this can save you a small fortune
- Fixed post and delivery costs including insurance so you know exactly how much is the maximum you can possibly spend where-ever you live
  - £200,000 + stamps to bid on ensures plenty of bargains to be had.

YES! I'd like to learn what stamps really sell for – please send me a free copy of your next postal auction catalogue

Name: ....
(BLOCK CAPITALS PLEASE)

Address: ....

....

....

....

Postcode: .... Country: ....

Tel. No (in case of query): ....

Mail to: UNIVERSAL PHILATELIC POSTAL AUCTIONS, P.O. Box 5678, HELENSBURGH G84 9WE, Argyll & Bute, Scotland. Tel: 01993 831666. Fax: 01993 831211. E-mail: gillian@upastampauctions.co.uk Ad code:BSMV

Leading Buyers
and
Recognised Valuers

Est. **40** Years

Serious professional buyers of all things philatelic

Corbitts would welcome the opportunity to discuss the sale of your collection by your preferred method.

PUBLIC AUCTION ❧ OUTRIGHT PURCHASE ❧ PRIVATE TREATY

We need all types of Philatelic material from general ranges and accumulations to specialised studies, good singles and covers. We buy it all.

So if you are considering selling part or all of your collection - I urge you to call now and discuss the many advantages of selling through Corbitts.

For a friendly and personal service, call Freephone 0800 525804 and ask for David McMonagle or Richard Vincent.

CORBITTS

5 Mosley Street, Newcastle upon Tyne NE1 1YE
Tel: 0191 232 7268 Fax: 0191 261 4130
Email: info@corbitts.com Website: www.corbitts.com

PLEASE CONTACT US FOR
A COMPLIMENTARY CATALOGUE

 Members of Philatelic Traders Society > American Stamp Dealers Association > American Philatelic Society

BOOKLET PANES

Only those from stitched booklets are listed here. Those from prestige stamp books are listed with their respective books. Prices are for mint panes.

PVA gum panes of four
Two **2p** with two ½p
vertically se-tenant	5.00
horizontally se-tenant, original coated paper	9.00
horizontally se-tenant, fluorescent coated paper	4.00

Two **1p** with two ½p
vertically se-tenant	5.00
horizontally se-tenant, original coated paper	6.00
horizontally se-tenant, fluorescent coated paper	3.00

PVA gum panes of six
Five ½p with label 'B ALAN LTD for GB STAMPS'
perforated label	4.00
imperforate label	7.50

Five ½p with label 'LICK battery failure'
perforated label	4.00
imperforate label	10.00

Five ½p with label 'MAKE YOUR LUCKY FIND PAY'
imperforate label only	2.00

Four **2½p** (one centre band) with labels 'UNIFLO STAMPS' and 'STICK FIRMLY'
perforated label	4.00
imperforate label	9.00

Five **2½p** (one centre band) with label 'STICK FIRMLY'
perforated label	4.50
imperforate label	9.00

Five **2½p** (one centre band) with label 'TEAR OFF to ESSO'
perforated label	4.50
imperforate label	9.00

Five **2½p** (one centre band) with label 'STAMP COLLECTIONS'
imperforate label only	3.50

Four **2½p** (one centre band) with labels 'DO YOU COLLECT GB STAMPS' and 'BUYING or SELLING'
imperforate label only	3.50

Five **2½p** (one centre band) with label 'B ALAN'
imperforate label only	3.75

Five **3p** (two bands) with label '£4,315 FOR YOU'
perforated label	3.00
imperforate label, OCP	12.00
imperforate label, FCP	1.75

Four **3p** (two bands) with two 2½p (one band at left)
OCP	10.00
FCP	5.00

Six **3p** (two bands)
OCP	5.00
FCP	2.50

Five **3p** (one centre band) with blank imperforate label	12.50
Five **3½p** (two bands) with blank imperforate label	7.50

PVAD gum panes of four
Two **2p** horizontally se-tenant with two ½p	2.00
Two **1p** horizontally se-tenant with two 1½p	2.00

PVAD gum panes of six
Five **3p** (one centre band) with blank imperforate label	10.00

Five **3½p** (two bands) with blank imperforate label	2.50
Five **3½p** (one centre band) with blank imperforate label	2.50
Five **4½p** (two bands) with blank imperforate label	3.00

NON-VALUE INDICATORS

These were issued in booklets. All are from retail stamp books (and can have at least one edge imperforate), except those marked * which are from prestige stamp books.

■ **2nd class bright blue (first issued August 22, 1989)**
Printed in gravure by Harrison		
With one centre phosphor band	0.80	0.75
With one phosphor band at right*	3.00	1.85
Printed in litho by Walsall		
With one centre phosphor band	0.45	0.50
Printed in litho by Questa		
With one centre phosphor band	0.70	0.65
With one phosphor band at left*	1.00	1.05
With one phosphor band at right*	1.20	1.25

■ **2nd class deep blue (first issued August 7, 1990)**
Printed in gravure by Harrison		
With one centre phosphor band	0.80	0.85
Printed in litho by Walsall		
With one centre phosphor band	0.55	0.55
Printed in litho by Questa		
With one centre phosphor band	0.55	1.35
With one phosphor band at left*	1.25	1.30

■ **1st class brownish black (first issued August 22, 1989)**
Printed in gravure by Harrison		
On phosphor paper	0.90	0.80
Two phosphor bands*	2.50	2.00
Printed in litho by Walsall		
With two phosphor bands	1.30	1.35
Printed in litho by Questa		
On phosphor paper	1.60	1.00

■ **1st class orange red (first issued August 7, 1990)**
Printed in gravure by Harrison		
On phosphor paper	0.60	0.65

MACHINS

Printed in litho by Walsall

On phosphor paper. Perf: 14	0.60	0.65
On phosphor paper. Perf: 13	1.75	1.70

Printed in litho by Questa

On phosphor paper	0.90	0.85
With two phosphor bands*	1.20	1.00
With two phosphor bands*	1.40	1.40

ELLIPTICAL PERFORATIONS, 1993-date

An elliptical perforation was introduced along each vertical side of the stamp as a security measure.

◼ 1993-2005

Printed in gravure by Enschedé. Issued in sheets. Two phosphor bands (except where stated). Variations in phosphor and gum are noted by specialists, but are outside the scope of this publication.

1p crimson (June 8, 1993)	0.30	0.30
2p deep green (April 11, 1995)	0.30	0.30
4p new blue (December 14, 1993)	0.35	0.35
5p claret (June 8, 1993)	0.37	0.35
6p lime green (April 27, 1993)	0.35	0.35
10p orange (June 8, 1993)	0.40	0.40
20p sea green (December 14, 1993)	0.75	0.70
25p salmon pink (October 10, 1995)	0.85	0.80
29p light grey (October 26, 1993)	0.90	0.85
30p grey-green (July 27, 1993)	1.00	1.00
31p deep purple (June 25, 1996)	0.80	0.85
35p deep yellow (August 17, 1993)	0.90	0.90
35p lime-green (Apr 5, 2005) (phos band)	0.80	0.85
36p ultramarine (October 26, 1993)	0.90	0.90
37p amethyst (June 25, 1996)	1.00	1.05
38p rosine (October 26, 1993)	1.00	1.00
39p magenta (June 25, 1996)	0.90	0.95
41p stone (October 26, 1993)	1.00	1.00
43p chocolate-brown (June 25, 1996)	1.35	1.35
50p ochre (December 14, 1993)	1.30	1.35
63p emerald (June 25, 1996)	1.60	1.40
£1 bluish-violet (August 22, 1995)	2.40	2.50
Stamp card (£1 stamp)	7.50	15.00

◼ 1993 to date

Printed by Harrisons, then by De La Rue.

1p crimson (April 1, 1997)	0.25	0.25
2p deep green (May 27, 1997)	0.30	0.25
4p new blue (May 27, 1997)	0.35	0.30
5p claret (May 27, 1997)	0.35	0.30
6p lime green (April 1, 1997)	0.30	0.30
7p light grey (April 20, 1999)	0.75	0.75
7p bright magenta (April 1, 2004)	0.25	0.30
8p deep yellow (April 25, 2000)	0.35	0.30
9p deep orange (April 5, 2005)	0.35	0.30
10p orange (May 8, 1997)	0.40	0.35
12p turquoise (August 1, 2006)	0.30	0.30
14p salmon pink (August 1, 2006)	0.35	0.35
19p olive (Oct 26, 1993) (one phos band)	0.45	0.40
20p bright green		
(June 25, 1996) (centre phos band)	0.45	0.50
(September 23, 1997) (phos band at right)	1.00	1.10

(April 20, 1999) (two phos bands)	0.45	0.50
25p salmon-pink		
(October 26, 1993) (phos coated paper)	0.60	0.60
(December 20, 1994)	0.60	0.60
26p reddish brown (June 25, 1996)	0.60	0.60
26p gold (April 29, 1997)	0.50	0.55
30p grey-green (May 12, 1997)	0.65	0.65
31p deep mauve (August 26, 1997)	0.65	0.70
33p slate-blue (April 25, 2000)	0.75	0.75
35p yellow (Nov 1, 1993) (phos coated paper)	5.00	1.50
35p sepia (April 1, 2004)	0.70	0.75
35p lime-green (April 26, 2005)	0.70	0.75
37p amethyst (July 8, 1996)	1.00	1.05
37p bright mauve (August 7, 1997)	0.80	0.85
37p deep grey (July 4, 2002)	0.95	0.90
37p olive green (March 28, 2006)	0.65	0.70
38p ultramarine (April 20, 1999)	0.90	0.75
39p magenta (May 12, 1997)	0.80	0.85
39p grey (April 1, 2004)	0.80	0.80
40p greyish blue (April 20, 1999)	0.80	0.85
40p turquoise (April 1, 2004)	0.80	0.80
41p drab (Nov 1, 1993) (phos coated paper)	5.25	1.50
41p rosine (April 20, 1999)	0.90	0.90
42p olive-grey (July 4, 2002)	0.80	0.85
43p chocolate-brown (July 8, 1996)	1.30	0.95
43p brown (March 21, 1997)	1.00	1.00
43p emerald (April 1, 2004)	0.90	0.95
44p stone (April 20, 1999)	0.95	0.75
44p ultramarine (March 28, 2006)	0.75	0.75
45p mauve (April 20, 1999)	0.80	0.85
46p light brown (April 5, 2005)	0.75	0.80
47p turquoise green (July 4, 2002)	0.85	0.85
49p rust (March 28, 2006)	0.90	0.80
50p ochre (April 1, 1997)	0.90	0.90
63p emerald (December 12, 1996)	1.40	1.45
64p sea green (April 20, 1999)	1.35	1.35
65p greenish blue (April 25, 2000)	1.20	1.30
68p grey-brown (July 4, 2002)	1.35	1.35
72p red (March 28, 2006)	1.20	1.20
£1 bluish-violet (April 1, 1997)	1.95	0.90

◼ May 22, 2000. Stamp Show 2000 Exhibition Souvenir

Des: Jeffery Matthews. Printed by De La Rue. Phosphor paper. Miniature sheet comprising 4p blue, 5p claret, 6p lime green, 10p orange, 31p purple, 39p magenta, 64p sea-green, £1 bluish violet, plus the Royal Mail crest and the Jeffery Matthews colour palette.

Miniature sheet	10.00	10.00
First day cover		10.00

◼ 1994-1996

Printed in litho by Questa. Two phosphor bands, except where stated. Specialists note differences in the shape of the elliptical perforation, but these are outside the scope of this publication.

1p crimson (July 8, 1995)		
from £1 booklets	1.00	0.55
6p lime-green (July 26, 1994)		
from Northern Ireland prestige stamp book	6.50	6.75
10p deep orange (April 25, 1995)		
from National Trust prestige stamp book	2.25	2.25

19p olive green (July 26, 1994) (phos band at left)
from Northern Ireland & National Trust PSBs 2.50 | 2.50
(April 25, 1995) (phos band at right)
from National Trust prestige stamp book 1.10 | 1.20
20p bright green (July 8, 1996) (centre phos band)
from £1 and £2 booklets 1.90 | 1.90
25p salmon-pink (July 26, 1994)
from £1 and £2 booklets, and Northern
Ireland & National Trust PSBs 1.00 | 1.00
26p red-brown (July 8, 1996)
from £1 and £2 booklets 0.90 | 0.90
30p grey-green (April 25, 1995)
from National Trust prestige stamp book 2.50 | 2.50
35p deep yellow (April 25, 1995)
from National Trust prestige stamp book 1.50 | 1.60
41p drab (April 25, 1995)
from National Trust prestige stamp book 2.00 | 2.00

■ 1998-1999
Printed in gravure by Questa. Two phosphor bands, except
where stated.
1p crimson (December 1, 1998)
from £1 booklets and World Changers PSB 1.00 | 1.00
2p myrtle-green (April 26, 1999)
from £1 booklets 0.60 | 0.60
19p olive green (Apr 26, 1999) (centre phos band)
from £1 and £2 booklets
and World Changers PSB 1.00 | 1.00
20p bright green (Dec 1, 1998) (centre phos band)
from £1 and £2 stamp booklets 1.50 | 1.50
26p red-brown (December 1, 1998)
from £1 and £2 booklets and
World Changers PSB 0.90 | 0.90

■ 1993-1996
Printed in litho by Walsall. Two phosphor bands.
25p salmon-pink (November 1, 1993)
from £1 booklets 1.30 | 1.30
35p deep yellow (November 1, 1993)
from £1.40 booklets 1.50 | 1.50
37p amethyst (July 8, 1996)
from £1.48 booklets 9.75 | -
41p stone (November 1, 1993)
from £1.64 booklets 1.50 | 1.50
60p slate-blue (March 19, 1996)
from £2.40 booklets 2.50 | 2.50
63p emerald (July 8, 1996)
from £2.52 booklets 2.50 | 2.50

■ 1997-2000
Printed in gravure by Walsall. Two phosphor bands, except
where stated.
10p deep orange (October 13, 1998)
from Breaking Barriers prestige stamp book 1.50 | 1.55
19p olive-green (Feb 15, 2000) (phos band at right)
from Special By Design prestige stamp book 1.00 | 1.10
30p grey-green (May 5, 1998)
from £1.20 booklet 1.00 | 1.10
37p amethyst (August 26, 1997)
from £1.48 booklets 0.85 | 0.95

38p ultramarine (April 26, 1999)
from £1.52 booklet 1.50 | 1.50
38p ultramarine (February 15, 2000) (perf: 14)
from Special By Design prestige stamp book 1.00 | 1.00
40p grey-blue (April 27, 2000)
from £1.60 booklets 1.00 | 1.00
43p chocolate brown (October 13, 1998)
from Breaking Barriers prestige stamp book 1.50 | 1.50
63p emerald (August 26, 1997)
from £2.52 booklets 1.50 | 1.60
64p sea-green (April 26, 1999)
from £2.56 booklets 1.50 | 1.50
65p greenish blue (April 27, 2000)
from £2.60 booklets 1.50 | 1.50

■ 1993-1999. Non-value indicators
All these stamps are issued in booklets or coils. The 2nd class
stamps have one centre phosphor band; the others have two
phosphor bands, except where otherwise stated.
Specialists note differences in the phosphor and gum in
these issues, but these are outside the scope of this
publication.

Printed in photogravure by Harrison
2nd bright blue (September 7, 1993) 0.50 | 0.50
1st orange-red
(April 6, 1993) (phos coated paper) 0.65 | 0.65
(April 4, 1995) (two phosphor bands) 0.75 | 0.70
1st gold (April 21, 1997)* 0.70 | 0.75
E deep blue (October 5, 1999) 0.80 | 0.85
Stamp card (1st gold) 0.75 | 3.00
(* The 1st class gold is also found in the 75 Years Of The BBC
prestige stamp book, and the 1st class orange-red in the Profile
On Print prestige stamp book.)

Printed in litho by Walsall
2nd bright blue (April 6, 1993) 0.75 | 0.80
1st orange-red (April 6, 1993) 0.60 | 0.65

*Printed in gravure by Walsall (specialists note differences in the shape
of the elliptical perforation, but these are outside the scope of this
publication)*
2nd bright blue (April 29, 1997) 0.70 | 0.75
(Oct 13, 1998) (phos band at left, perf: 14)
from Breaking Barriers prestige stamp book 1.00 | 1.00
(Oct 13, 1998) (phos band at right, perf: 14)
from Breaking Barriers prestige stamp book 1.20 | 1.05
1st gold (April 21, 1997) 1.00 | 1.00
1st orange-red (August 26, 1997) 0.75 | 0.75
E deep blue (January 19, 1999) 0.90 | 0.90

Printed in litho by Questa
2nd bright blue (April 6, 1993) 0.60 | 0.65
1st orange-red (April 6, 1993) 0.60 | 0.65

Printed in gravure by Questa
2nd bright blue (Dec 1, 1998) (perf: 14) 0.95 | 0.95
2nd bright blue (Apr 27, 2000) (perf: 15x14) 0.70 | 0.65
1st orange-red (Dec 1, 1998) (perf: 14) 0.95 | 0.90
1st orange-red (Apr 27, 2000) (perf: 15x14) 0.80 | 0.80

■ 1994-1997. Greetings card sheetlets

Small sheets including a 1st class orange-red stamp sold in conjunction with greetings cards, initially through Boots, and subsequently other retail outlets.

Printed in litho by Questa

1st sheetlet with Boots logo (Aug 17, 1994)	2.00	2.00
1st sheetlet with no logo (Sep 11, 1995)	1.50	1.50

Printed in litho by Enschedé

1st sheetlet with no logo (Apr 29, 1997)	0.95	0.95

SELF-ADHESIVES

All in vertical format except where otherwise stated.

■ 1993, October 19

Des: Jeffery Matthews. Printed in litho by Walsall. Horizontal format. Issued only in booklets of 20.

1st orange-red	1.00	1.00
Stamp card	7.50	10.00

■ 1997, March 18

Des; Jeffery Matthews. Printed in gravure by Enschedé. Horizontal format with 'st' or 'nd' in large size. Issued only in rolls of 100 stamps.

2nd bright blue	1.00	1.00
1st orange-red	1.00	1.00

■ 1998, April 6

Perf: 15 x 14. Printed in gravure by Enschedé in rolls of 200, by Walsall in business sheets of 100, by Questa in business sheets of 100 (1st class only) and by Enschedé in business sheets of 100.

2nd bright blue	1.00	1.00
2nd bright blue (Perf: 14½ x 14)	125.00	125.00
1st orange-red	0.70	0.70
1st orange-red (Perf: 14½ x 14)	125.00	125.00

(* Perf: 14½ x 14 stamps were printed only by Walsall, and sold only individually through Royal Mail's Tallents House)

■ 1999, February 6

Embossed and litho printed by Walsall. Self-adhesive. Found only in the Profile In Print prestige stamp book.

1st pale grey	1.30	1.40

(* This stamp is also listed under large format Machin definitives)

■ 2002, June 5

Printed by gravure by De La Rue, Questa and Walsall in retail stamp booklets, and by Enschedé and Walsall in business sheets of 100.

1st gold	0.60	0.60

■ 2002, July 4

Printed in gravure by Walsall. Issued only in retail books.

E deep blue	0.80	0.80
42p olive-grey	1.00	1.05
68p grey-brown	1.40	1.45

■ 2003-2004. Overseas rates with airmail chevrons

Des: Sedley Place. Printed in gravure by Walsall. Issued only in booklets, although individual stamps were sold through Royal Mail's Tallents House.

Europe (March 27, 2003)	1.25	1.20
Worldwide (March 27, 2003)	1.75	1.90
Worldwide Postcard (April 1, 2004)	0.75	0.80
First day cover (March 27, 2003)		4.25
First day cover (April 1, 2004)		3.25
Stamp card	0.75	3.25

■ 2006, Pricing in Proportion

Des: Mike Dempsey. Printed in gravure by De La Rue. Normal gum.

2nd blue (August 1, 2006)	0.50	0.55
2nd Large blue (August 1, 2006)	0.60	0.65
1st gold (August 1, 2006)	0.65	0.65
1st Large gold (August 1, 2006)	0.75	0.75

PENNY BLACK DEFINITIVES, 1990

These featured the head of Queen Victoria alongside that of Queen Elizabeth II.

■ 1990, January 10. 150th Anniversary of the Penny Black
Des: Jeffery Matthews. Issued in sheets and booklets; the stamps from booklets can have one or more edges imperforate.

Printed in photogravure by Harrison (from sheets and booklets)
15p bright blue (one centre phos band)	0.75	0.60
(one phos band at left)*	1.80	1.80
(one phos band at right)*	3.00	3.00
20p brownish-black and cream (phos paper)	0.60	0.65
(two phos bands)*	1.75	1.75
29p mauve (phosphor paper)	1.00	1.10
(two phosphor bands)*	5.50	5.50
34p blue-grey	1.10	1.10
37p rosine	1.20	1.25

(* these stamps come from the London Life prestige stamp book issued on March 20, 1990)

Printed in litho by Walsall (only from booklets)
15p bright blue (one centre phos band)	0.90	1.00
20p brownish-black and cream (phos paper)	1.00	1.00

Printed in litho by Questa (only from booklets)
15p bright blue (one centre phos band)	1.25	1.30
20p brownish-black (phos paper)	1.50	1.60

Printed in gravure by Walsall (only for the £7.50 Special by Design prestige stamp book issued on February 15, 2000)
1st brownish black and cream	1.00	1.05

LARGE FORMAT DEFINITIVES
■ 1999, February 6
These stamps come only from the Profile In Print prestige stamp book.

Embossed and litho printed by Walsall. Self-adhesive.
1st pale grey	1.30	1.40

(* This stamp is also listed under self-adhesive definitives)

Recess printed by Enschedé. Engraved by C. Slania. Two phos bands.
1st grey-black	1.30	1.40

Printed in typography by Harrison. Two phos bands.
1st black	1.30	1.40

MILLENNIUM DEFINITIVES, 2000

Issued as part of the Millennium celebrations.

■ 2000, January 6
The Machin portrait against a white background. Des: R. Scholey.

Printed in gravure by Harrison. Perf: 15 x 14. Issued in sheets.
1st olive-brown	0.65	0.65

Printed in gravure by Walsall. Perf: 15 x 14. Issued in retail books.
1st olive-brown	0.80	0.75

Printed in gravure by Walsall. Perf: 14. Issued in the Special By Design and Treasury Of Trees prestige stamp books.
1st olive-brown	1.00	1.05

Printed in gravure by Questa. Perf: 14. Issued in retail stamp booklets.
1st olive-brown	0.70	0.65

Printed in gravure by Questa. Perf: 15 x 14. Issued in the Queen Elizabeth The Queen Mother prestige stamp book.
1st olive-brown	1.00	1.00

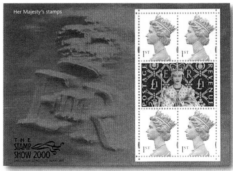

■ 2000, May 23. Her Majesty's Stamps Miniature Sheet. Stamp Show 2000.
Des: Delaney Design Consultants. Printed in gravure by De La Rue. Comprising four 1st class Millennium definitives, plus the 1953 Coronation design by Edmund Dulac, with face value £1.
Miniature sheet	15.00	15.00
First day cover		20.00
Stamp cards	20.00	25.00

£1.33 lilac, deep blue (Aug 28, 1984)	6.00	6.00
£1.41 deep blue, pale blue, green (Sep 17, 1985)	6.00	6.00
£1.50 rose-lilac, blue-black (Sep 2, 1986)	5.00	5.00
£1.60 buff, blue-green (Sep 15, 1987)	5.00	4.00
£2 emerald, deep purple	4.25	1.00
£5 pink, blue	10.00	1.90
Set	30.00	19.50
Gutter pair	70.00	
Traffic light gutter pair	80.00	
First Day Cover (£1, £2, £5)		10.00
First Day Cover (£1.30)		8.00
First Day Cover (£1.33)		7.50
First Day Cover (£1.41)		7.50
First Day Cover (£1.50)		7.00
First Day Cover (£1.60)		7.00

HIGH VALUES

■ 1970, June 17

Des: Arnold Machin. Printed in recess by Bradbury, Wilkinson.
No wmk. Perf: 12.

10p cerise, phos paper	1.00	0.70
20p olive-green	0.80	0.50
50p ultramarine	1.00	0.40
£1 black (Dec 6, 1972)	3.00	0.80

(* Initially the £1 was identical to that issued on March 5, 1969, but was printed in sheets of 100 instead of sheets of 40. However, on December 6, 1972 it was re-released with the denomination in a different typeface.)

■ 1977, February 2

Des: Arnold Machin. Printed in photogravure by Harrison. Perf: 14x15.

£1 olive, deep green	2.50	0.75
£1.30 steel blue, buff (Aug 3, 1983)	6.50	6.50

■ March 9, 1999. Small format

Printed in intaglio by Enschedé. Engraved by C. Slania.
£1.50, £2, £3, £5

Set	20.00	10.00
First Day Cover		17.50

■ April 11, 2000

Printed in intaglio by De La Rue.
£1.50, £2, £3, £5

Set	18.50	10.00
First Day Cover		20.00

■ July 1, 2003

Printed in gravure by De La Rue.
£1.50, £2, £3, £5

Set	18.00	10.00
First Day Cover		20.00

Stamp Magazine is Britain's best for GB collectors

Every issue includes:

■ Five pages of GB news
■ Full details of latest issues
■ The best first day covers
■ Newly discovered errors

Available from newsagents, or visit www.stampmagazine.co.uk

The latest valuations
Old fashioned values

Building a stamp collection can take years, so the decision to sell is not taken lightly.

Which is why it makes good sense to entrust the sale to someone who understands your feelings and your needs.

Tony Lester is a fellow philatelist and provides a service based on the old fashioned values of care, friendliness, consideration and total sensitivity, whether buying or selling.

However, when it comes to the 'bottom line' - you will be hard pressed to find someone offering a better valuation or a quicker response.

All you need to do now is to decide how you would like us to deal with your collection. We offer two choices.

1 PURCHASE
From modest collections of just a few hunded pounds up to collections in excess of £100,000, we can and do deal with all - and provide immediate payment.

2 AUCTION
We run regular auctions throughout the year, each attracting wide interest both nationally and internationally and covering a wide range including stamps, postal history, postcards and cigarette cards. Our commission charges are attractively low.

We offer a free 'visiting' service to view and value suitable lots, alternatively we can arrange collection, or you can forward any material by registered post for our written valuation by return. All with no obligation.

TONY LESTER *Auctions*

For a friendly and personal service just call **01926 634 809** and speak directly to me or to Robin Taylor.

Tony Lester, The Sidings, Birdingbury Road, Marton, Nr. Rugby CV23 9RX. Email: stamps@ukonline.co.uk
Web: www.tonylester.co.uk

We are long standing members of the Philatelic Traders' Society, complying with its strict code of ethics.

QUEEN ELIZABETH II
DECIMAL SPECIAL ISSUES

In this section, prices are quoted in two columns: mint (left) and fine used (right).

Most issues are priced for complete sets only, except where a variety of an individual design has extra value. Gutter pairs, traffic light gutter pairs and stamp cards are also priced for a complete set except where stated.

Gutter pairs appear from November 1972, traffic light gutter pairs from November 1972 to January 1980, blue tinted polyvinyl alcohol dextrin (**PVAD**) gum from November 1973 and phosphor coated paper from September 1979.

'A Mountain Road' by Flanagan (3p)
'Deer's Meadow' by Carr (7½p)
'Slieve na brock' by Middleton (9p)

■ 1971, June 16. Ulster Paintings
Des: S. Rose.

Set	0.50	0.60
First day cover		1.00

John Keats (3p)
Thomas Gray (5p)
Sir Walter Scott (7½p)

■ 1971, July 28. Literary Anniversaries
Des: Rosalind Dease.

Set	0.50	0.60
First day cover		1.00

British Legion: Servicemen and a nurse (3p)
City of York: A Roman Centurion (7½p)
Rugby Football Union: Rugby Players (9p)

■ 1971, August 25. Anniversaries
Des: F. Wegner.

Set	0.50	0.60
First day cover		1.10

University College, Aberystwyth (3p)
University of Southampton (5p)
University of Leicester (7½p)
University of Essex (9p)

■ 1971, September 22. University Buildings
Des: N. Jenkins.

Set	0.75	1.00
First day cover		1.10

'Dream of the Wise Men' (2½p)
'Adoration of the Magi' (3p)
'Ride of the Magi' (7½p)

■ 1971, October 13. Christmas
Des: Clarke, Clement and Hughes based on stained glass windows at Canterbury Cathedral.

Set	0.30	0.40
First day cover		1.00

Sir James Clarke Ross (3p)
Sir Martin Frobisher (5p)
Henry Hudson (7½p)
Captain Scott (9p)

■ 1972, February 16. Polar Explorers
Des: Marjorie Seynor.

Set	0.60	0.75
First day cover		1.10

Tutankhamun (3p)
Coastguard (7½p)
Ralph Vaughan Williams (9p)

■ **1972, April 26. Anniversaries**
Des: Rosalind Dease (3p), F. Wegner (7½p), C. Abbott (9p)
Set   0.50   0.60
First day cover   1.10

St. Andrew's, Greensted-juxta-Ongar, Essex (3p)
All Saints, Earls Barton, Northants (4p)
St. Andrew's, Lethringsett, Norfolk (5p)
St. Andrew's, Helpringham, Lincs (7½p)
St. Mary the Virgin, Huish Episcopi, Somerset (9p)

■ **1972, June 21. Village Churches**
Des: R. Maddox.
Set   0.75   1.00
First day cover   1.50

Microphones (3p)
Horn Loudspeaker (5p)
Colour Television (7½p)
Oscillator and Spark Transmitter (9p)

■ **1972, September 13. 50th Anniversary of the BBC**
Des: D. Gentleman.
Set   0.75   0.80
First day cover   1.10

Angel with trumpet (2½p)
Angel with lute (3p)
Angel with harp (7½p)

■ **1972, October 19. Christmas**
Des: Sally Stiff.
Set   0.25   0.40
First day cover   0.60

Queen Elizabeth II and Prince Phillip (3p), (20p)

■ **1972, November 20, Royal Silver Wedding**
Des: J. Matthews from photograph by Norman Parkinson.
All-over phosphor (3p), no phosphor (20p).
i) Printed on a Rembrandt machine
Set   0.50   0.60
First day cover   0.60
ii) Printed on a Jumelle machine.
3p deep blue, brown, silver   0.20   0.20
Gutter pair   0.30
Traffic light gutter pair   8.00
(* The portraits tend to be lighter on the Jumelle printing)

Jigsaw pieces representing Europe (3p), (5p)

■ **1973, January 3, European Communities**
Des: P. Murdoch.
Set   0.50   0.75
First day cover   0.80

Oak Tree (9p)

■ **1973, February 28. British Trees**
Des: D. Gentleman.

9p multicoloured	0.25	0.25
First day cover		0.50

David Livingstone (3p)
H.M. Stanley (3p)
Francis Drake (5p)
Walter Raleigh (7½p)
Charles Sturt (9p)

■ **1973, April 18. British Explorers**
Des: Marjorie Seynor. All-over phosphor.

Set	1.00	1.00
First day cover		1.10

About to bat (3p)
Watching the ball (7½p)
Leaving the wicket (9p)

■ **1973, May 16. County Cricket**
Des: E Ripley, based on drawings by Harry Furniss of W.G. Grace.

Set	1.00	1.00
First day cover		1.25
Stamp card (of 3p design)	50.00	

Self portrait of Joshua Reynolds (3p)
Self portrait of Henry Raeburn (5p)
'Nelly O'Brien' by Reynolds (7½p)
'Rev. R. Walker' by Raeburn (9p)

■ **1973, July. British Painters**
Des: S. Rose.

Set	0.55	0.65
First day cover		1.00

Court Masque Costumes (3p)
St Paul's church, Covent Garden (3p)
Prince's Lodging, Newmarket (5p)
Court Masque Stage Scene (5p)

■ **1973, August 15. 400th Anniversary of Birth of Inigo Jones**
Des: Rosalind Dease. Printed in litho and typo by Bradbury, Wilkinson.

Set	0.50	0.65
First day cover		0.90
Stamp card (of 3p St Paul's)	125.00	£225

Palace of Westminster from Whitehall (8p)
Palace of Westminster from Millbank (10p)

■ **1973, September 12. Commonwealth Parliamentary Conference**
Des: R. Downer. Printed in recess and litho by Bradbury, Wilkinson.

Set	0.40	0.50
First day cover		0.75
Stamp card (of 8p)	25.00	£150

Princess Anne and Captain Mark Phillips (3½p), (20p)

1973, November 14. Royal Wedding
Des: C. Clements and E. Hughes based on photograph by Lord Lichfield

Set	0.50	0.55
Gutter pair	1.50	
Traffic light gutter pair	50.00	
First day cover		0.60
Stamp card (of 3½p design)	5.00	30.00

(*The 3½p exists from sheets guillotined in the wrong place giving incorrect inscriptions within the gutter: priced at £30.)

Good King Wenceslas (five different 3p designs)
Good King Wenceslas, the Page and the Peasant (3½p)

1973, November 28. Christmas
Des: D. Gentleman. 3p values have one phosphor band. These stamps exist with either gum Arabic (3p), PVA gum (3½p) or dextrin gum (both values); prices are the same.

Set	1.00	1.50
First day cover		1.20

Horse Chestnut (10p)

1974, February 27. British Trees
Des: D. Gentleman.

10p	0.20	0.25
Gutter pair	1.00	
Traffic light gutter pair	30.00	
First day cover		0.50
Stamp card	95.00	75.00

First Motor Fire Engine 1904 (3½p)
Fire Engine 1863 (5½p)
Steam Fire Engine (8p)
Fire Engine 1766 (10p)

1974, April 24. Fire Engines
Des: D. Gentleman. Dextrin gum except where stated.

3½p with PVA gum	0.90	-
Set	0.75	0.80
Gutter pairs	1.75	
Traffic light gutter pairs	30.00	
First day cover		1.25
Stamp card (of 3½p)	75.00	75.00

P&O Packet Steamer 'Peninsular' (3½p)
Coronation Airmail 1911 (5½p)
Blue Airmail Van (8p)
Imperial Airways Flying boat (10p)

1974, June 12. Centenary of the UPU
Des: Rosalind Dease.

Set	0.50	0.75
Gutter pairs	1.50	
Traffic light gutter pairs	25.00	
First day cover		0.75

Robert the Bruce (4½p)
Owain Glyndwr (5½p)
Henry V (8p)
The Black Prince (10p)

1974, July 10. Famous Britons
Des: F. Wegner.

Set	0.55	0.75
Gutter pairs	2.50	
Traffic light gutter pairs	30.00	
First day cover		1.00
Stamp card (set)	16.00	50.00

Lord Warden of the Cinque Ports (4½p)
Prime Minister (5½p)
Secretary for War and Air (8p)
War Correspondent in South Africa (10p)

■ **1974, October 9. Birth Centenary of Winston Churchill**
Des: C. Clements and E. Hughes.

8p with PVA gum	1.25	-
Set	0.90	0.85
Gutter pairs	1.75	
Traffic light gutter pairs	17.50	
First day cover		1.00
Stamp card (of 5½p)	3.50	17.00

'Adoration of the Magi' (3½p)
'The Nativity' (4½p)
'Virgin and Child' (8p)
'Virgin and Child' (10p)

■ **1974, November 27. Christmas**
Des: Peter Hatch Partnership based on church roof bosses.

3½p with phos band to right	0.20	0.25
Set	0.50	0.60
Gutter pairs	2.25	
Traffic light gutter pairs	25.00	
First day cover		0.90

Invalid in Wheelchair (4½p + 1½p)

■ **1975, January 22. Health and Handicap Charities**
Des: P. Sharland. Surcharge donated to charity.

4½p + 1½p	0.15	0.15
Gutter pair	0.30	
Traffic light gutter pair	0.50	
First day cover		0.50

'Peace: Burial at Sea' (4½p)
'Snowstorm' (5½p)
'The Arsenal, Venice' (8p)
'St. Laurent' (10p)

■ **1975, February 19. Bicentenary of the Birth of Turner**
Des: S. Rose.

Set	0.50	0.60
Gutter pairs	1.25	
Traffic light gutter pairs	4.00	
First day cover		0.80
Stamp card (of 5½p)	22.00	17.00

Charlotte Square, Edinburgh (7p)
The Rows, Chester (7p)
Royal Observatory, Greenwich (8p)
St. George's Chapel, Windsor (10p)
National Theatre, London (12p)

■ **1975, April 23. European Architectural Heritage Year.**
Des: P. Gauld.

Set	0.75	0.80
Gutter pairs	2.25	
Traffic light gutter pairs	12.00	
First day cover		1.00
Stamp cards (7p and 8p)	6.00	22.00

Sailing Dinghies (7p)
Racing Keel Boats (8p)
Cruising Yachts (10p)
Multihulls (12p)

1975, June 11. Sailing
Des: A. Restall. Printed in photogravure and recess by Harrison.

Set	0.50	0.60
Gutter pairs	1.50	
Traffic light gutter pairs	12.00	
First day cover		0.90
Stamp card (of 8p)	4.00	15.00

*The 7p exists from sheets guillotined in the wrong place, giving gutter pairs with the wrong inscriptions, priced at £45.)

Stephenson's 'Locomotion' (7p)
Waverley Class (8p)
Caerphilly Class (10p)
High Speed Train (12p)

1975, August 13. Railways
Des: B. Cracker.

Set	0.80	0.75
Gutter Pairs	2.00	
Traffic light gutter pairs	6.00	
First day cover		1.00
Stamp cards (set)	35.00	35.00

Palace of Westminster (12p)

1975, September 3. Inter-Parliamentary Union Conference
Des: R. Downer

12p	0.25	0.25
Gutter pair	0.60	
Traffic light gutter pair	1.25	
First day cover		0.50

Emma and Mr. Woodhouse (8½p)
Catherine Morland (10p)
Mr. Darcy (11p)
Mary and Henry Crawford (13p)

1975, October 22. Jane Austen Birth Bicentenary
Des: Barbara Brown.

Set	0.65	0.60
Gutter pairs	1.40	
Traffic light gutter pairs	3.25	
First day cover		0.90
Stamp cards (set)	12.00	30.00

Angel with harp and lute (6½p)
Angel with mandolin (8½p)
Angel with horn (11p)
Angel with trumpet (13p)

1975, November 25. Christmas
Des: R. Downer. Dextrin gum except where stated. The 8½p has the phosphor in the green printing ink

6½p with PVA gum	0.50	-
Set	0.65	0.60
Gutter pairs	1.40	
Traffic light gutter pairs	4.00	
First day cover		0.75

Housewife with telephone (8½p)
Policeman with telephone (10p)
District Nurse with telephone (11p)
Industrialist with telephone (13p)

1976, March 10. Centenary of First Telephone Conversation
Des: P. Sharland.

Set	0.75	0.60
Gutter pairs	1.50	
Traffic light gutter pairs	3.25	
First day cover		0.75

Mining coal: Thomas Hepburn (8½p)
Machinery: Robert Owen (10p)
Sweeping a chimney: Lord Shaftesbury (11p)
Prison Bars: Elizabeth Fry (13p)

■ 1976, April 28. Social Reformers
Des: D. Gentleman.

Set	0.70	0.60
Gutter pairs	1.50	
Traffic light gutter pairs	3.25	
First day cover		0.75
Stamp card (of 8½p)	4.00	11.00

Benjamin Franklin (11p)

■ 1976, June 2. American Bicentennial
Des: P. Sharland.

11p	0.25	0.25
Gutter pair	0.50	
Traffic light gutter pair	0.85	
First day cover		0.50
Stamp card	3.50	12.00

Elizabeth of Glamis (8½p)
Grandpa Dickson (10p)
Rosa Mundi (11p)
Sweet Briar (13p)

■ 1976, June 30. Roses
Des: Kristin Rosenberg.

Set	0.70	0.60
Gutter pairs	1.50	
Traffic light gutter pairs	4.50	
First day cover		0.90
Stamp card	17.00	25.00

Archdruid (Royal National Eisteddfod) (8½p)
Morris Dancing (10p)
Highland Gathering (11p)
Harpist (Royal National Eisteddfod) (13p)

■ 1976, August 4. Cultural Traditions
Des: Marjorie Seynor.

Set	0.70	0.60
Gutter pairs	1.50	
Traffic light gutter pairs	4.50	
First day cover		0.75
Stamp card	9.00	17.00

'The Canterbury Tales' (8½p)
'The Tretyse of Love' (10p)
'The Game and Playe of Chesse' (11p)
Printing Press (13p)

■ 1976, September 29. 500th Anniversary of British Printing
Des: R. Gay.

Set	0.70	0.60
Gutter pairs	1.50	
Traffic light gutter pairs	3.50	
First day cover		0.75
Stamp card	7.00	17.00

irgin and Child (6½p)
ngel (8½p)
ngel with Shepherds (11p)
he Three Kings (13p)

1976, November 24. Christmas.
es: Enid Marx (based on English embroideries)

½p with one phos band	0.15	0.10
et	0.60	0.60
utter pairs	1.50	
raffic light gutter pairs	3.00	
irst day cover		0.75
tamp card	2.50	15.00

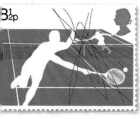

awn Tennis (8½p)
able Tennis (10p)
quash (11p)
adminton (13p)

1977, January 12. Racket Sports
es: A. Restall.

et	0.65	0.60
utter pairs	1.75	
raffic light gutter pairs	3.25	
irst day cover		0.80
tamp card	4.00	15.00

eroids (8½p)
tamin C (10p)
arch Chromatography (11p)
lt Crystallography (13p)

■ 1977, March 2. Centenary of the Royal Institute of Chemistry
Des: J. Karo.

Set	0.65	0.60
Gutter pairs	1.75	
Traffic light gutter pairs	3.50	
First day cover		0.75
Stamp card	4.00	10.00

ER (8½p, 9p, 10p, 11p, 13p)

■ 1977, May 11. Silver Jubilee.
Des: Professor R. Guyatt. 9½p issued on June 15.

Set	0.80	0.75
Gutter pairs	1.80	
Traffic light gutter pairs	2.50	
First day cover (8½p, 10p, 11p, 13p)		0.60
First day cover (9p)		0.50
Stamp card	7.00	11.00

Symbol of Pentagons (13p)

■ 1977, June 8. Commonwealth Heads of Government Meeting
Des: P. Murdoch. Printed in photogravure and recess by Harrison.

13p	0.25	0.25
Gutter pair	0.50	
Traffic light gutter pair	0.60	
First day cover		0.50
Stamp card	3.00	4.00

Hedgehog *Erinaceus europaeus*

Hedgehog (9p)
Hare (9p)
Red Squirrel (9p)
Otter (9p)
Badger (9p)

■ **1977, October 5. Wildlife.**
Des: P Oxenham. All multicoloured

Se-tenant strip of five	0.75	0.90
Gutter strip	1.25	
Traffic light gutter strip	2.50	
First day cover		1.00
Stamp card	1.75	5.00

(* Gutter strips normally comprise a strip of four designs separated from the fifth design by the gutter.)

THE TWELVE DAYS OF CHRISTMAS

Three French Hens, two Turtle Doves and a Partridge in a Pear Tree (7p)
Six Geese, five Gold Rings, four Colley Birds (7p)
Eight Maids, seven Swans (7p)
Ten Pipers, nine Drummers (7p)
Twelve Lords, eleven Ladies (7p)
A Partridge and Pears (9p)

■ **1977, November 23. Christmas**
Des: D. Gentleman based on the Christmas song 'The Twelve Days of Christmas'. The 7p values, issued se-tenant, have one phosphor band.

Set	0.75	0.85
Gutter pairs	1.50	
Traffic light gutter pairs	2.75	
First day cover		0.80
Stamp card	2.00	4.50

(* Gutter pairs of the 7p values comprise two horizontal se-tenant strips of the stamps separated by a horizontal gutter.)

OIL

North Sea Oil (9p)
Coal Pithead (10½p)
Natural Gas Flame (11p)
Electricity (13p)

■ **1978, January 25. Energy**
Des: P. Murdoch.

Set	0.65	0.75
Gutter pairs	1.50	
Traffic light gutter pairs	2.25	
First day cover		0.80
Stamp card	1.75	4.00

Tower of London–The White Tower

Tower of London (9p)
Holyroodhouse (10½p)
Caernarvon Castle (11p)
Hampton Court (13p)

■ **1978, March 1. Historic Buildings**
Des: R. Maddox.

Set	0.75	0.80
Gutter pairs	1.60	
Traffic light gutter pairs	2.25	
First day cover		0.90
Stamp card	4.00	3.00
Miniature sheet	0.80	0.85
Miniature sheet FDC		1.00

(* The miniature sheet, designed by J. Matthews, was sold at 53½p, the extra 10p being donated to assist the finances of staging the International Stamp Exhibition. London 1980, which the sheet itself publicised.)

ate Coach (9p)
, Edward's Crown (10½p)
overeign's Orb (11p)
mperial State Crown (13p)

1978, May 31. 25th Anniversary of the Coronation
es: J. Matthews.

et	0.75	0.75
utter pairs	1.60	
raffic light gutter pairs	2.25	
irst day cover		0.75
ouvenir Pack	1.75	
tamp card	2.00	3.00

ire Horse (9p)
etland Pony (10½p)
Velsh Pony (11p)
horoughbred (13p)

1978, July 5. Horses
es: P. Oxenham.

et	0.70	0.75
utter pairs	1.50	
raffic light gutter pairs	2.25	
irst day cover		0.75
tamp card	1.75	3.00

Penny Farthing and Safety Bicycle of 1884 (9p)
Touring bicycles (10½p)
Small-Wheel Bicycles (11p)
Road-racers (13p)

■ 1978, August 2. Cycling
Des: F. Wegner.

Set	0.70	0.75
Gutter pairs	1.60	
Traffic light gutter pairs	2.25	
First day cover		0.75
Stamp card	1.50	3.00

Dancing around a Christmas Tree (7p)
The Waits (9p)
Carol Singers (11p)
Carrying the Boar's Head (13p)

■ 1978, November 22. Christmas
Des: Faith Jacques. 7p has one phos band.

Set	0.65	0.75
Gutter pairs	1.25	
Traffic light gutter pairs	2.25	
First day cover		0.75
Stamp card	2.00	3.00

Old English Sheepdog (9p)
Welsh Springer Spaniel (10½p)
West Highland Terrier (11p)
Irish Setter (13p)

■ 1979, February 7. British Dogs
Des: P. Barrett.

Set	0.70	0.75
Gutter pairs	1.25	
Traffic light gutter pairs	2.25	
First day cover		0.75
Stamp card	1.75	3.00

Primrose (9p)
Daffodil (10½p)
Bluebell (11p)
Snowdrop (13p)

■ 1979, March 21. Spring Flowers
Des: P. Newcombe.

Set	0.70	0.75
Gutter pairs	1.50	
Traffic light gutter pairs	2.25	
First day cover		0.75
Stamp card	1.50	3.00

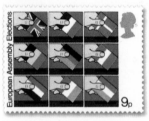

Hands placing 'flag' voting papers into ballot boxes
(9p, 10½p, 11p, 13p, designs vary slightly)

■ 1979, May 9. Direct Elections to the European Assembly
Des: S. Cliff.

Set	0.70	0.75
Gutter pairs	1.50	
Traffic light gutter pairs	2.25	
First day cover		0.75
Stamp card	1.50	3.00

Saddling Mahmoud for the Derby (9p)
The Liverpool Great National Steeple Chase (10½p)
The First Spring Meeting, Newmarket (11p)
Racing at Dorsett Ferry, Windsor (13p)

■ 1979, June 6. Horse Racing
Des: S. Rose.

Set	0.70	0.75
Gutter pairs	1.50	
Traffic light gutter pairs	2.25	
First day cover		0.75
Stamp card	1.50	3.00

The Tale of Peter Rabbit (9p)
The Wind in the Willows (10½p)
Winnie the Pooh (11p)
Alice's Adventures in Wonderland (13p)

■ 1979, July 11. International Year of the Child
Des: E. Hughes.

Set	0.85	0.80
Gutter pairs	1.75	
Traffic light gutter pairs	2.25	
First day cover		0.75
Stamp card	1.60	3.00

Sir Rowland Hill (10p)
London Post (11½p)
General Post (13p)
Penny Post (15p)

1979, August 22. Centenary of Death of Sir Rowland Hill

Des: E Stemp.

Set	0.75	0.75
Gutter pairs	1.60	
Traffic light gutter pairs	2.25	
First day cover		0.75
Stamp card	1.50	3.00
Miniature sheet	0.75	0.75
Miniature sheet FDC		0.75

(* The miniature sheet, designed by J. Matthews and issued October 24, 1979, was sold at 59½p, the extra 10p being donated towards the finances of staging the International Stamp Exhibition, London 1980, which the sheet itself publicised.)

Policeman talking to two children (10p)
Street Patrol (11½p)
Policewoman on horseback (13p)
River police (15p)

1979, September 26. Metropolitan Police 150th Anniversary

Des: B. Sanders.

Set	0.80	0.85
Gutter pairs	1.60	
Traffic light gutter pairs	2.25	
First day cover		0.85
Stamp card	1.50	3.00

The Kings following the Star (8p)
The Angel appearing to the Shepherd (10p)
The Manger Scene (11½p)
Joseph and Mary travelling to Bethlehem (13p)
The Annunciation (15p)

1979, November 21. Christmas

Des: F. Wegner. 8p has one phosphor band.

Set	0.90	0.90
Gutter pairs	1.80	
Traffic light gutter pairs	2.25	
First day cover		0.90
Stamp card	1.50	3.00

Kingfisher (10p)
Dipper (11½p)
Moorhen (13p)
Yellow Wagtail (15p)

1980, January 16. Water Birds

Des: Michael Warren.

Set	0.80	0.80
Gutter pairs	2.00	
First day cover		0.90
Stamp card	1.50	3.00

The Rocket (12p)
First and second class carriages (12p)
Third class carriage and cattle truck (12p)
Open coach on truck and horsebox (12p)
Goods wagon and mail coach (12p)

1980, March 12. 150th Anniversary of the Liverpool & Manchester Railway

Des: D. Gentleman.

Se-tenant strip of five	0.85	0.85
Gutter pairs	2.25	
First day cover		1.00
Stamp card	1.50	3.50

(* The gutter pairs comprise two horizontal se-tenant strips of the stamps separated by a horizontal gutter.)

INTERNATIONAL STAMP EXHIBITION

Montage of London buildings and monuments (50p)

■ 1980, April 9. London 1980, International Stamp Exhibition

Des: J. Matthews. Printed by line-engraving. No phosphor.

50p	0.90	0.75
Gutter pair	2.00	
First day cover		0.75
Stamp card	0.50	1.50
Miniature sheet	0.90	1.25
Miniature sheet FDC		1.25

(* The miniature sheet, issued on May 7, 1980, was sold at 75p, the extra 25p being donated towards the finances of staging the International Stamp Exhibition, London 1980.)
(* The stamp is known to exist in shades of green: the shades were caused by the speed of the ink-drying operation. Attempts have been made to create artificially the 'green' shades.)

$10\frac{1}{2}^{P}$ Buckingham Palace

Buckingham Palace (10½pp)
Albert Memorial (12p)
Royal Opera House (13½p)
Hampton Court (25p)
Kensington Palace (17½p)

■ 1980, May 7. London Landmarks

Des: Sir Hugh Casson.

Set	1.00	0.90
Gutter pairs	2.50	
First day cover		1.00
Stamp card	1.50	3.50

Charlotte Bronte (12p)
George Eliot (13½p)
Emily Bronte (15p)
Mrs. Gaskell (17½p)

■ 1980, July 9. Famous Women/Europa 1980

Des: Barbara Brown.

Set	1.10	0.75
Gutter pairs	2.50	
First day cover		0.90
Stamp card	1.75	3.00

Her Majesty Queen Elizabeth The Queen Mother (12p)

■ 1980, August 4. The Queen Mother's 80th Birthday

Des: Jeffery Matthews.

12p multicoloured	0.40	0.30
Gutter pair	1.00	
First day cover		0.60
Stamp card	0.60	1.00

r Henry Wood (12p)
r Thomas Beecham (13½p)
r Malcolm Sargent (15p)
r John Barbirolli (17½p)

1980, September 10. Music: British Conductors
es: Peter Gauld

et	0.90	0.80
utter pairs	2.25	
rst day cover		0.90
:amp card	1.50	2.50

These stamps exist on paper which reveals differences in the gree of 'shine' on the surface.)

thletics (12p)
ugby (13½p)
oxing (15p)
ricket (17½p)

1980, October 10. Sports
es: Robert Goldsmith. Printed in litho by Questa.

et	0.90	0.80
iutter pairs	2.25	
irst day cover		0.90
:amp card	1.50	2.50

hristmas tree (10p)
:andles, ivy and ribbon (12p)
listletoe and apples (13½p)
aper chains with crown and bell (15p)
lolly wreath and ornaments (17½p)

1980, November 10. Christmas
Des: Jeffery Matthews. 10p has one phosphor band.

Set	1.00	0.90
Gutter pairs	2.50	
First day cover		1.00
Stamp card	1.50	2.50

(* These stamps exist on paper which reveals differences in the degree of 'shine' on the surface.)

St. Valentine's Day (14p)
Morris Dancers (18p)
Lammastide (22p)
Medieval Mummers (25p)

1981, February 6. Folklore/Europa 1981
Des: Fritz Wegner.

Set	1.60	1.00
Gutter pairs	3.50	
First day cover		1.00
Stamp card	3.00	2.25

Blind Man and Guide Dog (14p)
Deaf and Dumb Alphabet (18p)
Person in Wheelchair (22p)
Foot Artist (25p)

1981, March 25. International Year of Disabled People
Des: John Gibbs.

Set	1.10	1.00
Gutter pairs	2.75	
First day cover		0.90
Stamp card	1.50	2.25

Small Tortoiseshell

Small tortoiseshell (14p)
Large Blue (18p)
Peacock (22p)
Chequered Skipper (25p)

■ 1981, May 13. Butterflies
Des: Gordon Beningfield.

Set	1.10	1.00
Gutter pairs	2.75	
First day cover		0.90
Stamp card	1.50	3.00

Glenfinnan, Scotland (14p)
Derwentwater, England (18p)
Stackpole Head, Wales (20p)
Giant's Causeway, Northern Ireland (22p)
St. Kilda, Scotland (25p)

■ 1981, June 24. National Trusts
Des: Michael Fairclough.

Set	1.20	1.15
Gutter pairs	3.00	
First day cover		1.20
Stamp card	1.50	3.00

Prince Charles and Lady Diana Spencer(14p and 25p)

■ 1981, July 22. Wedding of Prince Charles and Lady Diana Spencer
Des: Jeffery Matthews, from a portrait by Lord Snowdon.

Set	1.00	0.75
Gutter pair	2.50	
First day cover		1.50
Souvenir Pack	2.00	
Stamp card	1.75	3.00

(* A folder containing these two stamps with text printed in Japanese, was sold at the international stamp exhibition in Tokyo in 1981. A modified version of this was made available through the British Philatelic Bureau. A folder was also prepared for a promotion with Cadbury Typhoo.)

Expeditions (14p)
Skills (18p)
Service (22p)
Recreation (25p)

■ 1981, August 12. Duke of Edinburgh's Award 25th Anniversary
Des: Philip Sharland. Printed in Litho by Waddingtons.

Set	1.10	1.00
Gutter pairs	2.75	
First day cover		1.00
Stamp card	1.50	2.25

Cockle Dredging (14p)
Hauling Side Trawl (18p)
Lobster Potting (22p)
Hauling Seine Net (25p)

■ 1981, September 23. Fishing
Des: Brian Saunders.

Set	1.10	1.00
Gutter pairs	2.75	
First day cover		1.10
Stamp card	1.50	2.25

11½p

Samantha Brown, age 5

...ther Christmas with sacks of toys (11½p)
...he head of Christ (14p)
...ngel in flight (18p)
...seph and Mary with Donkey (22p)
...he Three Wise Man on their camels following the star (25p)

1981, November 18. Christmas
...es: Samantha Brown (11½p), Tracy Jenkins (14p), Lucinda
...ackmore (18p), Stephen Moore (22p), Sophie Sharp (25p). The
...½p has one phosphor band

...et	1.25	1.20
...utter pairs	3.00	
...irst day cover		1.10
...tamp card	1.50	3.00

15½p   C. Darwin

...arwin and Giant Tortoises (15½p)
...arwin and Iguanas (19½p)
...arwin and Darwin's Finches (26p)
...arwin and Prehistoric Skulls (29p)

1982, February 10. Centenary of the death of Charles
...arwin.
...es: David Gentleman.

...et	1.20	1.10
...utter pairs	3.00	
...irst day cover		1.20
...tamp cards	1.50	3.50

15½p

Boy's Brigade (15½p)
Girl's Brigade (19½p)
Scouts (26p)
Guides and Brownies (29p)

■ 1982, March 24. Youth Organisations
Des: Brian Sanders.

Set	1.20	1.10
Gutter pairs	3.00	
First day cover		1.20
Stamp cards	1.50	3.50

15½p

Ballet (15½p)
Pantomime (19½p)
Shakespearean drama (26p)
Opera (29p)

■ 1982, April 28. British Theatre/Europa
Des: Adrian George.

Set	2.50	1.10
Gutter pairs	6.00	
First day cover		1.20
Stamp cards	1.50	3.00

15½p

HENRY VIII/MARY ROSE

Henry VIII and 'Mary Rose' (15½p)
Admiral Blake and 'Triumph' (19½p)
Lord Nelson and 'HMS Victory' (24p)
Lord Fisher and 'HMS Dreadnought' (26p)
Viscount Cunningham and 'HMS Warspite' (29p)

■ 1982, June 16. Maritime Heritage
Des: Marjorie Seynor. Printed in recess and photogravure by
Harrison.

Set	2.00	1.25
Gutter pairs	5.00	
First day cover		1.25
Stamp cards	1.75	4.00

'Strawberry Thief', 1883 by William Morris (15½p)
'Scarlet Tulips', 1906 by F. Steiner and Co (19½p)
'Cherry Orchard', 1930 by Paul Nash (26p)
'Chevrons', 1973 by Andrew Foster (29p)

■ 1982, July 23. British Textiles
Des: Peter Hatch Patnership.

Set	1.25	1.40
Gutter pairs	3.00	
First day cover		1.20
Stamp cards	1.75	3.50

'History of Communications (15½p)
'Technology Today' (26p)

■ 1982, September 8. Information Technology Year
Des: Brian Delaney and Darrell Ireland.

Set	0.75	0.80
Gutter pair	2.00	
First day cover		0.90
Stamp cards	1.00	2.50

Austin Seven and Metro (15½p)
Ford Model T and Escort (19½p)
Jaguar SS1 and XJ6 (26p)
Rolls Royce Silver Ghost and Silver Spirit (29p)

■ 1982, October 13. British Motor Cars
Des: Stanley Paine. Printed in litho by Questa.

Set	1.40	1.25
Gutter pairs	3.25	
First day cover		1.25
Stamp cards	1.75	3.50

While Shepherds Watched (12½p)
The Holly and the Ivy (15½p)
I Saw Three Ships (19½p)
We Three Kings of Orient Are (26p)
Good King Wenceslas (29p)

■ 1982, November 17. Christmas
Des: Barbara Brown. 12½p has one phosphor band.

Set	1.50	1.25
Gutter pairs	3.50	
First day cover		1.25
Stamp cards	1.75	4.00

Salmon (15½p)
Pike (19½p)
Trout (26p)
Perch (29p)

■ 1983, January 26. British River Fishes
Des: Alex Jardine.

Set	1.50	1.40
Gutter pairs	3.50	
First day cover		1.20
Stamp cards	1.75	4.00

apical island (15½p)
t arid desert (19½p)
sh arable land (26p)
ld mountainous region (29p)

983, March 9. Commonwealth Day.
s: Donald Hamilton Fraser based on an original idea by
fford Cliff.

t	1.50	1.40
utter pairs	3.50	
rst day cover		1.20
amp cards	1.75	3.50

e Humber Bridge (16p)
names Flood Barrier (20½p)
lair' Emergency Support Vessel (28p)

1983, May 25. Europa: Engineering Achievements
es: Michael Taylor.

et	2.00	1.50
utter pairs	5.00	
irst day cover		1.20
camp cards	2.50	3.00

Musketeer and pikeman of the Royal Scots (16p)
The Royal Welch Fusiliers (20½p)
Riflemen of the 95th Rifles: The Royal Green Jacket (26p)
Irish Guards (28p)
The Parachute Regiment (31p)

■ 1983, July 6. The British Army
Des: Eric Stemp.

Set	1.50	1.60
Gutter pairs	3.50	
First day cover		1.50
Stamp cards	1.75	4.00

Sissinghurst (16p)
Biddulph Grange (20½p)
Blenheim (28p)
Pitmedden (31p)

■ 1983, August 24. British Gardens
Des: Liz Butler. Printed in litho by Waddingtons.

Set	1.40	1.20
Gutter pairs	3.25	
First day cover		1.20
Stamp cards	1.75	3.50

Merry-go-round (16p)
Menagerie and fairground rides (20½p)
Side shows (28p)
Trading in farm produce (31p)

■ 1983, October 5. Fairs and Shows.
Des: Andrew Restall.

Set	1.40	1.20
Gutter pairs	3.25	
First day cover		1.20
Stamp cards	1.75	3.50

Flurry of birds posting Christmas greetings (12½p)
Chimney pots with a dove and cat (16p)
Dove and blackbird under an umbrella (20½p)
Dove and blackbird under a street lamp (28p)
Hedge sculpture in shape of dove (31p)

1983, November 16. Christmas
Des: Tony Meeuwissen. 12½p has one phosphor band.

Set	1.50	1.40
Gutter pairs	3.50	
First day cover		1.30
Stamp cards	1.75	3.50

Arms of The College of Arms (16p)
Arms of Richard III (20½p)
Arms of The Earl Marshal (28p)
Arms of the City of London (31p)

1984, January 17. Quincentenary of The College of Arms
Des: Jeffrey Matthews.

Set	1.40	1.25
Gutter pairs	3.25	
First day cover		1.25
Stamp cards	1.75	4.00

Highland Cow (16p)
Chillingham Wild Bull (20½p)
Hereford Bull (26p)
Welch Black Bull (28p)
Irish Moiled Cow (31p)

1984, March 6. Cattle
Des: Barry Driscoll.

Set	1.60	1.40
Gutter pairs	4.00	
First day cover		1.25
Stamp cards	1.75	4.00

Liverpool: International Garden Festival (16p)
Durham: Milburngate Shopping Centre (20½p)
Bristol: Bush House, City Docks Area (28p)
Perth: Commercial Street Housing Scheme (31p)

1984, April 19. Urban Renewal
Des: Trickett and Webb and Ronald Maddox.

Set	1.50	1.25
Gutter pairs	3.50	
First day cover		1.25
Stamp cards	1.75	3.50

Europa 'bridge' and CEPT emblem (16p, both values)
Europa abducted by Zeus in the shape of a bull and the emblem
of the European Parliament (20½p, both values)

1984, May 15. 25th Anniversary of CEPT and Second Direct Elections to the European Parliament
Des: J. Larriviere (16p), Fritz Wegner (20½p). The two designs were printed in se-tenant pairs throughout the sheet.

Set	2.00	2.00
Gutter pairs	5.00	
First day cover		2.00
Stamp cards	3.00	3.50

VENDING MACHINE LABELS

From May 1, 1984 until April 30, 1985, machines were installed at four locations which printed labels for the basic 1st class rate, 2nd class rate or any denomination from ½p to 16p (17p from August 28).

They had a red value and frame with the Queen's portrait printed on phosphor-coated white security paper with a grey-green background design.

Pack of 3½p, 12½p and 16p	1.25
Pack of 16½p and 17p labels	1.50
Pack of all values from ½p to 16p	11.00
First day cover bearing 3½p, 12½p and 16p	2.50

caster House and flags of participating nations (31p)

1984, June 5. London Economic Summit.
s: Paul Hogarth.

p	0.60	0.70
utter pair	1.75	
st day cover		1.00
amp cards	0.50	2.00

e Earth from space (16p)
vigational chart of the English Channel (20½p)
rial photograph of the Greenwich Observatory (28p)
y's transit telescope (31p)

1984, June 21. Centenary of the Greenwich Meridian
s: Jerry Barney and Howard Walker. Printed in litho by
esta.

t	1.50	1.40
utter pairs	3.50	
st day cover		1.25
amp cards	1.75	3.50

iginal Bath Mail Coach of 1784 (16p)
tack on the Exeter Mail in 1816 (16p)
e Norwich Mail in a thunderstorm 1827 (16p)
e Holyhead and Liverpool Mails 1828 (16p)
e Edinburgh Mail snowbound in 1831 (16p)

■ **1984, July 31. 200th Anniversary of the Frst Mail Coach
Run from Bristol and Bath to London**
Des: Keith Bassford and Stanley Paine. Printed in recess and
photogravure by Harrison.

Set	1.50	1.40
Gutter pairs	3.50	
First day cover		1.25
Stamp cards	1.75	4.00

(* Gutter pairs comprise two horizontal se-tenant strips of the
five stamps separated by a gutter.)

'Education for development' (17p)
'Promoting the arts' (22p)
'Technical training' (31p)
'Language and libraries' (34p)

■ **1984, September 25. 50th Anniversary of the British
Council.**
Des: Francis Newell, John Sorrell and Brian Sanders.

Set	1.50	1.30
Gutter pairs	3.50	
First day cover		1.25
Stamp cards	1.75	3.50

(* Sheets of these stamps sold at the international stamp
exhibition held in Melbourne, Australia, in September 1984 had
the gutter margins overprinted with the exhibition logo.)

Holy Family (13p)
Arrival in Bethlehem (17p)
Shepherd and Lamb (22p)
Virgin and Child (31p)
Offering of Frankincense (34p)

■ **1984, November 20. Christmas**
Des: Yvonne Gilbert. 13p has one centre phosphor band.

13p (stars printed on back)	0.60	
Set	1.60	1.60
Gutter pairs	4.00	
First day cover		1.25
Stamp cards	1.75	3.00
Booklet	5.50	

(* The booklet, with a Manger Scene cover and containing 20 x
13p stamps, sold at £2.30, a discount of 30p. The stamps had an
all-over five-pointed star pattern printed on the back.)

Flying Scotsman (17p)
Golden Arrow (22p)
Cheltenham Flyer (29p)
Royal Scot (31p)
Cornish Riviera (34p)

■ 1985, January 22. Famous Trains
Des: Terence Cuneo.

Set	2.75	2.10
Gutter pairs	7.00	
First day cover		2.25
Stamp cards	3.25	9.00

Buff-tailed Bumble Bee (17p)
Seven-Spotted Ladybird (22p)
Wart-biter Bush-cricket (29p)
Stag Beetle (31p)
Emperor Butterfly (34p)

■ 1985, March 12. Insects
Des: Gordon Beningfield.

Set	2.00	1.60
Gutter pairs	4.00	
First day cover		1.60
Stamp cards	1.75	4.50

'Water Music' by Handel (17p)
'The Planet Suite' by Holst (22p)
'The First Cuckoo' by Delius (31p)
'Sea Picture' by Elgar (34p)

■ 1985, May 14. European Music Year. British Composer
Des: Wilson McLean.

Set	3.00	1.75
Gutter pairs	7.50	
First day cover		1.50
Stamp cards	1.75	4.00

RNLI Lifeboat and dinghy in distress (17p)
Beachy Head Lighthouse (22p)
Marecs A Satellite (31p)
Trinity House Buoy (34p)

■ 1985, June 18. Safety at Sea
Des: Newell and Sorell. Printed in litho by Waddingtons.

Set	1.60	1.50
Gutter pairs	4.00	
First day cover		1.40
Stamp cards	1.75	3.50

Datapost motorcyclist and plane (17p)
Postbus in countryside (22p)
Parcel delivery (31p)
Postman delivering letters (34p)

■ 1985, July 30. 350th Anniversary of Royal Mail Service to the Public
Des: Paul Hogarth.

17p 'D' pattern printed on gummed side		0.60
Set	1.60	1.50
Gutter pairs	4.00	
First day cover		1.40
Stamp cards	1.75	3.50
Booklet	3.00	

(* The booklet, containing 10 x 17p, sold at a discounted price
£1.53. Each stamp had a 'D' pattern printed on the gummed s.
The cover shows a Datapost van and plane, and Concorde.)

King Arthur and Merlin (17p)
The Lady of the Lake (22p)
Guinevere and Lancelot of the Lake (31p)
Sir Galahad (34p)

1985, September 3. Arthurian Legend.

Des: Yvonne Gilbert.

Set	1.60	1.50
Gutter pairs	4.00	
First day cover		1.40
Stamp cards	1.75	4.00

Peter Sellers from photograph by Bill Brandt (17p)
David Niven by Cornel Lucas (22p)
Charles Chaplin by Snowdon (29p)
Vivien Leigh by Angus McBean (31p)
Alfred Hitchcock by Howard Coster (34p)

1985, October 8. British Film Year

Des: Keith Bassford.

Set	2.25	2.10
Gutter pairs	6.00	
First day cover		2.25
Stamp cards	1.75	5.00

Principal Boy (12p)
Genie (17p)
Pantomime Dame (22p)
Good Fairy (31p)
Pantomime Cat (34p)

1985, November 19. Christmas: Pantomime

Des: Adrian George. 12p has one phosphor band.

12p ('stars' on gummed side)	0.55	
Set	1.60	1.50
Gutter pairs	4.00	
First day cover		1.50
Stamp cards	1.75	4.50
Christmas card pack (50 × 12p)	30.00	
Booklet	5.00	

(* The booklet contained 20 × 12p, sold at £2.40. Cover shows Cinderella's slipper on a cushion.)

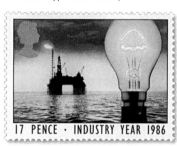

North Sea Drilling Rig and light bulb (17p)
Thermometer and laboratory (22p)
Garden hoe and steelworks (31p)
Loaf of bread and cornfield (34p)

1986, January 14. Industry Year

Des: Keith Bassford. Printed in litho by Questa.

Set	1.50	1.40
Gutter pairs	4.00	
First day cover		1.40
Stamp cards	1.75	3.50

Edmund Halley as the Comet (17p)
The Giotto space probe (22p)
'Maybe twice in a lifetime' (31p)
The Comet's Orbit (34p)

1986, February 18. Halley's Comet

Des: Ralph Steadman.

Set	1.50	1.40
Gutter pairs	4.00	
First day cover		1.40
Stamp cards	2.25	3.50

Sixtieth Birthday 17p

The Queen at the age of 2, 16 and 26 (17p and 34p)
The Queen at the age of 32, 47 and 56 (17p and 34p)

■ **1986, April 21. The Queen's 60th Birthday**
Des: Jeffrey Matthews.

Set	2.25	2.00
Gutter pairs	5.00	
First day cover		2.20
Stamp cards	1.75	4.00

Barn Owl (17p)
Pine Marten (22p)
Wild Cat (31p)
Natterjack Toad (34p)

■ **1986, May 20. Europa: Nature Conservation**
Des: Ken Lilly.

Set	2.75	1.80
Gutter pairs	7.00	
First day cover		1.75
Stamp cards	3.50	4.00

The peasant working on his land (17p)
The freeman and his craft (22p)
The knight and his retinue (31p)
The lord at head of table (34p)

■ **1986, June 17. Medieval Life. 900th Anniversary of the Domesday Book**
Des: Tayburn.

Set	1.60	1.50
Gutter pairs	4.00	
First day cover		1.50
Stamp cards	1.75	3.50

Sprinter's feet on starting blocks (17p)
Oarsman (22p)
Weightlifter with bar (29p)
Man looking through the sights of a rifle (31p)
Hockey player (34p)

■ **1986, July 15. Sport**
Des: Nick Cudworth.

Set	1.90	1.75
Gutter pairs	4.50	
First day cover		1.75
Stamp cards	2.25	4.50

Prince Andrew and Miss Sarah Ferguson (12p and 17p)

■ **1986, July 22. Royal Wedding**
Des: Jeffery Matthews.

Set	0.75	0.75
Gutter pairs	2.00	
First day cover		1.00
Stamp cards	1.25	3.00

Ballot-paper cross (34p)

1986, August 19. Commonwealth Parliamentary Association Conference
Des: John Gibbs. Printed in litho by Questa.

34p	0.75	0.80
Gutter pairs	2.00	
First day cover		0.80
Stamp cards	0.50	1.50

Lord Dowding and the Hurricane (17p)
Lord Tedder and the Typhoon (22p)
Lord Trenchard and the DH 9A (29p)
Sir Arthur Harris and the Lancaster (31p)
Lord Portal and the Mosquito (34p)

1986, September 16. Royal Air Force
Des: Brian Sanders.

Set	2.25	2.00
Gutter pairs	5.00	
First day cover		2.00
Stamp cards	2.25	5.50

The Glastonbury Thorn (12p), (13p)
The Tanad Valley Plygain (18p)
The Hebrides Tribute (22p)
The Dewsbury Church Knell (31p)
The Hereford Boy Bishop (34p)

1986, November 18. Christmas Traditions
Des: Lynda Gray. 12p has one phosphor band and was issued on December 2, 1986; 13p has one phosphor band

13p ('stars' printed on gummerd side)	0.50	
Set	2.00	2.00
Gutter Pairs	5.00	
First day cover		2.50
Stamp cards	1.75	5.00
Pack (36 × 13p, stars on gum)	9.00	

Gaillardia (18p)
Echinops (22p)
Echeveria (31p)
Colchicum (34p)

1987, January 6. Flowers
Des: Jeffery Matthews from photographs by Alfred Lammer.

Set	1.50	1.60
Gutter pairs	4.00	
First day cover		1.75
Stamp cards	1.75	4.00

(* A card with a Flowers design, stamped and cancelled with the 31p and 34p stamps, was made available at several stamp exhibitions, starting with Capex 87 in Toronto in June 1987.)

An apple (18p)
Planets moving around the sun (22p)
Flask of water and refraction of light (31p)
The earth and an artificial satellite (34p)

1987, March 24. Sir Isaac Newton
Des: Sarah Goodwin.

Set	1.50	1.60
Gutter pairs	4.00	
First day cover		1.75
Stamp cards	1.75	3.50

Willis Faber Dumas Building, Ipswich (18p)
Pompidou Centre, Paris (22p)
Staatgalerie, Stuttgart (31p)
European Investment Bank, Luxembourg (34p)

■ **1987, May 12. British Architects in Europe.
CEPT**
Des: Minale Tattersfield Studio.

Set	2.75	1.75
Gutter pairs	7.00	
First day cover		1.70
Stamp cards	4.00	3.50

Arms of the Lord Lyon, King of Arms (18p)
Arms of His Royal Highness The Duke of
Rothesay (22p)
Arms of the Royal Scottish Academy of Painting,
Sculpture and Architecture (31p)
Arms of The Royal Society of Edinburgh (34p)

■ **1987, July 21. Scottish Heraldry**
Des: Jeffery Matthews.

Set	1.50	1.60
Gutter pairs	4.00	
First day cover		1.70
Stamp cards	1.75	4.00

First aid duties in 1887 (18p)
First aid in wartime (22p)
First aid at events (31p)
Transplant organs flights (34p)

■ **1987, June 16. St John Ambulance
Centenary**
Des: Debbie Cook. Printed in litho by Questa.

Set	1.50	1.60
Gutter pairs	4.00	
First day cover		1.70
Stamp cards	1.75	3.50

Landseer's painting 'Monarch of the Glen', the Great Exhibition,
Grace Darling's Rescue (18p)
Launching of Brunel's 'Great Eastern', Mrs Beeton's Book of
Household Management, Prince Albert (22p)
The Albert Memorial, Benjamin Disraeli, the first ballot
box (31p)
Marconi's broadcast to Paris, Queen Victoria's diamond jubilee,
the Boer War (34p)

■ **1987, September 8. Victorian Britain**
Des: Carroll and Dempsey Studio. Printed in recess and
photogravure by Harrison.

Set	1.75	1.60
Gutter pairs	4.00	
First day cover		1.70
Stamp cards	1.75	4.00

Pottery by Bernard Leach (18p)
Pottery by Elizabeth Fritsch (26p)
Pottery by Lucie Rie (31p)
Pottery by Hans Coper (34p)

■ 1987, October 13. Studio Pottery
Des: Tony Evans.

Set	1.50	1.60
Gutter pairs	4.00	
First day cover		1.70
Stamp cards	1.75	3.50

Decorating the Christmas tree (13p)
Child looking out of a window (18p)
Father Christmas in sleigh and child asleep (26p)
A child reading a book surrounded by toys (31p)
Child playing a recorder and a snowman (34p)

■ 1987, November 17. Christmas
Des: M. Foreman. 13p has one phosphor band.

13p (double lined star on gummed side)		0.50
Set	1.75	1.75
Gutter pairs	4.00	
First day cover	1.60	
Stamp cards	1.75	3.50
Folder (36 x 13p with star on gum)	8.50	

Short-spined seascorpion (18p)
Yellow waterlily (26p)
Bewick's Swan (31p)
Morchella esculenta (34p)

■ 1988, January 19. Bicentenary of Linnean Society
Des: E. Hughes.

Set	1.50	1.50
Gutter pairs	4.00	
First day cover		1.50
Stamp cards	1.75	3.25

Revd William Morgan (18p)
William Salesbury (26p)
Bishop Richard Davies (31p)
Bishop Richard Parry (34p)

■ 1988, March 1. 400th Anniversary of the Welsh Bible
Des: K. Bowen.

Set	1.50	1.50
Gutter pairs	4.00	
First day cover		1.50
Stamp cards	1.75	3.25

Gymnastics (18p)
Downhill skiing (26p)
Tennis (31p)
Football (34p)

■ 1988, March 22. Sports Organisations
Des: J. Sutton.

Set	1.50	1.50
Gutter pairs	4.00	
First day cover		1.50
Stamp cards	1.50	3.25

'Mallard' (18p)
'Queen Elizabeth' (26p)
Glasgow tram (31p)
Handley Page H.P.45 'Horatius' (34p)

■ 1988, May 10. Transport and Mail Services. Europa
Des: M. Dempsey.

Set	2.50	1.75
Gutter pairs	6.00	
First day cover		1.70
Stamp cards	3.25	3.00

Settler and clipper (18p)
British and Australian Parliament Buildings
and Queen Elizabeth II (18p)
W. G. Grace and tennis racquet (34p)
Shakespeare, John Lennon and Sydney Opera House (34p)

■ 1988, June 21. Australian Bicentenary
Des: G. Emery. Printed in litho by Questa.

Set of four in two se-tenant pairs	1.50	1.50
Gutter pairs	4.00	
First day cover		1.50
Stamp cards	1.25	3.50

Spanish off The Lizard (18p)
English Fleet leaving Plymouth (18p)
Fighting off the Isle of Wight (18p)
English attacking at Calais (18p)
Armada in the North Sea (18p)

■ 1988, July 19. Spanish Armada
Des: G. Evernden.

Set of five in se-tenant strip	1.50	1.75
Gutter pairs	4.00	
First day cover		1.75
Stamp cards	1.50	4.50

The Owl and the Pussy cat (19p)
Edward Lear as a bird (27p)
'Cat' (32p)
There was a Young Lady whose bonnet (35p)

■ 1988, September 6. Centenary of the Death of Edward Lear
Des: M. Swatridge and S. Dew.

Set	1.75	1.90
Gutter pairs	4.00	
First day cover		1.75
Stamp cards	1.25	3.50
Miniature sheet	2.75	3.00
First day cover		3.75

(* The miniature sheet, containing one of each value, was sold with a surcharge to help fund the international stamp exhibition, Stamp World London 90, Issued on September 27, 1988.)

Carrickfergus Castle (£1)
Caernarfon Castle (£1.50)
Edinburgh Castle (£2)
Windsor Castle (£5)

■ 1988, October 18. Castle high value definitives
Engraved by C. Matthews from photographs by Prince Andrew.
Recess printed by Harrison.

Set	16.00	4.50
Gutter pairs	35.00	
Centre cross gutter blocks of four	75.00	
First Day Cover		20.00

Journeying to Bethlehem (14p)
Shepherds following the Star (19p)
Three Wise Men (27p)
The Nativity (32p)
The Annunciation (35p)

■ 1988, November 15. Christmas
Des: L. Trickett. 14p has one phosphor band.

Set	1.75	1.75
Gutter pairs	4.00	
First day cover		1.75
Stamp cards	1.50	3.50

Atlantic Puffin (19p)
Avocet (27p)
Oystercatcher (32p)
Northern Gannet (35p)

■ 1989, January 17. Centenary of the Royal Society for the Protection of Birds
Des: D. Cordery.

Set	1.75	1.75
Gutter pairs	4.00	
First day cover		1.75
Stamp cards	1.50	4.25

Teddy Bear (19p)
Rose (19p)
Cupid (19p)
Yachts (19p)
Fruit (19p)

■ 1989, January 31. Greetings stamps
Des: P. Sutton. Se-tenant strip of five Issued in booklets in panes of ten containing two of each design.

Se-tenant strip	12.00	12.00
Booklet pane of 10	15.00	
Booklet	30.00	
First day cover		9.00
Stamp cards	5.00	10.00

Fruit and vegetables (19p)
Meat (27p)
Dairy products (32p)
Cereals (35p)

■ 1989, March 7. Food and Farming Year
Des: Sedley Place Ltd.

Set	1.75	1.75
Gutter pairs	4.00	
First day cover		1.60
Stamp cards	1.25	3.25

Firework display: Mortar board (19p)
Firework display: Cross on ballot paper (19p)
Firework display: Posthorn (35p)
Firework display: Globe (35p)

■ 1989, April 11. Anniversaries & Events
Des: Lewis Moberly. 19p and 35p issued in se-tenant pairs.

Set of two se-tenant pairs	1.75	1.75
Gutter pairs	4.00	
First day cover		1.60
Stamp cards	1.25	4.00

Toy aeroplane and locomotive (19p)
Building bricks (27p)
Board games and dice (32p)
Robot, boat and doll's house (35p)

■ **1989, May 16. Toys and Games. Europa**
Des: D. Fern.

Set	2.75	1.75
Gutter pairs	6.00	
First day cover		1.50
Stamp cards	4.00	3.25

Ironbridge, Shropshire (19p)
Tin mine, St Agnes Head, Cornwall (27p)
Cotton Mills, New Lanark, Strathclyde (32p)
Pontcysylite Aqueduct, Clwyd (35p)

■ **1989, July 4. Industrial Archaeology**
Des: R. Maddox.

Set	1.60	1.75
Gutter pairs	4.00	
First day cover		1.50
Stamp cards	2.25	2.50
Miniature sheet	2.50	2.25
First day cover		3.50

(* The miniature sheet contained one of each value, but with
the designs in a horizontal format, with a surcharge to help fund
the international stamp exhibition, Stamp World London 90.
Issued on July 25, 1989.)

Snowflake (19p)
Fly (27p)
Blood cells (32p)
Microchip (35p)

■ **1989, September 5. 150th Anniversary of the
Microscopical Society**
Des: K. Bassford. Printed in litho by Questa.

Set	1.60	1.70
Gutter pairs	4.00	
First day cover		1.50
Stamp cards	1.25	3.25

Royal Mail coach (20p)
The Blues and Royals (20p)
Lord Mayor's coach (20p)
St Paul's Cathedral (20p)
Blues and Royals Drum Horse (20p)

■ **1989, October 17. Lord Mayor's Show.**
Des: P. Cox.

Set in se-tenant strip	1.50	1.50
Gutter pairs	4.00	
First day cover		1.50
Stamp cards	1.50	4.00

Peasants, from stained glass window (15p)
Arches and Roundels, West Front (15p + 1p)
Octagon Tower (20p + 1p)
Arcade from West Transept (34p + 1p)
Triple Arch from West Front (37p + 1p)

■ **1989, November 14. Christmas. 800th Anniversary of Ely Cathedral**
Des: D. Gentleman. 15p and 15+1p have one phosphor band.

Set	1.75	1.75
Gutter pairs	4.25	
First day cover		1.75
Stamp cards	1.50	4.00

(* Four of the stamps carried a surcharge for charity.)

■ **1990, January 10. 150th Anniversary of the Penny Black**
See under Machin decimal definitives

Kitten (20p)
Rabbit (29p)
Duckling (34p)
Puppy (37p)

■ **1990, January 23. 150th Anniversary of the Royal Society for the Prevention of Cruelty to Animals**
Des: T. Evans. Printed in litho by Questa.

Set	1.75	1.80
Gutter pairs	4.50	
First day cover		1.75
Stamp cards	1.50	4.50

Teddy Bear (20p)
Dennis the Menace (20p)
Punch (20p)
Cheshire Cat (20p)
The Man in the Moon (20p)
The Laughing Policeman (20p)
Clown (20p)
Mona Lisa (20p)
Queen of Hearts (20p)
Stan Laurel (20p)

■ **1990, February 6. Greetings stamps: Smiles**.
Des: Michael Peters and Partners. Stamps se-tenant in booklet panes of ten containing one of each design.

Booklet pane of 10	14.00	14.00
Booklet	17.50	
First day cover		11.00

Alexandra Palace (20p)
Glasgow School of Art (20p)
British Philatelic Bureau, Edinburgh (29p)
Templeton Carpet Factory, Glasgow (37p)

■ **1990, March 6. Europa and Glasgow 1990 European City of Culture**
Des: P. Hogarth.

Set	2.75	2.00
Gutter pairs	7.50	
First day cover		1.75
Stamp cards	3.50	3.50

(* The two 20p designs were issued in separate sheets, not as se-tenant pairs. The 20p Alexandra Palace design also appears as a pane of four in the £5 'London Life' prestige stamp booklet issued on March 20, 1990.)

Export Achievement Award (20p and 37p)
Technological Achievement Award (20p and 37p)

■ 1990, April 10. 25th Anniversary of The Queen's Awards for Export and Technology
Des: S. Broom. Printed in litho by Questa.

Set of four in two se-tenant pairs	1.60	1.60
Gutter pairs	4.00	
First day cover		1.60
Stamp cards	1.50	3.50

Portraits of Queen Victoria and Queen Elizabeth II (20p)

■ 1990, May 3. Stamp World London 90 International Exhibition
Des: Sedley Place Design; engraved by C. Matthews. Printed in recess and photogravure by Harrison. Issued only as a miniature sheet.

Miniature sheet	1.75	2.25
First day cover		2.50

(* The border of the sheet includes the Penny Black and Britannia from the 1913-1934 'Seahorse' design. The sheets were sold at £1 each, the surcharge being used to help fund the exhibition.)

Cycad and Sir Joseph Banks Building (20p)
Stone Pine and Princess of Wales Conservatory (29p)
Willow Tree and Palm House (34p)
Cedar Tree and Pagoda (37p)

■ 1990, June 5. 150th Anniversary of Kew Gardens
Des: P. Leith.

Set	1.60	1.60
Gutter pairs	4.00	
First day cover		1.60
Stamp cards	1.50	3.50

Thomas Hardy and Clyffe Clump, Dorset (20p)

■ 1990, July 10. 150th Anniversary of the birth of Thomas Hardy
Des: J. Gibbs.

20p	0.40	0.40
Gutter pair	1.00	
First day cover		0.70
Stamp card	0.50	2.50

Queen Elizabeth The Queen Mother (20p)
Queen Elizabeth (29p)
Elizabeth, Duchess of York (34p)
Lady Elizabeth Bowes-Lyon (37p)

1990, August 2. 90th birthday of Queen Elizabeth The Queen Mother

Des: J. Gorham from photographs by Norman Parkinson, Dorothy Wilding, B. Park and Rita Martin.

Set	3.00	2.25
Gutter pairs	7.50	
First day cover		2.25
Stamp cards	2.75	6.00

(*The same designs were used in 2002 in memory of the Queen Mother although the borders were changed to black.)

Victoria Cross (20p)
George Cross (20p)
Distinguished Service Cross and Distinguished Service Medal (20p)
Military Cross and Military Medal (20p)
Distinguished Flying Cross and Distinguished Flying Medal (20p)

1990, September 11. Gallantry Awards

Des: J. Gibbs and J. Harwood.

Set	2.50	1.50
Gutter pairs	6.00	
First day cover		1.70
Stamp cards	1.75	4.00

(*The 20p also appears on the miniature sheet and in the Prestige stamp book for the Victoria Cross issued on September 21, 2006.)

Armagh Observatory, Jodrell Bank & La Palma Telescopes (22p)
Early telescope and diagram of Moon & Tides by Newton (26p)
Greenwich Old Observatory and astronomical equipment (31p)
Stonehenge, Gyroscope and Navigation by the stars (37p)

1990, October 16. Astronomy

Des: J. Fisher. Printed in litho by Questa.

Set	2.00	2.00
Gutter pairs	5.00	
First day cover		1.75
Stamp cards	1.50	4.00

Building a snowman (17p)
Fetching a Christmas tree (22p)
Carol singers (26p)
Tobogganing (31p)
Ice-skating (37p)

1990, November 13. Christmas

Des: J. Gorham and A. Davidson. 17p has one phosphor band.

Set	2.00	1.75
Gutter pairs	5.00	
First day cover		1.75
Booklet (20 x 17p)	7.00	
Stamp cards	1.75	4.00

(*The 17p was also sold in £3.40 booklets containing a pane of 20 stamps.)

King Charles Spaniel (22p)
Pointer (26p)
Two Hounds in a landscape (31p)
A Rough Dog (33p)
Fino and Tiny (37p)

1991, January 8. Dogs: paintings by George Stubbs

Des: Carroll, Dempsey and Thirkell Ltd.

Set	2.25	2.00
Gutter pairs	5.50	
First day cover		2.00
Stamp cards	2.25	4.00

Thrush's Nest (1st)
Shooting Star and Rainbow (1st)
Magpies and Charm Bracelet (1st)
Black cat (1st)
Kingfisher and key (1st)
Mallard and frog (1st)
Four-leaf clover, boot and matchbox (1st)
Pot of Gold at the end of the Rainbow (1st)
Butterflies (1st)
Wishing Well and sixpence (1st)

■ **1991, February 5. Greetings stamps: Good luck**
Des: J. Meeuwissen. Issued in booklets in panes of ten containing
one of each design.

Booklet pane of 10	7.00	7.00
Booklet	7.00	
First day cover		7.00

Michael Faraday (22p)
Charles Babbage (22p)
Sweep of radar of East Anglia (31p)
Gloster Whittle E28/39 airplane over East Anglia (37p)

■ **1991, March 5. Scientific Achievements**
Des: P. Till (22p values), J. Harwood (31p, 37p).

Set	1.75	1.75
Gutter pairs	4.25	
First day cover		1.75
Stamp cards	1.75	3.50

■ **1991, March 26. Greetings stamps: Smiles**
Designs as for the Greetings stamps of February 6, 1990, but
the values in each case changed to 1st. Issued in booklets in
panes of ten containing one of each design.

Booklet pane of 10	5.50	5.50
Booklet	6.00	
First day cover		5.50

(*These designs were also used for Smilers sheets in
2000 and 2001.)

Man looking at Space (design over two se-tenant 22p values)
Space looking at Man (design over two se-tenant 37p values)

■ **1991, April 23. Europe in Space. Europa**
Des: J-M. Folon.

Set of two se-tenant pairs	3.00	2.00
Gutter pairs	7.50	
First day cover		1.80
Stamp cards	3.50	3.50

Fencing (22p)
Hurdling (26p)
Diving (31p)
Rugby (37p)

■ **1991, June 11. World Student Games, Sheffield and
World Cup Rugby Championships, London**
Des: Huntley Muir Partners.

Set	1.75	1.75
Gutter pairs	4.25	
First day cover		1.75
Stamp cards	1.50	3.50

ver Jubilee (22p)
me Alfred Carrière (26p)
sa Moyesii (31p)
rvest Fayre (33p)
utabilis (37p)

1991, July 16. Ninth World Conference of Roses, Belfast
es: Yvonne Skargon. Printed in litho by Questa.

t	2.00	2.00
utter pairs	5.00	
rst day cover		2.00
amp cards	1.75	4.50

Iguanodon, **Owen's Dinosauria 1841**

uanodon (22p)
egosaurus (26p)
rannosaurus (31p)
otoceratops (33p)
iceratops (37p)

1991, August 20. 150th Anniversary of the identification
Dinosaurs by Owen
es: B. Kneale.

et	2.25	2.25
utter pairs	5.00	
rst day cover		1.75
amp cards	1.75	4.50

ORDNANCE SURVEY
1 7 9 1 - 1 9 9 1

ap of Hamstreet in 1816 (24p)
ap of Hamstreet in 1906 (28p)
ap of Hamstreet in 1959 (33p)
ap of Hamstreet in 1991 (39p)

■ 1991, September 17. Bicentenary of Ordnance Survey
Des: H. Brown. Printed in recess and litho by Harrison (24p), in litho by Harrison (28p) and in litho by Questa (33p, 39p).

Set	2.00	2.00
Gutter pairs	5.00	
First day cover		1.75
Stamp cards	1.75	3.25

(* Examples of the 28p are known with the denomination of 26p, from supplies printed before an increase in postage rates affected the denominations of this set.)

Adoration of the Magi (18p)
Mary with Jesus in stable (24p)
The Holy Family and angel (28p)
The Annunciation (33p)
The Flight into Egypt (39p)

■ 1991, November 12. Christmas
Des: D. Driver. 18p has one phosphor band.

Set	2.00	2.00
Gutter pairs	5.00	
First day cover		1.75
Booklet (pane of 20 × 18p)	6.25	
Stamp cards	1.75	4.00

(* The 18p was also sold in £3.60 booklets containing a pane of 20 stamps.)

Fallow deer (18p)
Hare (24p)
Fox (28p)
Redwing (33p)
Welsh Mountain sheep (39p)

■ 1992, January 14. Wintertime (The Four Seasons)
Des: J. Gorham and K. Bowen. 18p has one phosphor band.

Set	2.25	1.90
Gutter pairs	5.00	
First day cover		1.75
Stamp cards	2.75	4.50

(* The 39p also appears as a pane of four in the Cymru Wales prestige stamp booklet issued on February 25, 1992.)

Spray of flowers (1st)
Double locket (1st)
Key (1st)
Toy car and cigarette cards (1st)
Compass and map (1st)
Pocket watch (1st)
Penny red stamp and pen (1st)
Pearl necklace (1st)
Marbles (1st)
Starfish and a bucket and spade (1st)

■ 1992, January 28. Greetings stamps: Memories
Des: Trickett and Webb Ltd. Issued in booklets in panes of ten
containing one of each design.

Booklet pane of 10	6.50	6.50
Booklet	7.00	
First day cover		5.50

Queen Elizabeth II,
In Coronation robes (24p)
In Garter robes (24p)
With Prince Andrew as a baby (24p)
At Trooping the Colour (24p)
With emblem of the Commonwealth (24p)

■ 1992, February 6. 40th Anniversary of the Accession
Des: Why Not Associates. Printed in litho by Questa.

Set in se-tenant strip	3.00	3.25
Gutter pairs	7.50	
First day cover		2.50
Stamp cards	2.75	5.50

Tennyson in 1888 (24p)
In 1856 (28p)
In 1864 (33p)
As a young man (39p)

■ 1992, March 10. Centenary of the death of Alfred, Lor Tennyson
Des: Irene von Treskow.

Set	2.00	1.75
Gutter pairs	5.00	8.00
First day cover		1.75
Stamp cards	2.50	3.50

British Olympic Association logo (24p)
British Paralympic Association symbol (24p)
Santa Maria, Christopher Columbus (24p)
Kaisei, Operation Raleigh (39p)
British Pavilion at Expo '92 in Seville (39p)

■ 1992, April 7. International Events
Des: K. Bassford (BOA, BPA and Expo), K. Bassford and S. Paine
(Santa Maria and Kaisei). Printed in litho by Questa and in
recess and litho by Harrison. The BOA and BPA designs were
issued as a se-tenant pair.

Set	3.00	2.00
Gutter pairs	7.00	
First day cover		1.75
Stamp cards	4.00	5.00

arrickfergus Castle (£1)
aernarfon Castle (£1.50)
inburgh Castle (£2)
indsor Castle (£5)

1992, March 24. Castle definitives
s issue of October 18, 1988, but Queen's head is in silhouette
inted in optically variable ink which changes colour from
ld to green depending on the angle at which it is viewed. In
dition, an elliptical perforation is included along the side of
ch stamp.

et	19.50	4.00
utter pairs	40.00	
entre cross gutter blocks of four	85.00	
rst Day Cover		15.00
camp cards	10.00	40.00

The £1.50, £2 and £5 exist with either blue tinted PVAD gum,
' white PVA gum. The date of release of the stamp cards is not
e day of issue of the stamps.)

THE CIVIL WAR 1642-51
fought between the forces of KING
& PARLIAMENT: Pikeman ♚♚♚♚

keman (24p)
rummer (28p)
usketeer (33p)
andard bearer (39p)

1992, June 16. 350th Anniversary of the Civil War
es: J. Sancha.

et	1.85	1.75
utter pairs	4.50	
rst day cover		1.75
camp cards	2.50	3.25

GILBERT & SULLIVAN
The Yeomen of the Guard

Gilbert and Sullivan operas:
The Yeoman of the Guard (18p)
The Gondoliers (24p)
The Mikado (28p)
The Pirates of Penzance (33p)
Iolanthe (39p)

**■ 1992, July 21. 150th Anniversary of the birth of Sir
Arthur Sullivan**
Des: Lynda Gray. 18p has one phosphor band.

Set	2.00	1.75
Gutter pairs	5.00	
First day cover		1.75
Stamp cards	2.75	3.25

Acid rain kills (24p)
Ozone layer (28p)
Greenhouse effect (33p)
Bird of hope (39p)

■ 1992, September 15. Protection of the Environment
Des: C. Hall (24p), L. Fowler (28p), S. Warren (33p) and
A. Newton-Mold (39p). All paintings by children, in conjunction
with the BBC Television programme Blue Peter.

Set	1.75	1.75
Gutter pairs	4.50	
First day cover		1.75
Stamp cards	2.75	3.00

European Star (24p)

■ 1992, October 13. Single European Market
Des: D. Hockney.

24p	0.50	0.45
Gutter pair	1.50	
First day cover		0.65
Stamp card	0.50	2.00

Angel Gabriel (18p)
Madonna and Child (24p)
King carrying Gold (28p)
Shepherds (33p)
Kings with Frankincense and Myrrh (39p)

■ 1992, November 10. Christmas
Des: Carroll, Dempsey and Thirkell Ltd. 18p has one phosphor band.

Set	2.25	1.75
Gutter pairs	6.00	
First day cover		1.75
Booklet (pane of 20 x 18p)	6.25	
Stamp cards	2.75	4.00

(* The 18p was also sold in £3.60 booklets containing a pane of 20 stamps.)

Mute Swan Cob (18p)
Cygnet and Decoy (24p)
Swans and Cygnet (28p)
Eggs in nest (33p)
Young swan (39p)

■ 1993, January 19. 600th Anniversary of Abbotsbury Swannery
Des: David Gentleman. 18p has one phosphor band.

Set	3.50	3.00
Gutter pairs	8.50	
First day cover		3.00
Stamp cards	4.25	5.50

William (1st)
Long John Silver (1st)
Tweedledum and Tweedledee (1st)
Mole and Toad (1st)
Teacher and Wilfred (1st)
Peter Rabbit and Mrs Rabbit (1st)
Snowman and Father Christmas (1st)
The Big Friendly Giant and Sophie (1st)
Bill Badger and Rupert Bear (1st)
Aladdin and the Genie (1st)

■ 1993, January 28. Greetings stamps: Gift Giving
Des: Newell and Sorell. Issued in booklets in panes of ten containing one of each design.

Booklet pane of 10	6.00	5.50
Booklet	6.50	
First day cover		5.50
Stamp cards	10.00	15.50

(* The Peter Rabbit and Mrs Rabbit design also appears as a pane of four in the Story of Beatrix Potter prestige stamp book issued on August 10, 1993.)

Decorated dial (24p)
Escapement, Remontoire and Eusée (28p)
Balance, Spring and Temperature compensator (33p)
Movement seen from back (39p)

■ 1993, February 16. 300th Anniversary of the birth of John Harrison
Des: H. Brown and D. Penny. Printed in litho by Questa.

Set	2.00	2.00
Gutter pairs	5.00	
First day cover		1.75
Stamp cards	3.25	4.50

Britannia (£10)

■ 1993, March 2. £10 Definitive.
Des: B. Craddock and Roundel Design Group. Printed in litho by
Questa, also including die-stamping and embossing of Braille.

£10	20.00	7.50
First Day Cover		15.00
Stamp card	4.50	50.00

Dendrobium hellwigianum (18p)
Paphiopedilum Maudiae 'Magnificum' (24p)
Cymbidium lowianum (28p)
Vanda Rothschildiana (33p)
Dendrobium vexillarius var albiviride (39p)

**■ 1993, March 16. 14th World Orchid Conference,
Glasgow**
Des: Pandora Sellars. 18p has one phosphor band.

Set	2.25	2.00
Gutter pairs	5.50	
First day cover		1.75
Stamp cards	4.25	5.50

Family Group' by Henry Moore (24p)
Kew Gardens' by Edward Bawden (28p)
St Francis and the Birds' by Stanley Spencer (33p)
Still Life: Odyssey 1' by Ben Nicholson (39p)

1993, May 11. Contemporary Art. Europa
Des: A. Dastor.

Set	2.50	2.00
Gutter pairs	6.50	
First day cover		1.75
Stamp cards	4.25	4.50

Emperor Claudius (24p)
Emperor Hadrian (28p)
Goddess Roma (33p)
Christ (39p)

■ 1993, June 15. Roman Britain
Des: J. Gibbs.

Set	1.85	1.75
Gutter pairs	4.50	
First day cover		1.75
Stamp cards	3.25	4.50

Grand Union Canal (24p)
Stainforth and Keadby Canal (28p)
Brecknock and Abergavenny Canal (33p)
Crinan Canal (39p)

■ 1993, July 20. Inland Waterways
Des: T. Lewery. Printed in litho by Questa.

Set	1.80	1.75
Gutter pairs	4.50	
First day cover		1.75
Stamp cards	3.25	4.50

Horse Chestnut (18p)
Blackberry (24p)
Hazel (28p)
Rowan (33p)
Pear (39p)

■ 1993, September 14. Autumn (The Four Seasons)
Des: Charlotte Knox. 18p has one phosphor band.

Set	2.25	1.75
Gutter pairs	6.00	
First day cover		1.75
Stamp cards	4.25	5.50

The Reigate Square (24p)
The Hound of the Baskervilles (24p)
The Six Napoleons (24p)
The Greek Interpreter (24p)
The Final Problem (24p)

■ 1993, October 12. Sherlock Holmes
Des: A. Davidson. Printed in litho by Questa.

Set in se-tenant strip of five	2.00	2.00
Gutter pairs	5.00	
First day cover		2.50
Stamp cards	4.25	5.50

Bob Cratchit and Tiny Tim (19p)
Mr and Mrs Fezziwig (25p)
Scrooge (30p)
The Prize Turkey (35p)
Scrooge's nephew (41p)

■ 1993, November 9. Christmas: 'A Christmas Carol' by Charles Dickens
Des: Q. Blake. 19p has one phosphor band.

Set	2.25	2.00
Gutter pairs	6.00	
First day cover		2.00
Booklet (20 x 19p)	7.00	
Booklet (10 x 25p)	5.75	
Stamp cards	4.25	5.50

Class 5 and Class B1 on the West Highland Line (19p)
Class A1 at Kings Cross (25p)
Class 4 at Blythe North (30p)
Class 4 near Wigan Central (35p)
Castle Class crossing Worcester and Birmingham Canal (41p)

■ 1994, January 18. The Age of Steam
Des: B. Delaney, from photographs by Colin Gifford. 19p has one phosphor band.

Set	2.50	2.25
Gutter pairs	7.00	
First day cover		2.25
Stamp cards	4.25	5.50

Dan Dare (1st)
The Three Bears (1st)
Rupert Bear (1st)
Alice (1st)
Noggin and the Ice Dragon (1st)
Peter Rabbit (1st)
Little Red Riding Hood (1st)
Orlando the Marmalade Cat (1st)
Biggles (1st)
Paddington Bear (1st)

■ 1994, February 1. Greetings stamps: Messages
Des: Newell and Sorell. Issued in booklets in panes of ten containing one of each design.

Booklet pane of 10	6.50	5.50
Booklet	7.00	
First day cover		5.50
Stamp cards	10.00	15.50

Castell Y Waun/Chirk Castle, Clwyd, Wales (19p)
Ben Arkle, Sutherland, Scotland (25p)
Mourne Mountains, County Down, Northern Ireland (30p)
Dersingham, Norfolk, England (35p)
Dolwyddelan, Gwynedd, Wales (41p)

■ 1994, March 1. 25th Anniversary of the Investiture of The Prince of Wales

Paintings by the Prince of Wales. 19p has one phosphor band.

Set	2.25	2.00
Gutter pairs	6.00	
First day cover		2.00
Stamp cards	4.25	5.50

(* The 30p also appears as a pane of four in the Northern Ireland prestige stamp book issued on July 26, 1994.)

Bathing at Blackpool (19p)
Where's My Little Lad (25p)
Wish You Were Here (30p)
Punch and Judy Show (35p)
'The Tower Crane' machine (41p)

■ 1994, April 12. Centenary of Picture Postcards

Des: M. Dempsey and B. Dare. Printed in litho by Questa. 19p has one phosphor band, others have two.

Set	2.25	1.75
Gutter pairs	6.00	
First day cover		2.25
Stamp cards	4.25	5.50

British Lion and French Cockerel (25p and 41p)
Hands over a train (25p and 41p)

■ 1994, May 3. Opening of Channel Tunnel

Des: G. Hardie (Lion & Cockerel), J.-P. Cousin (Hands & train)

Set of two se-tenant pairs	2.25	2.50
Gutter pairs	6.00	
First day cover		2.25
Stamp cards	3.25	4.50

Douglas Boston and groundcrew (25p)
HMS Warspite (25p)
Commandos on Gold Beach (25p)
Infantry on Sword Beach (25p)
Tank and infantry (25p)

■ 1994, June 6. 50th Anniversary of D-Day

Des: K. Bassford. Printed in litho by Questa.

Set of five in se-tenant strip	2.50	2.25
Gutter pairs	6.00	
First day cover		2.25
Stamp Cards	4.25	5.50

St Andrew's (19p)
Muirfield (25p)
Carnoustie (30p)
Royal Troon (35p)
Turnberry (41p)

■ 1994, July 5. British Golf Courses

Des: P. Hogarth. 19p has one phosphor band.

Set	2.25	2.25
Gutter pairs	6.00	
First day cover		2.25
Stamp cards	4.25	5.50

Royal Welsh Show, Llanelwedd (19p)
Wimbledon Tennis Championships (25p)
Cowes Week (30p)
Test Match at Lord's (35p)
Braemar Gathering (41p)

■ 1994, August 2. Summertime (The Four Seasons)

Des: M. Cook. 19p has one phosphor band.

Set	2.25	2.00
Gutter pairs	6.00	
First day cover		2.25
Stamp cards	4.25	5.50

Ultrasonic imaging (25p)
Scanning electron microscopy (30p)
Magnetic resonance imaging (35p)
Computed tomography (41p)

■ 1994, September 27. Medical Discoveries. Europa
Des: P. Vermier and J.-P. Tibbles. Printed in photogravure by
Enschedé.

Set	2.50	2.25
Gutter pairs	6.50	
First day cover		2.25
Stamp cards	3.25	4.50

Mary and Joseph (19p)
Three Wise Men (25p)
Mary with doll (30p)
Shepherds (35p)
Angels (41p)

■ 1994, November 1. Christmas: Children's Nativity Plays
Des: Yvonne Gilbert. 19p has one phosphor band.

Set	2.00	2.00
Gutter pairs	5.00	
First day cover		2.00
Booklet (20 × 19p)	6.75	
Booklet (10 × 25p)	4.25	
Stamp cards	4.25	5.50

Black cat (19p)
Siamese and tabby cat (25p)
Ginger cat (30p)
Tortoiseshell and Abyssinian cat (35p)
Black and white cat (41p)

■ 1995, January 17. Cats
Des: Elizabeth Blackadder. Printed in litho by Questa. 19p has
one phosphor band, other two phosphor bands.

Set	2.25	2.00
Gutter pairs	6.00	
First day cover		2.25
Stamp cards	5.25	7.50

Dandelion (19p)
Chestnut leaves (25p)
Garlic leaves (30p)
Hazel leaves (35p)
Spring grass (41p)

■ 1995, March 14. Springtime (The Four Seasons)
Plant sculptures by Andy Goldsworthy. 19p has one phosphor
band, other two phosphor bands.

Set	2.25	2.00
Gutter pairs	6.00	
First day cover		2.25
Stamp cards	5.25	6.50

'La Danse à la Campagne' by Renoir (1st)
'Troilus and Criseyde' by Peter Brookes (1st)
'The Kiss' by Rodin (1st)
'Girls on the Town' by Beryl Cook (1st)
'Jazz' by Andrew Mockett (1st)
'Girls performing a Kathak Dance' (1st)
'Alice Keppel with her daughter' by Alice Hughes (1st)
'Children Playing' by L. S. Lowry (1st)
'Circus Clowns' by Emily Firmin and Justin Mitchell (1st)
'All the Love Poems of Shakespeare' (detail) by Eric Gill (1st)

1995, March 21. Greetings Stamps: Art

es: Newell and Sorell. Printed in litho by Walsall. Issued in oklets in panes of ten containing one of each design.

oklet pane of 10	5.25	5.50
oklet	6.00	
st day cover		5.50
amp cards	10.00	15.50

The National Trust
Celebrating 100 Years **19**

eplace decoration (19p)
ak seedling (25p)
rved table leg (30p)
David's Head, Dyfed, Wales (35p)
zabethan window (41p)

1995, April 11. Centenary of The National Trust

es: T. Evans. One phosphor band (19p), two phosphor bands 5p, 35p), phosphor paper (30p, 41p).

t	2.25	2.00
utter pairs	6.00	
st day cover		2.25
amp cards	5.25	6.50

The 25p also appeared in a pane of six in the National Trust estige stamp book issued on April 25, 1995.)

tish troops and French civilians (19p)
nds and Red Cross (19p)
rchlights in a 'V' over St Paul's Cathedral 25p)
nd releasing Dove of Peace (25p)
nbolic hands (30p)

■ 1995, May 2. Peace & Freedom. Europa

Des: J-M. Folon (Red Cross 19p, Dove 25p, 30p), J. Gorham (Troops 19p, Seachlights 25p), One phosphor band (19p), two phosphor bands (others).

Set	2.25	2.00
Gutter pairs	6.00	
First day cover		2.00
Stamp cards	5.25	6.50

(* The design with St Paul's Cathedral was also used as a 1st class stamp in a miniature sheet in 2005.)

The Time Machine (25p)
The First Men in the Moon (30p)
The War of the Worlds (35p)
The Shape of Things to Come (41p)

■ 1995, June 6. Novels of H. G. Wells

Des: Siobhan Keaney. Printed in litho by Questa.

Set	2.25	1.85
Gutter pairs	6.00	
First day cover		2.00
Stamp cards	4.25	5.50

The Swan, 1595 (25p)
The Rose, 1592 (25p)
The Globe, 1599 (25p)
The Hope, 1613 (25p)
The Globe, 1614 (25p)

■ 1995, August 8. Reconstruction of Shakespeare's Globe Theatre

Des: C. Hodges. Printed in litho by Walsall.

Set of five in se-tenant strip	2.25	2.25
Gutter pairs	6.00	
First day cover		2.00
Stamp cards	5.25	6.50

1995, August 22. Castle definitive
As issue of March 24, 1992, but new value, replacing the £1.

£3	8.50	1.35
Gutter pair	18.00	
Centre cross gutter block of four	40.00	
First Day Cover		5.00
Stamp card	9.00	20.00

(*This stamp exists with either blue tinted PVAD gum or white PVA gum.)

Sir Rowland Hill and Uniform Penny Postage Petition (19p)
Sir Rowland Hill and Penny Black (25p)
Marconi and early wireless (41p)
Marconi and 'Titanic' (60p)

1995, September 5. Pioneers of Communications
Des: The Four Hundred; engraved by C. Slania. Printed in recess and litho by Harrison. 19p has one phosphor band.

Set	2.25	2.00
Gutter pairs	6.00	
First day cover		2.00
Stamp cards	4.25	5.50

Harold Wagstaff (19p)
Gus Risman (25p)
Jim Sullivan (30p)
Billy Batten (35p)
Brian Bevan (41p)

1995, October 3. Centenary of Rugby League
Des: C. Birmingham. One phosphor band (19p), two phosphor bands (others).

Set	2.25	2.00
Gutter pairs	6.00	
First day cover		2.00
Stamp cards	5.25	7.50

Robin in letter box (19p)
Robin on railings (25p)
Robin on milk bottles (30p)
Robin on road sign (35p)
Robin on front door handle (41p)

1995, October 30. Christmas: Christmas Robins
Des: K. Lilly. One phosphor band (19p), two phosphor bands (others).

Set	2.25	2.25
Gutter pairs	6.00	
First day cover		2.40
Booklet (20 x 19p)	7.00	
Booklet (10 x 25p)	4.25	
Booklet (4 x 60p)	4.25	
Stamp cards	5.25	6.50

(*The 19p design was also used in Smilers sheets in 2000 and 2001.)

Wee, fleeket, cowran, tim'rous beastie (19p)
O, my Love's like a red, red rose (25p)
Scots, Wha hae wi Wallace bled (41p)
Should auld acquaintance be forgot (60p)

1996, January 25. Bicentenary of death of Robert Burns
Des: Tayburn Design Consultancy. Printed in litho by Questa. One phosphor band (19p), two phosphor bands (others).

Set	2.25	2.00
Gutter pairs	6.00	
First day cover		2.25
Stamp cards	4.25	5.50

I'm writing to you because you don't listen to a word I say . . (1st)
More! Love (1st)
Sincerely (1st)
Do you have something for the human condition? (1st)
Mental floss (1st)
4:55pm. Don't ring (1st)
Dear lottery prize winner (1st)
Fetch this, fetch that. Let the cat do it. (1st)
My day starts before I'm ready for it (1st)
The cheque in the post (1st)

■ 1996, February 26. Greetings Stamps: Cartoons
Des: M. Wolff. Printed in litho by Walsall. All-over phosphor.
Issued in booklets in panes of ten containing one of each design.

Booklet pane of 10	6.50	5.50
Booklet	6.00	
First day cover		5.50
Stamp cards	10.00	15.50

Muscovy Duck (19p)
Lapwing (25p)
White-front Goose (30p)
Bittern (35p)
Whooper Swan (41p)

1996, March 12. 50th Anniversary of the Wildfowl and Wetlands Trust
Des: Moseley Webb, from paintings by C. F. Tunnicliffe. 19p has one phosphor band.

Set	2.25	2.40
Gutter pairs	6.00	
First day cover		2.75
Stamp cards	5.25	6.50

Odeon (19p)
Laurence Olivier and Vivien Leigh (25p)
Cinema ticket (30p)
Pathé News (35p)
'Big Screen Showing' (41p)

■ 1996, April 16. Centenary of Cinema
Des: The Chase. One phosphor band (19p), two phosphor bands (others).

Set	2.25	2.25
Gutter pairs	6.00	
First day cover		2.60
Stamp cards	5.25	6.50

Dixie Dean (19p)
Bobby Moore (25p)
Duncan Edwards (30p)
Billy Wright (35p)
Danny Blanchflower (41p)

■ 1996, May 14. European Football Championships
Des: H. Brown. Printed in litho by Questa. One phosphor band (19p), two phosphor bands (others).

Set	3.00	2.25
Gutter pairs	7.50	
First day cover		2.25
Stamp cards	5.25	6.50

(* All of the stamps in this set also appeared as panes in the European Football Championships prestige stamp booklet, issued on May 14, 1996.)

Athlete (26p)
Throwing the Javelin (26p)
Basketball (26p)
Swimming (26p)
Athlete and Olympic rings (26p)

■ **1996, July 9. Olympic Games and Paralympic Games**
Des: N. Knight. Printed in litho by Questa.

Set of five in se-tenant strip	2.25	2.00
Gutter pairs	6.00	
First day cover		2.25
Stamp cards	5.00	6.50

Dorothy Hodgkin (20p)
Margot Fonteyn (26p)
Elizabeth Frink (31p)
Daphne du Maurier (37p)
Marea Hartman (43p)

■ **1996, August 6. Famous Women. Europa**
Des: Stephanie Nash. One phosphor band (20p), two phosphor bands (others).

Set	2.50	2.50
Gutter pairs	6.50	
First day cover		2.50
Stamp cards	3.75	6.50

Muffin the Mule (20p)
Sooty (26p)
Stingray (31p)
The Clangers (37p)
Dangermouse (43p)

■ **1996, September 3. 50th Anniversary of Children's Television**
Des: Tutssels. Printed in photogravure by Enschedé. One phosphor band (20p), two phosphor bands (others).

Set	2.25	2.25
Gutter pairs	6.00	
First day cover		2.50
Stamp cards	5.25	6.50

(* The 20p also appeared in the 75th Anniversary of the BBC prestige stamp booklet issued on September 23, 1997, but printed in photogravure by Harrison; priced at 60p mint.)

Triumph TR3 (20p)
MG TD (26p)
Austin Healey 100 (37p)
Jaguar XK120 (43p)
Morgan Plus 4 (63p)

■ **1996, October 1. Classic Sports Cars**
Des: S. Clay. One phosphor band (20p), two phosphor bands (others).

Set	3.00	2.50
Gutter pairs	7.50	
First day cover		2.40
Stamp cards	3.75	6.50

The Three Kings (2nd)
The Annunciation (1st)
The Journey to Bethlehem (31p)
The Nativity (43p)
The Shepherds (63p)

1996, October 28. Christmas
Des: Laura Stoddart. One phosphor band (2nd), two phosphor bands (others).

Set	2.50	2.25
Gutter pairs	6.50	
First day cover		2.75
Booklet (20 x 2nd)	7.00	
Booklet (10 x 1st)	4.25	
Stamp cards	5.25	6.50

1996, November 11. Greetings Stamps: Cartoons
As issue of February 26, but with two phosphor bands. Issued in booklets in panes of ten containing one of each design

Booklet pane of 10	20.00	20.00
Booklet	20.00	

* These designs were also used for Smilers sheets in 2001 and 2002.)

Iris latifolia (1st)
Gentiana acaulis (1st)
Magnolia grandiflora (1st)
Camellia japonica (1st)
Tulipa (1st)
Fuchsia 'Princess of Wales' (1st)
Tulipa gesneriana (1st)
Guzmania splendens (1st)
Hippeastrum rutilum (1st)
Passiflora coerulea (1st)

1997, January 6. Greetings stamps: Flower paintings
Des: Tutssls. Printed in litho by Walsall. Two phosphor bands. Issued in booklets in panes of ten containing one of each design.

Booklet pane of 10	6.50	6.00
Booklet	7.00	
First day cover		5.50
Stamp cards	10.00	15.50

The Gentiana acaulis, Tulipa and Iris latifolia designs also appear in the Glory of the Garden prestige stamp book of 2004. The designs were also used for a Smilers sheet in 2003.)

King Henry VIII (26p)
Catherine of Aragon (26p)
Anne Boleyn (26p)
Jane Seymour (26p)
Anne of Cleves (26p)
Catherine Howard (26p)
Catherine Parr (26p)

1997, February. 450th Anniversary of the Death of King Henry VIII
Des: Kate Stephens. Two phosphor bands. King Henry VIII design issued as a separate stamp in sheets, wives designs in a se-tenant strip

Set	3.00	3.25
Gutter pairs	7.50	
First day cover		3.75
Stamp cards	5.25	8.50

St Columba in boat (26p)
St Columba on Iona (37p)
St Augustine with King Ethelbert (43p)
St Augustine with a model of a cathedral (63p)

1997, March 11. Religious Anniversaries
Des: Claire Melinsky. Printed in photogravure by Enschedé. Two phosphor bands.

Set	2.25	2.25
Gutter pairs	6.00	
First day cover		2.60
Stamp cards	4.25	5.50

Dracula

Carriage horse (20p)
Lifeguards horse (26p)
Blues and Royals drum horse (43p)
Duke of Edinburgh's horse (63p)

Dracula (26p)
Frankenstein (31p)
Dr Jekyll and Mr Hyde (37p)
The Hound of the Baskervilles (43p)

■ 1997, May 13. Tales of Horror. Europa
Des: J. Pollock. Printed in photogravure by Walsall. Two phosphor bands.

Set	2.50	2.25
Gutter pairs	6.50	
First day cover		2.50
Stamp cards	4.25	5.50

■ 1997, July 8. All The Queen's Horses. 50th Anniversary of the British Horse Society
Des: J.-L. Benard. Printed in litho by Walsall. One phosphor band (20p), two phosphor bands (others).

Set	2.40	2.25
Gutter pairs	6.00	
First day cover		2.50
Stamp cards	4.25	5.50

■ 1997, July 29. Castle definitives
As £1.50, £2 and £5 of March 24, 1992, and £3 of August 8, 1995, but printed in recess and silk screen (for Queen's portrait) by Enschedé. Engraved by Inge Madlé.

Set	45.00	10.00
Gutter pairs	95.00	
Centre cross gutter blocks of four	200.00	
First Day Cover		25.00

Supermarine Spitfire MkIIA and Reginald Mitchell (20p)
Avro Lancaster MkI and Roy Chadwick (26p)
De Havilland Mosquito B MkXVI and Ronald Bishop (37p)
Gloster Meteor T Mk7 and George Carter (43p)
Hawker Hunter FGA Mk9 and Sir Sydney Camm (63p)
The faces of the aircraft designers feature in the cloud formations

Haroldswick, Shetland, Scotland

Haroldswick, Shetland (20p)
Painswick, Gloucestershire (26p)
Beddgelert, Gwynedd (43p)
Ballyroney, County Down (63p)

■ 1997, June 10. British Aircraft Designers
Des: Turner Duckworth. One phosphor band (20p), two phosphor bands (others).

Set	3.00	2.25
Gutter pairs	7.50	
First day cover		2.75
Stamp cards	3.75	6.50

■ 1997, August 12. Sub Post Offices
Des: T. Millington. Printed in photogravure by Enschedé. One phosphor band (20p), two phosphor bands (others).

Set	2.40	2.25
Gutter pairs	6.00	
First day cover		2.50
Stamp cards	4.25	5.50

Enid Blyton's *Malory Towers*

Malory Towers (63p)
Noddy (20p)
Famous Five (26p)
Secret Seven (37p)
Faraway Tree (43p)

1997, September 9. Centenary of the birth of Enid Blyton
Des: C. Birmingham. Printed in photogravure by Enschedé. One phosphor band (20p), two phosphor bands (others).

Set	2.50	2.50
Gutter pairs	6.50	
First day cover		2.50
Stamp cards	5.25	6.50

Children and Father Christmas pulling Christmas cracker (2nd)
Father Christmas with Christmas cracker (1st)
Father Christmas riding on a Christmas cracker (31p)
Father Christmas with a snowball (43p)
Father Christmas on a chimney (63p)

1997, October 27. Christmas. 150th Anniversary of the Christmas Cracker
Des: M. Thomas (1st) and J. Gorham (others). One phosphor band (2nd), two phosphor bands (others).

Set	2.50	2.50
Gutter pairs	6.50	
First day cover		2.50
Booklet (20 at 2nd)	6.75	
Booklet (10 at 1st)	5.00	
Stamp cards	5.25	6.50

(The 1st class design was also used for Smilers sheets in 2000 and 2001.)

Queen Elizabeth II and Prince Philip Wedding photograph of 1947 (20p and 43p)
Queen Elizabeth II and Prince Philip photographed in 1997 (26p and 63p)

■ 1997, November 13. Royal Golden Wedding
Des: D. Driver (20p, 43p), Lord Snowdon (26p, 63p). One phosphor band (20p), two phosphor bands (others).

Set	2.40	2.25
Gutter pairs	6.00	
First day cover		2.50
Stamp cards	5.25	5.50

Common Dormouse (20p)
Lady's Slipper Orchid (26p)
Song Thrush (31p)
Shining Ram's-horn Snail (37p)
Mole Cricket (43p)
Devil's Bolette (63p)

■ 1998, January 20. Endangered Species
Des: R. Maude. Printed in litho by Questa. One phosphor band (20p), two phosphor bands (others).

Set	3.25	3.00
Gutter pairs	8.00	
First day cover		3.00
Stamp cards	6.25	7.50

By Lord Snowdon (26p)
At British Lung Foundation function (26p)
Wearing tiara (26p)
During visit to Birmingham (26p)
In evening dress (26p)

■ **1998, February 3. Diana, Princess of Wales Memorial**
Des: B. Robinson. Two phosphor bands.

Set of five in se-tenant strip	2.00	2.25
Gutter pairs	5.00	
First day cover		2.25

Lion of England and Griffin of Edward III (26p)
Flacon of Plantagenet and Bull of Clarence (26p)
Lion of Mortimer and Yale of Beaufort (26p)
Greyhound of Richmond and Dragon of Wales (26p)
Unicorn of Scotland and Horse of Hanover (26p)

■ **1998, February 24. The Queen's Beasts. 650th Anniversary of the Order of the Garter**
Des: Jeffery Matthews. Printed in recess and litho by Harrison. Two phosphor bands.

Set of five in se-tenant strip	2.40	2.25
Gutter pairs	6.00	
First day cover		2.50
Stamp cards	5.25	6.50

■ **1998, March 10. Wilding definitives**
Des: Dew Gibbons Design Group, from original design by G. Knipe. Printed in gravure by Walsall. Issued only in the £7.49 The Wilding Definitives prestige stamp book.

20p light green (phos band at left)	0.70	0.75
20p light green (phos band at right)	0.70	0.75
26p red-brown	0.75	0.80
37p light purple	1.75	1.85

St John's Point Lighthouse (20p)
Smalls Lighthouse (26p)
Needles Rock Lighthouse (37p)
Bell Rock Lighthouse (43p)
Eddystone Lighthouse (63p)

■ **1998, March 24. Lighthouses**
Des: D. Davis and J. Boon. Printed in litho by Questa. One phosphor band (20p), two phosphor bands (others).

Set	3.00	2.50
Gutter pairs	7.50	
First day cover		2.60
Stamp cards	5.25	6.50

Tommy Cooper (20p)
Eric Morecambe (26p)
Joyce Grenfell (37p)
Les Dawson (43p)
Peter Cook (63p)

■ **1998, April 23. Comedians**
Des: Gerald Scarfe. Printed in litho by Questa. One phosphor band (20p), two phosphor bands (others).

Set	3.00	2.50
Gutter pairs	7.50	
First day cover		2.60
Stamp cards	5.25	6.50

(* Examples exist of the 37p design but with the denomination 30p, printed before an increase in postal rates, and issued in error.)

10,000 donors give blood every day NHS

20

CARNIVAL

20

Woman in costume of yellow feathers (20p)
Woman in blue costume (26p)
Children in white and gold robes (43p)
Child dressed as a tree (63p)

ands forming the shape of a heart (20p)
dult holding the hand of a child (26p)
ands forming a cradle (43p)
and taking a pulse (63p)

1998, June 23. 50th Anniversary of the National Health Service
es: V. Frost, using photographs by A. Wilson. Printed in litho
Questa. One phosphor band (20p), two phosphor bands
thers).

et	2.25	2.50
utter pairs	5.50	
irst day cover		2.60
tamp cards	4.25	5.50

■ 1998, August 25. Notting Hill Carnival. Europa
Des: T. Hazael. Printed in photogravure by Walsall. One
phosphor band (20p), two phosphor bands (others).

Set	2.50	2.50
Gutter pairs	6.50	
First day cover		2.60
Stamp cards	4.25	5.50

20

Sir Malcolm C...

ne Hobbit (20p)
ne Lion, The Witch and the Wardrobe (26p)
ne Phoenix and the Carpet (37p)
ne Borrowers (43p)
nrough The Looking Glass (63p)

Bluebird of Sir Malcolm Campbell (20p)
Sunbeam of Sir Henry Segrave (26p)
Babs of John G. Parry Thomas (30p)
Railton Mobil Special of John R. Cobb (43p)
Bluebird CN7 of Donald Campbell (63p)

1998, July 21. Children's Fantasy Novels
es: P. Malone. Printed in photogravure by De La Rue. One
osphor band (20p), two phosphor bands (others).

et	2.75	2.75
utter pairs	6.50	
rst day cover		2.75
tamp cards	6.00	6.50

■ 1998, September 29. British Land Speed Records
Des: Roundel Design Group. Printed in photogravure by De La
Rue. One centre phosphor band (20p), two phosphor bands
(others).

Set	2.60	2.75
Gutter pairs	6.50	
First day cover		2.75
Stamp cards	5.25	6.50

(*The 26p also appears in the Breaking Barriers prestige stamp
book issued on October 13, 1988, but printed in photogravure
by Walsall, and with one phosphor band printed on the left or
right of the stamp; priced at £1.00 mint.)

Angel with hands in blessing (20p)
Angel praying (26p)
Angel playing lute (30p)
Angel playing flute (43p)
Angel praying (63p)

■ 1998, November 2. Christmas. Angels

Des: Irene von Treskow. Printed in photogravure by De La Rue.
One phosphor band (20p), two phosphor bands (others).

Set	2.50	2.75
Gutter pairs	5.50	
First day cover		2.70
Booklet (20 at 20p)	6.50	
Booklet (10 at 26p)	4.50	
Stamp cards	5.25	6.50

During 1999 and 2000 Royal Mail embarked on a
programme of special stamp issues to mark the
new Millennium. Each design includes the inscription
'Millennium' and the year, and a serial number.

The designs for 1999 looked back over the previous
Millennium, by exploring twelve different 'tales'. The
designs for 2000 are of photographs of projects
undertaken to celebrate the Millennium.

Greenwich Meridian and clock (20p)
Worker and blast furnace (26p)
Photograph of leaves (43p)
Computer inside head (63p)

■ 1999, January 12. The Inventors' Tale

Des: David Gentleman (20p), P. Howson (26p), Z. and Barbara
Baran (43p), E. Paolozzi (63p). Printed in photogravure by
Enschedé (26p), or De La Rue (others). One phosphor band
(20p), two phosphor bands (others).

Set	2.50	2.50
Gutter pairs	6.25	
First day cover		3.25
Stamp cards	4.25	6.50

(* The 63p also appears in the World Changers prestige
stamp book issued on September 21, 1999, but printed in
photogravure by Questa; priced at £1.75 mint.)

Globe surrounded by aircraft (20p)
Woman on bicycle (26p)
Railway Station (43p)
Captain Cook and man (63p)

■ 1999, February 2. The Travellers' Tale

Des: G. Hardie (20p), Sara Fanelli (26p), J. Lawrence (43p), A.
Klimowski (63p). Printed in photogravure by Enschedé (20p
and 63p), by De La Rue (26p), or litho by Enschedé (43p). One
phosphor band (20p), two phosphor bands (others).

Set	2.50	2.60
Gutter pairs	6.25	
First day cover		3.25
Stamp cards	4.25	6.50

Cow with markings of child being vaccinated (20p)
Patient on trolley (26p)
Penicillin mould (43p)
Test tube baby (63p)

1999, March 2. The Patients' Tale

Des: P. Brookes (20p), Susan Macfarlane (26p), M. Dempsey (43p), A. Gormley (63p. Printed in photogravure by Questa. One phosphor band (20p), two phosphor bands (others).

Set	2.50	2.60
Gutter pairs	6.25	
First day cover		3.25
Stamp cards	4.25	6.50

(* The 20p also appears in the World Changers prestige stamp book issued on September 21, 1999.)

Norman and dove (20p)
Pilgrim Fathers and Red Indian (26p)
Sailing ship and emigration to Australia (43p)
Face superimposed on hummingbird (63p)

1999, April 6. The Settlers' Tale

Des: J. Byrne (20p), W. McLean (26p), J. Fisher (43p), G. Powell (63p). Printed in litho (20p) or photogravure (others) by Walsall. One phosphor band (20p), two phosphor bands (others).

Set	2.50	2.60
Gutter pairs	6.25	
First day cover		3.25
Stamp cards	4.25	6.50

The 26p also appears in a booklet issued on May 12, 1999.)

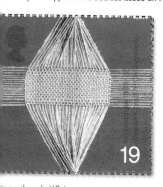

Woven threads (19p)
Salts Mill, Saltaire (26p)
Hull of ship on slipway (44p)
Lloyd's Building (64p)

1999, May 4. The Workers' Tale

Des: P. Collingwood (19p), D. Hockney (26p), R. Sanderson (44p), B. Neiland (64p). Printed in litho (19p) or photogravure (others) by De La Rue. One phosphor band (19p), two phosphor bands (others).

Set	2.50	2.60
Gutter pairs	6.25	
First day cover		3.25
Stamp cards	4.25	6.50

(* The 26p from this set also appears in a booklet issued on May 12, 1999, printed in photogravure by Walsall; priced at £1.50 mint.)

Freddie Mercury (19p)
Bobby Moore holding the World Cup (26p)
Dalek (44p)
Charlie Chaplin (64p)

1999, June 1. The Entertainers' Tale

Des: P. Blake (19p), M. White (26p), Lord Snowdon (44p), R. Steadman (64p). Printed in photogravure by Enschedé. One phosphor band (19p), two phosphor bands (others).

Set	2.50	2.60
Gutter pairs	6.25	
First day cover		3.25
Stamp cards	4.25	6.50

Prince Edward and Miss Sophie Rhys-Jones facing front (26p)
Facing sideways (64p)

1999, June 15. Royal Wedding

Des: J. Gibbs from photographs by John Swannell. Printed in photogravure by De La Rue.

Set	1.50	1.50
Gutter pairs	4.00	
First day cover		2.25
Stamp cards	3.25	3.50

Suffragette behind bars (19p)
Tap (26p)
Children (44p)
Magna Carta (64p)

■ 1999, July 6. The Citizens' Tale

Des: Natasha Kerr (19p), M. Craig-Martin (26p), A. Drummond (44p), A. Kitching (64p). Printed in photogravure by De La Rue. One phosphor band (19p), two phosphor bands (others).

Set	2.50	2.60
Gutter pairs	6.25	
First day cover		3.25
Stamp cards	4.25	6.50

DNA (19p)
Galapagos Finch and skeleton (26p)
Light polarised by magnetism (44p)
Saturn, from Hubble Space Telescope (64p)

■ 1999, August 3. The Scientists' Tale

Des: M. Curtis (19p), R. Harris Ching (26p), C. Gray (44p), photograph (64p). Printed in photogravure (19p, 64p) or litho (others) by Questa. One phosphor band (19p), two phosphor bands (others).

Set	2.50	2.60
Gutter pairs	6.25	
First day cover		3.25
Stamp cards	4.25	6.50

(* The 26p and 44p also appear in the World Changers prestige stamp book issued on September 21, 1999; priced at £3 for the pair mint.)

■ 1999, August 11. Solar Eclipse

Printed in photogravure by De La Rue. Miniature sheet, comprising four 64p values from issue of August 3.

Miniature sheet	12.00	12.00
First day cover		12.00

Upland landscape (19p)
Horse-drawn seed drill (26p)
Peeling potato (44p)
Combine harvester in field (64p)

■ 1999, September 7. The Farmers' Tale

Des: D. Tress (19p), C. Wormell (26p), Tessa Traeger (44p), R. Cooke (64p). Printed in photogravure by De La Rue. One phosphor band (19p), two phosphor bands (others).

Set	2.50	2.60
Gutter pairs	6.25	
First day cover		3.25
Stamp cards	4.25	6.50

(* The 26p also appears in a booklet issued on September 21, 1999, printed in photogravure by Walsall; priced at £1.50 mint.)

Robert the Bruce (19p)
Cavalier and horse (26p)
War Graves Cemetery (44p)
Soldiers with boy (64p)

■ 1999, October 5. The Soldiers' Tale

Des: A. Davidson (19p), R. Kelly (26p), D. McCullin (44p), C. Co (64p). Printed in litho (19p) or photogravure (others) by Walsa One phosphor band (19p), two phosphor bands (others).

Set	2.50	2.60
Gutter pairs	6.25	
First day cover		3.25
Stamp cards	4.25	6.50

rk the Herald Angels Sing' (19p)
g James I and Bible (26p)
Andrews Cathedral, Fife (44p)
tivity (64p)

1999, November 2. The Christians' Tale
s: B. Neuenschwander (19p), Claire Melinsky (26p), Catherine
s (44p), C. Aitchison (64p). Printed in photogravure by De La
e. One phosphor band (19p), two phosphor bands (others).

t	2.50	2.60
tter pairs	6.25	
st day cover		3.25
oklet (20 × 19p)	6.75	
oklet (10 × 26p)	4.75	
mp cards	4.25	6.50

orld of the Stage' (19p)
orld of Music' (26p)
orld of Literature' (44p)
w Worlds' (64p)

1999, December 7. The Artists' Tale
s: Allen Jones (19p), Bridget Riley (26p), Lisa Milroy (44p),
Howard Hodgkin (64p). Printed in photogravure by Walsall.
e phosphor band (19p), two phosphor bands (others).

t	2.50	2.60
tter pairs	6.25	
st day cover		3.25
mp cards	4.25	6.50

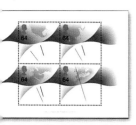

be showing North America (64p)
be showing Asia (64p)
be showing Middle East (64p)
be showing Europe (64p)

■ 1999, December 14. Millennium Timekeeper
Des: David Gentleman. Printed in gravure by De La Rue.
Miniature sheet containing 64p, 64p, 64p, 64p

Miniature sheet	14.00	11.00
First day cover		11.00
Stamp cards	9.50	18.50

(* The miniature sheet exists with the margin overprinted 'Earls
Court, London 22-28 May 2000 The Stamp Show 2000' sold
with tickets to The Stamp Show 2000 at £10: first put on sale
on March 1, 2000. Price: £15.00 mint.)

Barn owl (19p)
Night sky (26p)
River Goyt and textile mills (44p)
Cape Gannets (64p)

■ 2000, January 18. Above and Beyond
Printed in litho (44p) and gravure (others) by Questa. One
phosphor band (19p), two phosphor bands (others).

Set	2.50	2.60
Gutter pairs	6.25	
First day cover		3.25
Stamp cards	4.25	6.50

(* The 26p also appears as a 1st class value in a £2.70 stamp
booklet issued on May 26, 2000, printed in gravure by Walsall.
Priced at £1.50 mint.)

Millennium beacon (19p)
Garratt locomotive and train (26p)
Lightning (44p)
Floodlighting (64p)

■ 2000, February 1. Fire and Light
Printed in gravure by De La Rue. One phosphor band (19p),
two phosphor bands (others).

Set	2.50	2.60
Gutter pairs	6.25	
First day cover		3.25
Stamp cards	4.25	6.50

Pebbles (19p)
Frog's legs and water lilies (26p)
Cliff Broadwalk (44p)
Reflections in water (64p)

■ 2000, March 7. Water and Coast

Printed in litho (44p) or gravure (others) by Walsall. One phosphor band (19p), two phosphor bands (others).

Set	2.50	2.60
Gutter pairs	6.25	
First day cover		3.25
Stamp cards	4.25	6.50

River Braid (2nd)
South American leaf-cutter ants (1st)
Solar sensors (44p)
Hydroponic leaves (64p)

■ 2000, April 4. Life and Earth

Printed in gravure by De La Rue. One phosphor band (2nd), two phosphor bands (others).

Set	2.50	2.60
Gutter pairs	6.25	
First day cover		3.25
Stamp cards	4.25	6.50

(* The 1st also appears in a booklet issued on May 26, 2000.)

Pottery glaze (2nd)
Tate Modern (1st)
Road marking for bicycle (45p)
People in Salford (65p)

■ 2000, May 2. Art and Craft

Printed in gravure by Enschedé. One phosphor band (2nd), two phosphor bands (others).

Set	2.50	2.60
Gutter pairs	6.25	
First day cover		3.25
Stamp cards	4.25	6.50

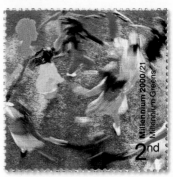

Children playing (2nd)
Millennium Bridge, Gateshead (1st)
Daisies (45p)
African hut and thatched cottage (65p)

■ 2000, June 6. People and Places

Printed in gravure (2nd, 45p) or litho (others) by Walsall. One phosphor band (2nd), two phosphor bands (others).

Set	2.50	2.60
Gutter pairs	6.25	
First day cover		3.25
Stamp cards	4.25	6.50

Raising the Stone (2nd)
Horse's hooves (1st)
Cyclist and reflection (45p)
Bluebell wood (65p)

2000, July 4. Stone and Soil

Printed in gravure in Enschedé. One phosphor band (2nd), two phosphor bands (others).

Set	2.50	2.60
Gutter pairs	6.25	
First day cover		3.25
Stamp cards	4.25	6.50

(* The 1st also appears in a £2.70 stamp booklet issued on September 5, 2000, printed in gravure by Walsall. Priced at 75p mint. The 65p also appears in the Treasury of Trees prestige stamp book issued on September 18, 2000, printed in gravure by Walsall; priced at £1.50 mint.)

Roots of trees (2nd)
Sunflower (1st)
Sycamore seeds (45p)
Doire Dach Forest (65p)

2000, August 1. Tree and Leaf

Printed in gravure in De La Rue. One phosphor band (2nd), two phosphor bands (others).

Set	2.50	2.60
Gutter pairs	6.25	
First day cover		3.25
Stamp cards	4.25	6.50

(* The 2nd, 45p and 65p also appear in the Treasury of Trees prestige stamp book issued on September 18, 2000, printed in gravure by Walsall; priced at £3 mint.)

Queen Elizabeth II (27p)
Prince William (27p)
The Queen Mother (27p)
Prince Charles (27p)

2000, August 4. 100th birthday of The Queen Mother

Des: J. Gibbs. Photograph by J. Swannell. Printed in gravure by De La Rue. Miniature sheet containing four 27p designs as part of the entire photograph.

Miniature sheet	4.00	4.00
First day cover		5.00
Stamp cards	9.50	10.50

(* The 27p design showing the Queen Mother, and the entire miniature sheet but in a slightly larger size, also appeared in the Life of the Century prestige stamp book issued on August 4, 2000, printed in gravure by Questa; stamp priced at £1.25 mint.)

Head of Gigantiops (2nd)
Gathering water lilies on Norfolk Broads (1st)
X-Ray of hand with computer mouse (45p)
Tartan wool holder (65p)

2000, September 5. Mind and Matter

Printed in litho by Walsall. One phosphor band (2nd), two phosphor bands (others).

Set	2.50	2.60
Gutter pairs	6.25	
First day cover		3.25
Stamp cards	4.25	6.50

Acrobats (2nd)
Footballers (1st)
Bather (45p)
Hen's egg (magnified) (65p)

2000, October 3. Body and Bone

Printed in litho (2nd) or gravure by Questa. One phosphor band (2nd), two phosphor bands (others).

Set	2.50	2.60
Gutter pairs	6.25	
First day cover		3.25
Stamp cards	4.25	6.50

Virgin and Child stained glass window (2nd)
Floodlit church (1st)
Latin gradual (45p)
Chapter House ceiling of York Minster (65p)

■ 2000, November 7. Spirit and Faith

Printed in gravure by De La Rue. One phosphor band (2nd), two phosphor bands (others).

Set	2.50	2.60
Gutter pairs	6.25	
First day cover		3.25
Booklet (20 x 2nd)	6.25	
Booklet (10 x 1st)	4.75	
Stamp cards	4.25	6.50

Church bells (2nd)
Eye (1st)
Top of a harp (45p)
Figure in latticework (65p)

■ 2000, December 5. Sound and Vision

Printed in gravure by De La Rue. One phosphor band (2nd), two phosphor bands (others).

Set	2.50	2.60
Gutter pairs	6.25	
First day cover		3.25
Stamp cards	4.25	6.50

Children's face painting: Flower (2nd)
Tiger (1st)
Owl (45p)
Butterfly (65p)

■ 2001, January 16. Looking to the Future

Des; Why Not Associates. Printed in gravure by De La Rue. One phosphor band (2nd), two phosphor bands (others).

Set	2.60	2.60
Gutter pairs	6.50	
First day cover		3.25
Stamp cards	5.00	6.50

Hallmarks: Love (1st)
Thanks (1st)
abc (1st)
Welcome (1st)
Cheers (1st)

■ 2001, February 6. Occasions stamps

Des: Springpoint Design. Printed in gravure by Enschedé.

Set	3.50	3.00
Gutter pairs	8.50	
First day cover		3.25
Stamp cards	8.00	7.50

(* These designs were also used for Smilers sheets in 2001.)

Dog in bath (1st)
Dog and man sitting on bench (1st)
Boxer (1st)
Cat handbag (1st)
Cat on gate (1st)
Dog in car (1st)
Cat at window (1st)
Dog looking over fence (1st)
Cat watching bird (1st)
Cat in wash basin (1st)

■ 2001, February 13. Cats and Dogs

Des: Johnson Banks. Printed in gravure by Walsall. Issued as a self-adhesive sheetlet which could be folded to form a booklet containing one of each of the ten designs.

Sheetlet	7.50	7.50
First day cover		6.50
Stamp Cards	10.00	15.50

(* The ten designs, with two 1st class definitives, were also issued in a £3.24 Cats and Dogs booklet on February 13, 2001

ections of a barometer:
Rain (19p)
Fair (27p)
Stormy (45p)
Very dry (65p)

2001, March 13. The Weather
Des: H. Brown and T. Meeuwissen. Printed in gravure by De La Rue. One phosphor band (19p), two phosphor bands (others).

Set	3.00	3.00
Gutter pairs	7.50	
First day cover		3.50
Stamp cards	5.25	8.50
Miniature sheet (1 x each value)	8.50	8.50
First day cover		8.50

Vanguard Class submarine (2nd)
Swiftsure Class submarine (1st)
Utility Class submarine (45p)
Holland type submarine (65p)

2001, April 10. Centenary of Royal Navy Submarine Service
Des: D. Davis. Printed in gravure by Questa. One phosphor band (2nd), two phosphor bands (others). Perf: 15 x 14. PVA gum.

Set	2.75	2.50
Gutter pairs	7.00	
First day cover		3.50
Stamp cards	4.75	6.50

(* The four stamps are also in the Unseen and Unheard prestige stamp book issued on October 22, 2001. Perf: 15 x 15; priced at £10.00 mint or used. The 1st class design also appears twice in self-adhesive form, together with four 1st class definitives, in a £1.62 stamp booklet issued on April 17, 2001; priced at £35 mint, £20 used.)

White Ensign (1st)
Union Jack (1st)
Jolly Roger (1st)
Flag of Chief of Defence Staff (1st)

2001, April 10. Centenary of Royal Navy Submarine Service. Flags.
Miniature sheet. Printed in gravure by Questa.
PVA gum.

Miniature sheet (1 x each value)	4.50	4.50
First day cover		4.50
Stamp cards	10.50	14.00

(* The White Ensign and Jolly Roger designs also appear in self adhesive form with four 1st class definitives in a £1.62 stamp booklet issued on October 22, 2001; priced at: £11 mint, £11 used per pair. The Union Jack design was used for a Smilers sheet in 2005.)

Leyland X2, B Type, Leyland Titan TD1, AEC Regent I (1st)
AEC Regent I, Daimler COG5, Guy Arab II, AEC Regent III RT (1st)
AEC Regent III, Bristol K, AEC Routemaster, Bristol Lodekka FSF (1st)
Bristol Lodekka FSF, Leyland PD3, Leyland Atlantean, Daimler Fleetline (1st)
Daimler Fleetline, MCW Metrobus, Leyland Olympian, Dennis Trident (1st)

2001, May 15. Double-deck buses
Des: M. English. Printed in gravure by Questa. The illustrations extend into the sheet margins, and across the sheet, so that some of the illustrations span two stamps.

Set of five in se-tenant strip	2.50	2.60
Gutter pairs	6.50	
First day cover		3.25
Miniature sheet (1 x each value)	5.50	5.00
First day cover		5.50
Stamp cards	10.50	15.50

Toque hat (1st)
Butterfly hat (E)
Top hat (45p)
Spiral hat (65p)

■ 2001, June 19. Hats

Des: Rose Design, from photographs by N. Knight.
Printed in litho by Enschedé.

Set	2.75	2.75
Gutter pairs	7.00	
First day cover		3.25
Stamp cards	4.75	6.50

Common frog (1st)
Great diving beetle (E)
Three-spined stickleback (45p)
Southern Hawker Dragonfly (65p)

■ 2001, July 10. Pond Life. Europa

Des: J. Gibbs. Printed in gravure by De La Rue.

Set	3.00	3.00
Gutter pairs	7.50	
First day cover		3.50
Stamp cards	4.75	6.50

Policeman (1st)
Mr Punch (1st)
Clown (1st)
Judy (1st)
Beadle (1st)
Crocodile (1st)

■ 2001, September 4. Punch and Judy

Des: K. Bernstein, from puppets made by Bryan Clarkez. Printed
in gravure by Walsall. PVA gum. Perf: 14 x 15.

Set of six in se-tenant strip	2.75	2.75
Gutter pairs	7.00	
First day cover		3.25
Stamp cards	6.25	8.50

(*The Mr Punch and Judy designs also appear in self-adhesive
form with four 1st class definitives in a £1.62 stamp booklet
issued on September 4, 2001, printed in gravure by Questa. Perf
14 x 15; priced at £10 mint, £10 used per pair.)

Carbon molecule, printed in litho and silk screen (2nd)
Globe, printed in litho and recess (1st)
Dove, printed in litho and embossing (E)
Crosses, printed in litho (40p)
'The Ad-dressing of Cats' by T. S. Eliot, printed in litho (45p)
Boron molecule, printed in litho with hologram (65p)

■ 2001, October 2. Nobel Prizes

Des: P. Vermier; engraved by Inge Madle (1st). Printed by
Enschedé. One phosphor band (2nd), phosphor band around
stamp (others).

Set	7.00	3.75
Gutter pairs	18.00	
First day cover		5.00
Stamp cards	6.25	8.50

Robins with snowman (2nd)
Robins on bird table (1st)
Robins skating on bird bath (E)
Robins with Christmas pudding hanging from tree (45p)
Robins in nest made of paper chains (65p)

■ 2001, November 6. Christmas. Robins
Des: A. Robins and H. Brown. Printed in gravure by De La Rue.
Self-adhesive.

Set	3.25	3.25
First day cover		5.00
Booklet (20 x 2nd)	7.50	
Booklet (10 x 1st)	5.50	
Stamp cards	5.25	7.50

(* The 2nd and 1st class values were also issued in separate
stamp books, in the form of folders. The same designs were
used for Smilers stamps in 2004.)

The Elephant's Child (1st)
How the Whale got his Throat (1st)
How the Camel got his Hump (1st)
How the Rhinoceros got his Skin (1st)
How the Leopard got his Spots (1st)
The Sing Song of Old Man Kangaroo (1st)
The Beginning of the Armadillos (1st)
The Crab that played with the Sea (1st)
The Cat that walked by Himself (1st)
The Butterfly that stamped (1st)

■ 2002, January 15. The Just So Stories by Rudyard Kipling
Des: I. Cohen. Printed in gravure by Walsall. Issued as a self-
adhesive sheetlet containing one of each of the ten designs.

Sheetlet	5.25	5.50
First day cover		5.50
Stamp Cards	7.00	21.00

Queen Elizabeth II in 1952, by Dorothy Wilding (2nd)
In 1968, by Cecil Beaton (1st)
In 1978, by Lord Snowden (E)
In 1984, by Yousef Karsh (45p)
In 1996, by Tim Graham (65p)

■ 2002, February 6. Golden Jubilee
Des: Kate Stephens. Printed in gravure by De La Rue. One phos
band (2nd), two phos bands (others). Wmk: 50 (sideways).

Set	3.50	3.00
Gutter pairs	8.50	
First day cover		3.75
Stamp cards	4.00	7.00

(* The stamps are also in the Gracious Accession prestige stamp
book, but with the Wmk upright; priced £7.50 mint, £8.00 used.)

Wilding design (1st)
Wilding design (2nd)

■ 2002, February 6. Wilding Design Decimal Definitives
Des: M. Farrar-Bell (2nd), Enid Marx (1st). Printed in gravure
by Enschedé. Wmk: 50. One phosphor band (2nd) or two
phosphor bands (1st). Only issued in the £7.29 A Gracious
Accession prestige stamp book issued on February 6, 2002.
One pane included a tilted 2nd, resulting in a diagonal
watermark.

2nd carmine-red	0.90	1.00
2nd carmine-red (Wmk diagonal)	2.50	2.50
1st green	0.90	1.00

Love (1st)
Rabbits, inscribed 'a new baby' (1st)
'Hello' written in sky (1st)
Bear pulling topiary tree in shape of house (1st)
Flowers inscribed 'best wishes' (1st)

■ 2002, March 5. Occasions
Des: I. Bilbey (Rabbits and Flowers), A. Kitching (Love), Hoop
Associates (Hello), G. Percy (Bear). Printed in litho by Questa.

Set	2.75	2.75
Gutter pairs	7.00	
First day cover		3.25
Stamp cards	4.00	7.00

(* The 'Hello' design also appears in a self-adhesive booklet,
with four 1st gold definitives, issued on March 4, 2003; priced at
£2.75. The designs were also used for Smilers sheets in 2002.)

Studland Bay (27p)
Luskentyre (27p)
Cliffs of Dover (27p)
Padstow Harbour (27p)
Broadstairs (27p)
St Abb's Head (27p)
Dunster Beach (27p)
Newquay (27p)
Portrush (27p)
Sand-spit (27p)

■ 2002, March 19. British Coastlines
Des: R. Cooke. Printed in litho by Walsall.

Set of ten in se-tenant block	4.50	4.50
Gutter pairs	12.00	
First day cover		5.25
Stamp cards	6.00	13.50

Slack wire act (2nd)
Lion tamer (1st)
Trick tri-cyclists (E)
Krazy kar (45p)
Equestrienne (65p)

■ 2002, April 10. Circus. Europa
Des: R. Fuller. Printed in gravure by Questa. One phosphor band (2nd), two phosphor bands (others).

Set	3.50	3.25
Gutter pairs	9.00	
First day cover		3.75
Stamp cards	4.00	7.00

20p design from the Queen Mother issue of 1990 (1st)
29p design (E)
34p design (45p)
37p design (65p)

■ 2002, April 25. The Queen Mother Memorial Issue
Des: J. Gorham. Printed in gravure by De La Rue.

Set	2.75	3.00
Gutter pairs	7.00	
First day cover		4.00

Airbus A340-600 (2nd)
Concorde (1st)
Trident (E)
VC 10 (45p)
Comet (65p)

■ 2002, May 2. Airliners
Des: Roundel. Printed in gravure by De La Rue. One phosphor band (2nd), two phosphor bands (others).

Set	3.50	3.25
Gutter pairs	9.00	
First day cover		3.75
Miniature sheet	5.00	5.00
First day cover		7.00
Stamp cards	4.00	12.00

(*The 1st class design also appears twice in self-adhesive form with four 1st class definitives in a £1.62 stamp booklet issued on May 2, 2002, printed in gravure by Questa; priced at £2.75 mint or used.)

Lion with shield of St George (1st)
Football with quarters: top left (1st)
Top right (1st)
Bottom left (1st)
Bottom right (1st)

2002, May 21. World Cup Football Championships

Des: Sedley Place (Lion), H. Brown (flag). Printed in gravure by Walsall.

1st (St George design)	1.25	1.25
Gutter pair	3.00	
First day cover	2.75	
Miniature sheet	3.50	3.50
First day cover		5.00
Stamp cards	4.00	7.50

(* The 1st class designs showing the top left and top right of the English flag also appear twice in self-adhesive form with four 1st class definitives in a £1.62 stamp booklet issued on May 21, 2002; priced at £4 per pair. The design showing the bottom right of the flag also appeared on Smilers sheets.)

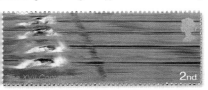

Swimming (2nd)
Running (1st)
Cycling (E)
Long jump (47p)
Wheelchair racing (68p)

2002, July 16. 17th Commonwealth Games, Manchester

Des: Madeleine Bennett. Printed in gravure by Enschedé. One phosphor band (2nd), two phosphor bands (others).

Set	3.25	3.25
Gutter pairs	9.00	
First day cover		4.00
Stamp cards	4.00	10.00

Tinkerbell (2nd)
Wendy, John and Michael Darling flying by Big Ben (1st)
Crocodile and the alarm clock (E)
Captain Hook (47p)
Peter Pan (68p)

2002, August 20. Peter Pan

Des: Tutsells. Printed in gravure by De La Rue. One phosphor band (2nd), two phosphor bands (others).

Set	4.00	3.25
Gutter pairs	10.00	
First day cover		4.00
Stamp cards	5.00	8.00

Millennium Bridge (2nd)
Tower Bridge (1st)
Westminster Bridge (E)
Blackfriars Bridge (47p)
London Bridge (68p)

2002, September 10. Bridges of London

Des: Sarah Davies and Robert Maude. Printed in litho by Questa. One phosphor band (2nd), two phosphor bands (others).

Set	4.00	3.50
Gutter pairs	10.00	
First day cover		4.00
Stamp cards	4.00	10.00

(* The 1st class design also appears twice in self-adhesive form with four 1st class definitives in a £1.62 booklet issued on September 10, 2002. Printed in gravure by Questa; priced at £2.00 mint, £2.50 used.)

Planetary nebula in Aquila (1st)
Seyfert 2 galaxy in Pegasus (1st)
Planetary nebula in Norma (1st)
Seyfert 2 galaxy in Circinus (1st)

2002, September 24. Astronomy

Des: Rose Design. Printed in gravure by Questa.
Miniature sheet, containing the four designs.

Miniature sheet	2.75	2.75
First day cover		2.75
Stamp cards	4.00	10.00

(* The design of the miniature sheet also appears in a larger size in the Across The Universe prestige stamp book issued on September 21, 2002.)

Pillar box of 1857 in green (2nd)
Pillar box of 1874 (1st)
Air mail box of 1934 (E)
Pillar box of 1939 (47p)
Pillar box of 1980 (68p)

■ 2002, October 8. 150th Anniversary of the first Pillar Box

Des: Silk Pearce; engraved by C. Slania. Printed in recess and litho by Enschedé. One phosphor band (2nd), two phosphor bands (others).

Set	4.25	3.25
Gutter pairs	11.00	
First day cover		4.00
Stamp cards	3.25	7.50

Blue spruce (2nd)
Holly (1st)
Ivy (E)
Mistletoe (47p)
Pine cone (68p)

■ 2002, November 5. Christmas. Christmas Flowers

Des: Rose Design. Printed in gravure by De La Rue. One phosphor band (2nd), two phosphor bands (others). Self-adhesive.

Set	3.25	3.25
First day cover		4.00
Booklet (24 x 2nd)	7.50	
Booklet (12 x 1st)	5.25	
Stamp cards	3.25	7.50

(*The 2nd and 1st class stamps also appear in folded stamp booklets.)

The Wilding definitives collection 1 ~ 1952 ~ 1953

Wilding Designs (1p, 2p, 5p, 2nd, 1st, 33p, 37p, 47p, 50p)

■ 2002, December 5. 50th Anniversary of the Wilding Definitives, 1st issue

Des: Rose Design (based on the original designs). Miniature sheet. Printed in gravure by De La Rue. One phosphor band (2nd), two phosphor bands (others). Wmk: 50.

Miniature sheet	5.50	6.00
First day cover		7.50
Stamp cards	5.00	15.00

Barn Owl Tyto alba

Barn Owl about to land, five different views (1st)
Kestrel in flight, five different views (1st)

■ 2003, January 14. Birds of Prey

Des: J. Gibbs from photographs by S. Dakon. Printed in litho by Walsall.

Set in se-tenant block of ten	6.00	5.50
Gutter pairs	15.00	
First day cover		5.50
Stamp cards	5.00	15.00

Gold star, See me, Playtime (1st)
I 'love' U (1st)
Angel, Poppet, Little terror (1st)
Yes, No, Maybe (1st)
Oops! Sorry, Will try harder (1st)
I did it! You did it! We did it! (1st)

2003, February 4. Occasions

Des: UNA, Sarah Wiegand and M. Exon. Printed in litho by Questa.

Set in se-tenant block of six	3.25	3.25
Gutter pairs	8.00	
First day cover		4.00
Stamp Cards	3.25	8.75

(* These designs also appeared as Smilers sheets.)

Genome **The End of the Beginning**

The genetic jigsaw (2nd)
Ape looking at scientist behind bars (1st)
DNA snakes and ladders (E)
Animals dressed as scientists (47p)
Looking into a DNA crystal ball (68p)

2003, February 25. 50th Anniversary of the Discovery of DNA

Des: William Murray Hamm and P. Brookes. Printed in litho by Enschedé. One phosphor band (2nd), two phosphor bands (others).

Set	3.25	3.25
Gutter pairs	8.00	
First day cover		4.25
Stamp cards	3.00	8.50

(* The 2nd and E designs also appear in the Microcosmos prestige stamp book issued on February 25, 2003.)

Red Pepper (1st)
Strawberry (1st)
Potato (1st)
Apple (1st)
Pear (1st)
Orange (1st)
Tomato (1st)
Lemon (1st)
Brussels sprout (1st)
Aubergine (1st)

2003, March 25. Fruit and Veg

Des: Johnson Banks. Printed in gravure by Walsall. Self-adhesive.

Set in se-tenant block of six	5.50	5.50
Gutter pairs	12.50	
First day cover		5.50
Stamp Cards	8.50	25.00

(* These stamps were issued with various self-adhesive stickers, such as of eyes, ears and mouths, so that the fruit and vegetables could be made to resemble faces. These designs were also used for a Smilers sheet in 2006.)

Amy Johnson with bi-plane (2nd)
1953 Everest team (1st)
Freya Stark in the desert (E)
Ernest Shackleton (42p)
Francis Chichester with Gipsy Moth IV (47p)
Robert Falcon Scott at the South Pole (68p)

2003, April 29. Extreme Endeavours

Des: H. Brown. Printed in gravure by Questa. One phosphor band (2nd), two phosphor bands (others). Perf: 15 x 14½.

Set	4.50	4.50
Gutter pairs	12.00	
First day cover		5.00
Stamp cards	4.00	9.50

(* The 1st class design also appears twice, in self adhesive form, with four 1st class definitives in a £1.62 stamp booklet issued on April 29, 2003. Printed in gravure by De La Rue. Perf: 14½; priced at £2.25 mint, £2.25 used.)

Wilding Designs (4p, 8p, 10p, 20p, 28p, 34p, E, 42p, 68p)

2003, May 20. 50th Anniversary of the Wilding Definitives, 2nd issue

Des: Rose Design (based on the original designs). Miniature sheet. Printed in gravure by De La Rue. One phosphor band (20p), two phosphor bands (others). Wmk: 50.

Miniature sheet	5.50	6.00
First day cover		6.50

Coronation procession (1st)
Children reading poster (1st)
The Queen seated in the Coronation Chair (1st)
Children producing Royal montage (1st)
The Queen in Coronation robes – by Cecil Beaton (1st)
Children racing during street party (1st)
Coronation Coach passing through Admiralty Arch (1st)
Children in fancy dress (1st)
Coronation Coach outside Buckingham Palace (1st)
Children at street party (1st)

■ 2003, June 2. 50th Anniversary of the Coronation
Des: Kate Stephens. Printed in gravure by De La Rue.

Set of ten in se-tenant block	4.75	4.75
Gutter pairs	12.00	
First day cover		5.25
Stamp cards	7.00	20.00

(* Eight of these designs also appear in the A Perfect
Coronation prestige stamp book issued on June 2, 2003.)

■ 2003, June 2. Wilding design decimal definitives
Des: as issue of March 10, 1998. Printed in gravure by Walsall.
Wmk: 50. Issued only in the £7.46 A Perfect Coronation
prestige stamp book.

47p bistre-brown	3.00	3.25
68p grey-blue	3.00	3.25

(* The booklet pane comprised two of each value, plus the 1953
Coronation design by Edmund Dulac with face value £1. This
stamp with Wmk: 50 priced at £25.00 mint, £25.00 used.)

Photographs of Prince William:
By Brendan Beirne (28p)
By Tim Graham (2000) (E)
By Camera Press (47p)
By Tim Graham (2001) (68p)

■ 2003, June 17. 21st Birthday of Prince William
Des: Madeleine Bennett. Printed in gravure by Walsall.

Set	3.75	3.00
Gutter pairs	10.00	
First day cover		4.00
Stamp cards	5.00	20.00

Loch Assynt, Sutherland (2nd)
Ben More, Isle of Mull (1st)
Rothiemurchus, Cairngorms (E)
Dalveen Pass, Lowther Hills (42p)
Glenfinnan Viaduct, Lochaber (47p)
Papa Little, Shetland Islands (68p)

■ 2003, July 15. A British Journey: Scotland
Des: Phelan Barker. Printed in gravure by De La Rue. One
phosphor band (2nd), two phosphor bands (others).

Set	4.25	4.25
Gutter pairs	11.00	
First day cover		5.00
Stamp cards	3.25	9.00

(* The 1st class design also appears twice, in self adhesive form,
with four 1st class definitives in a £1.68 stamp booklet issued
on July 15, 2003; priced at £2.50 mint, £2.25 used.)

The Station (1st)
Black Swan (E)
The Cross Keys (42p)
The Mayflower (47p)
The Barley Sheaf (68p)

■ 2003, August 12. Pub Signs. Europa
Des: Elmwood. Printed in gravure by De La Rue.

Set	5.00	4.25
Gutter pairs	12.50	
First day cover		4.50
Stamp cards	2.75	7.50

(* The 1st class design also appears in a Letters by Night
prestige stamp book issued on March 16, 2004.)

MECCANO
Constructor Biplane c1931

Meccano Constructor Biplane (1st)
Wells-Brimtoy bus (E)
Hornby M1 locomotive (42p)
Dinky Toys Ford Zephyr (47p)
Mettoy Space Ship Eagle (68p)

■ 2003, September 18. Toys
Des: Trickett and Webb. Printed in gravure by Enschedé.

Set	4.25	4.25
Gutter pairs	11.00	
First day cover		4.50
Stamp cards	3.50	13.50
Miniature sheet (1x each value)	4.00	4.00
First day cover		5.50

(* The 1st class design also appears twice, in self adhesive form, with four 1st class definitives in a £1.68 stamp booklet issued on September 18, 2003. Printed in gravure by De La Rue; priced at £2.75 mint, £2.75 used.)

Coffin of Denytenamun (2nd)
Alexander the Great (1st)
Sutton Hoo helmet (E)
Sculpture of Parvati (42p)
Mask of Xiuhtecuhtli (47p)
Hoa Hakananai'a (68p)

2003, October 7. Treasures from the British Museum
Des: Rose Design. Printed in gravure by Walsall. One phosphor band (2nd), band at right (42p, 68p), two phosphor bands (others).

Set	5.50	4.25
Gutter pairs	14.00	
First day cover		5.00
Stamp cards	3.25	9.00

Spiral (2nd)
Star (1st)
Wall (E)
Ball (42p)
Hole (47p)
Pyramids (68p)

■ 2003, November 4. Christmas. Ice Sculptures
Des: D. Davis, from ice Sculptures by Andy Goldsworthy. Printed in gravure by De La Rue. One phosphor band (2nd), two phosphor bands (others). Self-adhesive.

Set	5.00	5.25
First day cover		5.50
Booklet (24 x 2nd)	8.00	
Booklet (12 x 1st)	5.50	
Stamp cards	3.25	12.00

(* The 1st class and 2nd class design also appear in folded stamp booklets, and as Smilers sheets.)

England fans and England flag (1st)
England team standing in a circle (1st)
The Rugby World Cup (1st)
The England team after winning the Rugby World Cup (1st)

■ 2003, December 19. England winning the Rugby World Cup
Des: Why Not Associates. Printed in litho by Walsall. Miniature sheet, containing one of each design.

Miniature sheet	3.25	3.25
First day cover		4.50

'Dolgoch' 0-4-0T, Rheilffordd Talyllyn Railway, Gwynedd

'Dolgoch' on the Rheilffordd Tayllyn Railway (20p)
CR 439 on the Bo'ness and Kinneil Railway (28p)
GCR 8K on the Grand Central Railway (E)
GWR Manor on the Severn Valley Railway (42p)
SR West Country on the Bluebell Railway (47p)
BR Standard on the Keighley and Worth Valley Railway (68p)

■ 2004, January 13. Classic Locomotives
Des: Roundel. Printed in litho by De La Rue. One phosphor
band (2nd), two phosphor bands (others).

Set	4.50	4.50
Gutter pairs	12.00	
First day cover		5.00
Stamp cards	6.00	15.50
Miniature sheet (1 x each value)	15.00	15.00
First day cover		15.00

(* The 28p, E and 42p designs also appear in the Letters by
Night prestige stamp book issued on March 16, 2004.)

Postman (1st)
Face (1st)
Duck (1st)
Baby (1st)
Aircraft (1st)

■ 2004, February 3. Occasions.
Des: S. Kambayashi. Printed in litho by De La Rue.

Set of five in se-tenant strip	2.25	2.25
Gutter pairs	6.00	
First day cover		3.50
Stamp cards	2.25	7.50

(* These designs also appear as a Smilers sheet.)

J.R.R.TOLKIEN · THE LORD OF THE RINGS

Middle Earth (1st)
Forest of Lothlórien (1st)
The Fellowship of the Ring (1st)
Rivendell (1st)
The Hall at Bag End (1st)
Orthanc (1st)
Doors of Durin (1st)
Barad-dûr (1st)
Minas Tirth (1st)
Fangorn Forest (1st)

■ 2004, February 26. The Lord of The Rings by J. R. R. Tolkien
Des: HGV Design. Printed in litho by Walsall.

Set of ten in se-tenant block	5.00	5.00
Gutter pairs	12.50	
First day cover		5.00
Stamp cards	7.50	15.00

Ely Island, Lower Lough Erne (2nd)
Giant's Causeway, Antrim coast (1st)
Slemish, Antrim Mountains (E)
Banns Road, Mourne Mountains (42p)
Glenelly Valley, Sperrins (47p)
Islandmore, Strangford Lough (68p)

■ 2004, March 16. A British Journey: Northern Ireland
Des: Phelan Barker. Printed in gravure by Enschedé. One
phosphor band (2nd), two phosphor bands (others).

Set	3.75	4.00
Gutter pairs	9.00	
First day cover		5.00
Stamp cards	2.75	9.50

(* The 28p design also appears twice in self-adhesive form in a
£1.68 stamp booklet issued on March 16, 2004; priced at £2.00

'Lace 1 (trial proof) 1968' by Sir Terry Frost (28p)
'Coccinelle' by Sonia Delaunay (57p)

2004, April 6. Entente Cordiale

es: Rose Design. Printed in gravure by Walsall.

t	1.50	1.50
utter pairs	4.00	
affic light gutter pairs	6.50	
rst day cover		2.50
amp cards	4.00	4.00

Stamps in the same designs were issued by France.)

42

RMS Queen Mary 1936

MS Queen Mary 2 (1st)
Canberra (E)
MS Queen Mary (42p)
MS Mauretania (47p)
City of New York (57p)
Great Western (68p)

2004, April 13. Ocean Liners

es: J. Gibbs. Printed in gravure by De La Rue.

et	4.25	4.25
utter pairs	12.00	
rst day cover		5.25
amp cards	4.00	15.50
liniature sheet (1 x each value)	5.50	6.00
rst day cover		7.00

The 1st class design also appears in self-adhesive form with ur 1st class definitives in a £1.68 stamp booklet issued on pril 13, 2004; priced at £2.00 mint, £2.00 used.)

2nd

Royal Horticultural Society 1804-2004
Dianthus Allwoodii Group

ianthus Allwoodii group (2nd)
ahlia Garden Princess (1st)
lematis Arabella (E)
iltonia French Lake (42p)
ium Lemon Pride (47p)
elphinium Clifford Sky (68p)

2004, May 25. Bicentenary of the Royal Horticultural Society

Des: Rose Design. Printed in gravure by Enschedé. One phosphor band (2nd), two phosphor bands (others).

Set	4.25	4.25
Gutter pairs	11.00	
First day cover		5.00
Stamp cards	4.00	15.50
Miniature sheet (1 x each value)	4.50	4.50
First day cover		5.50

(* All values are also in the Glory of the Garden prestige stamp book of May 25, 2004., and the 1st class on Smilers sheets.)

Pont Abermaw, Cymru
Barmouth Bridge, Wales

Barmouth Bridge (2nd)
Hyddgen, Plynlimon (1st)
Brecon Beacons (40p)
Pen-pych, Rhondda Valley (43p)
Rhewl, Dee Valley (47p)
Marloes Sands (68p)

2004, June 15. A British Journey: Wales. Europa

Des: Phelan Barker. Printed in gravure by De La Rue. One phosphor band (2nd), two phosphor bands (others).

Set	3.75	3.75
Gutter pairs	9.00	
First day cover		5.00
Stamp cards	2.75	9.00

(* The 1st class design also appears in self-adhesive form in a £1.68 stamp booklet of June 15, 2004; priced at £2.50.)

1st
Sir Rowland Hill
was awarded the first RSA Albert Medal
in 1864 for his postal reforms and the
introduction of the Penny Post.
The Royal Society of Arts 1754–2004

Penny Black with citation to Sir Rowland Hill (1st)
William Shipley (40p)
R, S and A as typewriter keys (43p)
Brush for sweeping chimneys (47p)
Typeface by Eric Gill (57p)
Zero Waste (68p)

2004, August 10. 250th Anniversary of the Royal Society of Arts

Des: D. Birdsall. Printed in litho by Walsall.

Set	5.25	5.25
Gutter pairs	14.00	
First day cover		6.00
Stamp cards	2.75	9.50

Pine Marten (1st)
Roe Deer (1st)
Badger (1st)
Yellow-necked mouse (1st)
Wild Cat (1st)
Red Squirrel (1st)
Stoat (1st)
Natterer's Bat (1st)
Mole (1st)
Fox (1st)

■ 2004, September 16. Woodland Animals
Des: Kate Stephens. Printed in gravure by Enschedé.

Set of ten in se-tenant block	5.00	5.00
Gutter pairs	13.00	
First day cover		5.75
Stamp cards	4.25	15.00

Scotland definitives (40p, 1st, 2nd, 1st, 40p)

■ 2004, October 5. Opening of the Scottish Parliament Building
Des: H. Brown. Printed in gravure by De La Rue.
Miniature sheet, comprising one 2nd, two 1st and two 40p Scotland definitives.

Miniature sheet	3.25	3.50
First day cover		4.50

Pte McNamara (2nd)
Piper Muir (1st)
Sgt Major Edwards (40p)
Sgt Powell (57p)
Sgt Major Poole (68p)
Sgt Glasgow (£1.12)

■ 2004, October 12. The Crimean War
Des: Atelier Works, from photographs taken during The Crimean War. Printed in litho by Walsall. One phosphor band (2nd), two phosphor bands (others).

Set	5.25	5.25
Gutter pairs	12.50	
Traffic light gutter pairs	15.00	
First day cover		7.50
Stamp cards	2.75	9.00

Father Christmas on roof (2nd)
Father Christmas welcoming the sunrise (1st)
Father Christmas battling against the wind (40p)
Father Christmas holding umbrella (57p)
Father Christmas holding torch (68p)
Father Christmas sheltering by a chimney (£1.12)

■ 2004, November 2. Christmas
Des: R. Briggs. Printed in gravure by De La Rue. One phosphor band (2nd), two phosphor bands (others).

Set	5.25	5.25
First day cover		7.50
Booklet (24 x 2nd)	7.00	
Booklet (12 x 1st)	4.75	
Stamp cards	3.25	15.00
Miniature sheet (1 x each value, but conventionally gummed)	5.00	5.50
First day cover		7.50

(*The 1st class and 2nd class designs also appear in folded stamp booklets, and in Smilers sheets.)

Embden geese (1st)
British Saddleback pigs (1st)
Khaki Campbell ducks (1st)
Clydeside mare with foal (1st)
Dairy Shorthorn cattle (1st)
Border Collie (1st)
Light Sussex chickens (1st)
Suffolk sheep (1st)
Bagot goat (1st)
Norfolk Black turkeys (1st)

2005, January 11. Farm Animals
Des: C. Wormell. Printed in gravure by Enschedé.

Set of ten in se-tenant block	5.00	5.00
Gutter pairs	12.50	
First day cover		5.25
Stamp cards	4.25	15.50

Old Harry Rocks, Studland Bay (2nd)
Wheal Coates, St Agnes (1st)
Start Point, start Bay (40p)
Horton Down, Wiltshire (43p)
Chiselcombe, Exmoor (57p)
St James's Stone, Lundy (68p)

2005, February 8. A British Journey: South-West England
Des: J. Phelan and Lissa Barker. Printed in gravure by De La Rue. One phosphor band (2nd), two phosphor bands (others).

Set	4.25	4.25
Gutter pairs	11.00	
First day cover		5.50
Stamp cards	2.75	9.00

Rochester (2nd)
Come to me (1st)
the comfort of her bonnet (40p)
Ligne des Rats (57p)
refectory (68p)
inspection (£1.12)

2005, February 24. 150th Anniversary of the Death of Charlotte Brontë
Des: P. Willberg, from illustrations by Paula Rego. Printed in litho by Walsall. One phosphor band (2nd), two phosphor bands (others).

Set	5.50	5.50
Gutter pairs	14.00	
First day cover		7.00
Stamp cards	3.25	15.00
Miniature sheet (1 x each design)	5.00	5.50
First day cover		7.00

(*All designs also appear in the Brontë Sisters prestige stamp book issued on February 24, 2005.)

Heads or Tails (1st)
Rabbit and Top Hat (40p)
Coloured scarves and tube (47p)
Ace of Hearts (68p)
Three fezzes and pyramids (£1.12)

2005, March 15. Magic
Des: Tathem Design; illustration by George Hardie. Printed in gravure by Walsall. The designs include 'magical' features; rubbing the 1st class stamp with a coin reveals either the head or tail of a coin.

Set	5.50	5.50
Gutter pairs	14.00	
First day cover		6.50
Stamp cards	2.25	7.50

(*The 1st class design is also found in a Smilers sheet issued on March 15, 2005.)

Carrickfergus Castle (50p)
Caernarvon Castle (£1)
Edinburgh Castle (£1)
Windsor Castle (50p)

2005, March 22. The Castle Definitives of 1955
Des: Sedley Place (original illustrations by Lynton Lamb). Miniature sheet. Printed by intaglio and litho by Enschedé.

Miniature sheet	4.50	5.00
First day cover		6.50
Stamp cards	4.00	15.00

Hadrian's Wall (2nd)
Uluru Kata Tjuta National Park (2nd)
Stonehenge (1st)
Wet Tropics of Queensland (1st)
Blenheim Palace (47p)
Greater Blue Mountains Area (47p)
Heart of Neolithic Orkney (68p)
Pumululu National Park (68p)

■ 2005, April 21. World Heritage Sites

Des: Jason Godfrey from photographs by Peter Marlow. Litho printed by Enschedé. One phosphor band (2nd), two phosphor bands (others).

Set of four se-tenant pairs	5.00	5.25
Gutter pairs	12.50	
First day cover		7.00
Stamp cards	3.50	12.50

(* This is a joint issue with Australia Post.)

At the Mey Games in the Scottish Highlands (30p)
At Birkhall (68p)

■ 2005, April 8. The Wedding of Prince Charles and Mrs Camilla Parker Bowles

Des: Rose Design,, from photographs by Christopher Furlong (30p) and Carolyn Robb (68p). Printed in litho by Enschedé. Miniature sheet, containing two of the 30p and two of the 68p design.

Miniature sheet	3.25	3.50
First day cover		4.50

(* Whilst the first day handstamps and the miniature sheet are dated April 8, the wedding took place on April 9)

Ensign of the Scots Guards (2nd)
The Queen taking the salute (1st)
Trumpeter of the Household Cavalry (42p)
Welsh Guardsman (60p)
The Queen on horseback (68p)
The Queen with Duke of Edinburgh in an open carriage (£1.12

■ 2005, June 7. Trooping the Colour

Des: Why Not Associates. Printed in litho by Walsall. One phosphor band (2nd), two phosphor bands (others).

Set	5.50	5.50
Gutter pairs	14.00	
First day cover		6.50
Stamp cards	3.25	10.00
Miniature sheet (1 x each value)	5.00	5.50
First day cover		6.50

Searchlights in a 'V' over St Paul's Cathedral (1st)
Definitives (1st, 1st, 1st, 1st, 1st)

2005, July 5. End of the War

Des: Jeffery Matthews, using a stamp designed by J. Gorham and originally issued on May 2, 1995. Printed in gravure by Enschedé. Miniature sheet containing St Paul's Cathedral design plus five 1st class definitives.

Miniature sheet	3.00	3.25
First day cover		4.00

1991 **Norton F.1** road version of a race winner

Norton F.1 (1st)
BSA Rocket 3 (40p)
Vincent Black Shadow (42p)
Triumph Speed Twin (47p)
Brough Superior (60p)
Royal Enfield (68p)

2005, July 19. Motorcycles

Des: Atelier works, with illustrations by Michael English. Printed in litho by Walsall.

Set	4.50	4.75
Gutter pairs	12.00	
First day cover		6.00
Stamp cards	2.75	10.00

Athletes (1st, 1st, 1st, 1st, 1st, 1st, 1st)

2005, August 12. London 2012

Printed in litho by Walsall. Miniature sheet containing one of each of the five designs issued for the Olympic and Paralympic Games stamps of 1996, plus a second of the Athlete with Olympic rings design, but all inscribed '1st'

Miniature sheet	3.25	3.50
First day cover		4.50

Eating rice (2nd)
Drinking tea (1st)
Eating sushi (42p)
Eating pasta (47p)
Eating chips (60p)
Eating an apple (68p)

2005, August 23. Changing Tastes in Britain. Europa

Des: Rose Design, with illustrations by Catell Ronca. Printed in gravure by Enschedé. One phosphor band (2nd), two phosphor bands (others).

Set	4.25	4.25
Gutter pairs	12.00	
First day cover		5.50
Stamp cards	2.75	10.00

Inspector Morse (2nd)
Emmerdale (1st)
Rising Damp (42p)
The Avengers (47p)
The South Bank Show (60p)
Who Wants To Be A Millionaire? (68p)

2005, September 15. Classic ITV

Des: Kate Stephens.. Printed in litho by De La Rue. One phosphor band (2nd), two phosphor bands (others).

Set	4.25	4.50
Gutter pairs	12.00	
First day cover		5.50
Stamp cards	2.75	10.00

(*The 1st class design is also found on a Smilers sheet.)

Guzmania splendens (1st)
Hello (1st)
Love (1st)
Union flag (1st)
Teddy bear (1st)
Robin looking through pillar box slit (1st)

■ 2005, October 4. Pictorial definitives

Printed by litho by Walsall. Self-adhesive. Issued in booklets containing one of each of the six designs.

Booklet	2.75	
Booklet (with PiP information)	2.75	
First day cover		4.00

(* These designs were made available as a generic Smilers sheet on July 4, 2006.)

The Entrepreante with British Belle Isle (1st)
Nelson wounded (1st)
Entrepreante and the French Achille (42p)
The schooner Pickle (42p)
Nelson attacking in two columns (68p)
Putting to sea from Cadiz (68p)

■ 2005, October 18. Battle of Trafalgar

Des: Dick Davis from a painting by William Heath. Printed in litho by Walsall.

Set of three se-tenant pairs	4.75	4.75
Gutter pairs	13.00	
First day cover		6.00
Stamp cards	3.50	16.00
Miniature sheet (1 x each stamp)	4.50	4.75
First day cover		6.00

(* The stamps also appear in a Battle of Trafalgar prestige stamp book issued on October 18, 2005.)

THE ASHES ENGLAND WINNERS 2005

England team celebrating (two 1st designs)
England team in action (two 68p designs)

■ 2006, October 6. England Winning The Ashes

Des: Why Not Associates. Printed in litho by Cartor. Miniature sheet, comprising two 1st and two 68p.

Miniature sheet	3.50	4.00
First day cover		4.50

Haiti (2nd)
European (1st)
European (42p)
North American Indian (60p)
India (68p)
Australian Aborigine (£1.12)

■ 2005, November 1. Christmas. Madonna and Child

Des: Irene von Treskow. Printed in gravure by De La Rue. One phosphor band (2nd), two phoshor bands (others). Self-adhesive

Set	5.25	5.50
First day cover		6.50
Booklet (24 x 2nd)	7.00	
Booklet (12 x 1st)	4.75	
Stamp cards	3.50	17.50
Miniature sheet (all six stamps, but with normal gumming)	4.75	5.50
First day cover		6.50

(* The 2nd and 1st class stamps also appear in stamp books.)

The Tale of Mr Jeremy Fisher (2nd)
Kipper (2nd)
The Enormous Crocodile (1st)
More About Paddington (1st)
Comic Adventures of Boots (42p)
Alice's Adventures in Wonderland (42p)
The Very Hungry Caterpillar (68p)
Maisy's ABC (68p)

■ 2006. January 10. Animal Tales

Des: Rose Design. Printed in litho by De La Rue.

Set	5.00	5.00
Gutter pairs	12.50	
First day cover		6.50
Stamp cards	4.00	15.00

ırding Mill Valley, Shropshire (1st)
ıachey Head, Sussex (1st)
Paul's Cathedral (1st)
ancaster, Norfolk (1st)
ərwent Edge, Peak District (1st)
əbin's Hood Bay, Yorkshire (1st)
ıttermere, Lake District (1st)
ʰipping Campden, Cotswolds (1st)
Boniface Down, Isle of Wight (1st)
ʰamberlain Square, Birmingham (1st)

2006, February 7. England: A British Journey
əs: Phelan Parker Design Consultants. Printed in gravure by
ıe La Rue.

ət in block	4.75	4.80
ıutter pairs	12.50	
ʳst day cover		6.50
ːamp cards	4.50	15.00

ʸal Albert Bridge (1st)
ʷx Tunnel (40p)
ʲddington Station (42p)
S Great Britain (47p)
fton Suspension Bridge (60p)
ıidenhead Bridge (68p)

2006, February 23. Bicentenary of the birth of ımbard Kingdom Brunel
əs: Hat-trick Design. Printed in litho by Enschedé.

ət	4.50	4.75
ıutter pairs	12.00	
ʳst day cover		5.00
ıamp cards	4.50	15.00
ıniature sheet (1 x each value)	4.50	4.75
ʳst day cover		5.00

ıles definitives (68p, 1st, 2nd, 1st, 68p)

■ 2006, March 1. Welsh Assembly
Des: Silk Pearce. Printed in gravure by De La Rue.
Miniature sheet, comprising one 2nd, two 1st and two 68p
Welsh definitives.

Miniature sheet	3.50	3.50
First day cover		5.00

Sabre-tooth Cat (1st)
Giant Deer (42p)
Woolly Rhino (47p)
Woolly Mammoth (68p)
Cave Bear (£1.12)

■ 2006, March 21. Ice Age Animals
Des: Howard Brown (illustrations by Andrew Davidson). Printed
in litho by Enschedé.

Set	4.75	4.80
Gutter pairs	12.50	
First day cover		6.25
Stamp cards	2.50	15.00

The Queen in 1972 (2nd)
The Queen in 1985 (2nd)
The Queen in 1931 (1st)
The Queen in 2001 (1st)
The Queen in 1951 (44p)
The Queen in 1960 (44p)
The Queen in 1940 (72p)
The Queen in 1950 (72p)

■ 2006, April 18. The Queen's 80th birthday
Des: Sedley Place. Printed in gravure by Enschedé.

Set	5.50	5.50
Gutter pairs	14.00	
First day cover		7.00
Stamp cards	3.50	17.00

42

England (1st)
Italy (42p)
Argentina (44p)
Germany (50p)
France (64p)
Brazil (72p)

■ 2006, June 6. World Cup Winners
Des: Getty Images. Printed in litho by Walsall.

Set	4.75	4.80
Gutter pairs	12.50	
First day cover		6.25
Stamp cards	2.75	11.00

Downland Gridshell, Chichester (50p)
30 St Mary Axe, London (1st)
Maggie's Centre, Dundee (42p)
Selfridges, Birmingham (44p)
An Turas Isle of Tiree (64p)
The Deep, Hull (72p)

■ 2006, June 20. Modern Architecture
Des: Roundel. Printed in gravure by Walsall.

Set	4.75	4.80
Gutter pairs	12.50	
First day cover		6.25
Stamp cards	2.75	10.00

T. S. Eliot (1st)
Sir Winston Churchill (1st)
Sir Joshua Reynolds (1st)
Emmeline Pankhurst (1st)
Virginia Woolf (1st)
Sir Walter Scott (1st)
Mary Seacole (1st)
William Shakespeare (1st)
Dame Cicely Saunders (1st)
Charles Darwin (1st)

■ 2006, July 18. 150th Anniversary of the National Portrait Gallery
Des: Peter Willberg. Printed in gravure by De La Rue.

Set of ten in block	5.25	5.25
Gutter pairs	14.00	
First day cover		7.00
Stamp cards	5.00	16.00

■ 2006, August 31. The Year of the Three Kings
Des: Together Design. Printed in gravure by De La Rue.
Miniature sheet comprising £1 Machin definitive, and illustrating the 1d stamps of the reigns of King George V, King Edward VIII and King George VI.

Miniature sheet	4.00	4.50
First day cover		6.50

Agansing Rai, a Gurkha (1st)
Boy Seaman First Class Jack Cornwell (1st)
Midshipman Charles Lucas (64p)
Captain Noel Chavasse (64p)
Captain Alan Ball (72p)
Captain Charles Upham (72p)

2006, September 21. Victoria Cross
es: Atelier Works. Printed in litho by Enschedé.

t	4.50	4.50
utter pairs	11.00	
rst day cover		6.50
amp cards	3.50	15.00
iniature sheet (1 x each, plus the 20p Victoria		
oss stamp from September 1990)	4.50	4.50
rst day cover		6.50

sian sitar (1st)
aribbean base player (42p)
tin American maracas (44p)
ish fiddle (50p)
ack American Blues (72p)

2006, October 3. Sounds of Britain
es: CDT. Printed in litho by Cartor

et	3.50	3.50
utter pairs	10.00	
rst day cover		6.25
tamp cards	3.00	8.00

ew baby (1st)
est wishes (1st)
hank you (1st)
alloons (1st)
rework (1st)
hampagne, flowers and butterflies (1st)

2006, October 17. Pictorial definitives
inted by litho by Walsall. Self-adhesive. Issued in booklets
ontaining one of each of the six designs.

ooklet	2.75	
irst day cover		4.00

These designs were also available as a generic Smilers sheet.)

Poppies (1st), Country definitives (72p, 72p, 72p, 72p)

■ 2006, November 6. Lest We Forget
Des: Hat-Trick Design. Printed in gravure by De La Rue.
Miniature sheet with 1st class Poppies design, and 72p
definitives of England, Northern Ireland, Scotland and Wales.

Miniature sheet	5.00	5.00
First day cover		7.50

(* The 1st Poppies design was also made available as a generic
Smilers sheet.)

Snowman (2nd and 2nd Large)
Father Christmas sitting on chimney (1st and 1st Large)
Reindeer (72p)
Christmas tree (£1.19)

■ 2006, November 7. Christmas
Des: CDT. Printed in litho by De La Rue. Self-adhesive.

Set	4.50	4.50
Gutter pairs	11.00	
First day cover		6.25
Stamp cards	3.25	18.00
Miniature sheet (normal gum)	4.50	4.50
First day cover		6.25

Scottish flag (1st)
St Andrew (72p)
Edinburgh Castle (72p)
Scotland definitive (1st)

■ 2006, November 30. Celebrating Scotland
Des: P. Crowther, Claire Melinsky, Silk Pearce. Printed in gravure
by De La Rue. Miniature sheet.

Miniature sheet	3.50	3.50
First day cover		5.00
Stamp cards	2.50	10.00

(* The 1st Scotland definitive, self-adhesive, was also used for a
generic Smilers sheet issued on November 30, 2007.)

With The Beatles (1st)
Sgt Pepper's Lonely Hearts Club Band (1st)
Help! (64p)
Abbey Road (64p)
Revolver (72p)
Let It Be (72p)

Moon Jellyfish (1st)
Common Starfish (1st)
Beadlet Anemone (1st)
Bass (1st)
Thornback Ray (1st)
Lesser Octopus (1st)
Common Mussels (1st)
Grey Seal (1st)
Shore Carb (1st)
Common Sun Star (1st)

■ 2007, January 9. The Beatles
Des: Johnson Banks, from album sleeve covers. Printed in gravure by Walsall. Self-adhesive. Issued in se-tenant pairs.

Set	5.00	5.00
First day cover		7.00
Stamp cards (set & miniature sheet)	5.00	20.00

■ 2007, February 1. Sea Life
Des: A. Ross. Printed in litho by Cartor.

Set (in block)	5.00	5.00
Gutter pairs	12.50	
First day cover		7.00
Stamp cards	4.75	16.00

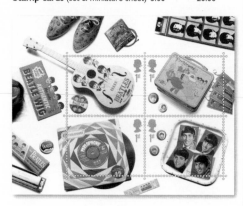

Saturn Nebula (1st)
Eskimo Nebula C39 (1st)
Cat's Eye Nebula C6 (50p)
Helix Nebula (50p)
Flaming Star Nebula C31 (72p)
The Spindle (72p)

Guitar (1st)
Yellow Submarine lunch box (1st)
Love Me Do (1st)
Tea Tray (1st)

■ 2007, February 13. The Sky at Night
Des: D. Davis, Printed in gravure by Walsall. Self-adhesive. Issue in se-tenant pairs. Stamps have description of designs on the backing paper.

Set	4.75	4.75
First day cover		6.50
Stamp cards	3.00	12.50

■ 2007, January 9. The Beatles
Miniature sheet, containing four at 1st: printed in litho by Walsall. Normal gum.

Miniature sheet	2.00	2.00
First day cover		4.00

Railway Bridge (1st)
Locomotive with railway track as 'steam' (1st)
Map of British Isles and Australia (64p)
Television and camera (64p)
Globe (72p)
Carrying suitcases on the Moon (72p)

■ 2007, March 1. World of Invention

Des: P. Willberg. Printed in gravure by De La Rue. Self-adhesive.
Issued in se-tenant pairs. Stamps have description of designs on
the backing paper. Miniature sheet has normal gum.

Set	5.00	5.00
Gutter pairs	12.50	
First day cover		7.00
Miniature sheet	5.25	5.25
Stamp cards	3.50	18.00

(* The same designs were also issued as normal gummed
stamps in the World of Invention prestige stamp book issued on
March 1, 2007.)

William Wilberforce (1st0
Olaudah Equiano (1st)
Granville Sharp (50p)
Thomas Clarkson (50p)
Hannah More (72p)
Ignatius Sancho (72p)

■ 2007, March 22. Abolition of the Slave Trade

Des: Howard Brown. Printed in litho by Cartor. Issued in se-
tenant pairs.

Set	4.75	4.75
Gutter pairs	12.00	
First day cover		6.50
Stamp cards	2.75	11.00

CELEBRATING ENGLAND

Flag of England (1st)
St George (78p)
Houses of Parliament (78p)

■ 2007, April 23. Celebrating England

Des; P. Crowther, Claire Melinsky, Silk Pearce. Printed in gravure
by De La Rue. Miniature sheet with 1st class England definitive
plus above three designs.

Miniature sheet	3.25	3.25
First day cover		5.00
Stamp cards	2.50	14.00

(* The 1st England definitive, self-adhesive, was also used for a
generic Smilers sheet.)

Ice cream cone (1st)
Sand castle (46p)
Merry-go-round (48p)
Beach huts (54p)
Deckchairs (69p)
Donkeys (78p)

■ 2007, May 15. Beside the Seaside

Des: Phelan Barker Design Consultants. Printed in gravure by
De La Rue.

Set	4.75	4.75
Gutter pairs	11.00	
First day cover		6.50
Stamp cards	3.00	10.00

Lion with shield of St George (1st)
England definitives (2nd, 2nd, 78p, 78p)

■ 2007, May 17. Opening of the New Wembley Stadium

Des: Roundel. Printed in gravure by De La Rue. Miniature sheet.

Miniature sheet	3.75	3.75
First day cover		6.00

(* The 1st Lion design was previously issued on May 21, 2002
with an inscription, and was also used for a Smilers sheet.)

Arnold Machin (1st)
4d Machin olive sepia-brown (1st)
Definitive (£1 bluish-violet)
Definitive (£1 ruby)

■ 2007, June 5. 40th Anniversary of the Machin Definitives

Des: J. Matthews and Together Design. Printed in gravure by De La Rue. Miniature sheet.

Miniature sheet	3.75	3.75
Press sheet	75.00	
First day cover		6.00
Stamp cards	1.50	9.00

(*The 1st Arnold Machin design was also used for a generic Smilers sheet. The two 1st class designs also appear in The Making of a Masterpiece prestige stamp book.)

Graham Hill (1st)
Stirling Moss (1st)
Jackie Stewart (54p)
Jim Clark (54p)
James Hunt (78p)
Nigel Mansell (78p)

■ 2007, July 3. Grand Prix

Des: True North, from photographs by James Callaghan. Printed in litho by Cartor.

Set	5.00	5.00
Gutter pairs	12.50	
First day cover		6.50
Stamp cards	2.50	10.00

Book covers:
Harry Potter and the Philosopher's Stone (1st)
Harry Potter and the Chamber of Secrets (1st)
Harry Potter and the Prisoner of Azkaban (1st)
Harry Potter and the Goblet of Fire (1st)
Harry Potter and the Order of the Phoenix (1st)
Harry Potter and the Half-blood Prince (1st)
Harry Potter and the Deathly Hallows (1st)

■ 2007, July 17. Harry Potter

Printed in litho by Walsall.

Set	5.00	5.00
Gutter pairs	12.50	
First day cover		6.50
Stamp cards	5.00	12.00

Symbol of Gryffindor (1st)
Symbol of Hufflepuff (1st)
Crest of Hogwarts (1st)
Symbol of Ravenclaw (1st)
Symbol of Slytherin (1st)

■ 2007, July 17. Harry Potter

Printed in litho by Walsall.

Miniature sheet	2.50	2.50
First day cover		4.00

(*These designs also appear on a generic Smilers sheet.)

Scout looking at the Moon (1st)
Scouts conquering a mountain (46p)
Scout planting a tree (48p)
Scout practicing archery (54p)
Scout piloting an aircraft (69p)
Group of Scouts (78p)

■ 2007, July 26. Scouts. Europa
Des: The Workroom. Printed in litho by Enschedé.

Set	4.50	4.50
Gutter pairs	11.00	
First day cover		6.00
Stamp cards	2.00	10.00

White-tailed Eagle (1st)
Bearded Tit (1st)
Red Kite (1st)
Cirl Bunting (1st)
Marsh Harrier (1st)
Avocet (1st)
Bittern (1st)
Dartford Warbler (1st)
Corncrake (1st)
Peregrine (1st)

■ 2007, September 4. Endangered Species. Birds
Des: Kate Stephens. Printed in litho by De La Rue. Issued in a se-tenant block.

Set (in block)	5.00	5.00
Gutter pairs	12.50	
First day cover		7.00
Stamp cards	4.75	16.00

NCO British Military Police 1999 (1st)
Tank Commander 5th Royal Tank Regiment 1944 (1st)
Observer Royal Field Artillery 1917 (1st)
Rifleman 95th Rifles (78p)
Grenadier Royal Regiment of Foot of Ireland 1704 (78p)
Trooper Earl of Oxford's Horse 1661 (78p)

■ 2007, September 23. British Army Uniforms
Des: Atelier Works. Printed in litho by Enschedé. Issued in se-tenant strips of three.

Set	4.50	4.50
Gutter pairs	11.00	
First day cover		6.50
Stamp cards	2.50	10.00

(*These stamps are also available in a prestige stamp book.)

Photographs of The Queen and Prince Philip:
2006 (1st)
1997 (1st)
1980 (54p)
1969 (54p)
1961 (78p)
1947 (78p)

■ 2007, October 16. Royal Diamond Wedding Anniversary
Des: Pentagram. Printed in gravure by Walsall. Normal gum. Issued in se-tenant pairs.

Set	4.50	4.50
Gutter pairs	11.00	
First day cover		6.50

Photographs of the Royal Family (1st, 1st, 69p, 78p)

■ 2007, October 16. Royal Diamond Wedding Anniversary
Des: Pentagram. Printed in gravure by Walsall. Miniature sheet. Self-adhesive. The reverse of the sheet shows photographs of the Royal couple leading up to their marriage.

Miniature sheet	3.25	3.25
First day cover		6.00
Stamp cards	5.00	12.00

Angels playing musical instruments (2nd, 2nd Large, 1st, 1st Large, 78p, £1.24)

■ 2007, November 6. Christmas
Des: Rose Design, with illustrations by Marco Ventura. Printed in gravure by De La Rue. Miniature sheet has normal gum.

Set	5.00	5.00
Gutter pairs	12.50	
First day cover		7.50
Miniature sheet	5.00	5.00
Miniature sheet first day cover		7.50
Stamp cards	4.50	16.00

(* The 2nd, 1st and 78p designs also appear as a generic Smilers sheet.)

■ 2007, November 6. Christmas
Madonna & Child designs.

Set	1.25	1.25
Gutter pairs	4.00	
First day cover		2.50

(* These stamps were produced for customers wishing to have 'religious' designs, and will be re-issued in future years.)

Part of poppy (1st)
Country definitives (78p, 78p, 78p, 78p)

■ 2007, November 8. Lest We Forget
Des: Hat-Trick Design. Printed in gravure by De La Rue. Miniature sheet.

Miniature sheet	4.50	4.50
First day cover		6.00

(* The 1st design also appeared in a generic Smilers sheet.)

Stamp Magazine is Britain's best for GB collectors

STAMP

Near perfect?

Every issue includes:
- Five pages of GB news
- Full details of latest issues
- The best first day covers
- Newly discovered errors
- Price analysis from dealers and eBay
- Features on everything from Queen Victoria classics to modern Smilers

Available from newsagents, or visit www.stampmagazine.co.uk

PROTECTIVE SHIELD

In a market filled with many pitfalls, it's good to know who you can rely on.

Members of the Philatelic Traders' Society agree to abide by a strict code of ethics, which ensures that you can deal with them in total confidence.

Established over 60 years, the PTS is the premier British dealer organisation with over 500 members respected throughout the philatelic community.

For more information on the society and its members, which also organises the world famous, twice yearly Stampex national stamp exhibitions held in London, go to
www.philatelic-traders-society.co.uk

The Philatelic Traders' Society Limited,
P.O. Box 371, Fleet, Hampshire GU52 6ZX.
Tel: 01252 628006 Fax: 01252 684674

OFFICIAL STAMPS

During the reigns of Queen Victoria and King Edward VII stamps were overprinted for use by Government Departments. The prices in this section are quoted in two columns: mint (left) and fine used (right). Dates in brackets refer to the stamps overprinted.

QUEEN VICTORIA

1d 'VR' official

■ Penny Black 'VR'

As the standard stamp but with the stars in the top corners replaced by the letters 'V' and 'R', but never officially issued.

1d black (with gum)	£20,000	-
1d black (without gum)	£10,000	-
1d black (with trial cancellation)	-	£30,000

■ Overprinted 'I.R OFFICIAL' for use by the Inland Revenue

½d green (1880 issue)	60.00	15.00
½d blue (1884 issue)	45.00	13.00
½d orange (1887 issue)	6.00	1.00
½d green (1900 issue)	8.00	3.50
1d lilac (1881 issue)	2.75	1.40
2½d lilac (1884 issue)	£250	50.00
2½d purple (1887 issue) (blue paper)	80.00	6.00
6d grey (1881 issue)	£280	50.00
6d purple (1887 issue) (red paper)	£250	45.00
1/- green (1884 issue)	£3,000	£750
1/- green (1887 issue)	£400	95.00
1/- green, red (1900 issue)	£2,000	£600
5/- red (1884 issue)	£2,800	£850
10/- blue (1884 issue)	£4,000	£1,250
£1 brown (1884 issue) Wmk: Imperial Crowns	£34,000	£17,000
£1 brown (1888 issue) Wmk: Orbs	£55,000	£30,000
£1 green (1891 issue)	£6,500	£1,400

■ Overprinted 'O.W OFFICIAL' for use by the Office of Works

½d orange (1887 issue)	£150	65.00
½d green (1900 issue)	£250	£100
1d lilac (1881 issue)	£250	65.00
5d purple, blue (1887 issue)	£1,600	£450
10d purple, red (1887 issue)	£3,250	£800

£1 green IR official

■ Overprinted 'ARMY OFFICIAL' for use by the Army

½d orange (1887 issue)	2.75	1.25
½d green (1900 issue)	3.00	5.00
1d lilac (1881 issue)	2.50	2.00
2½d purple (1887 issue) (blue paper)	25.00	10.00
6d purple (1887 issue) (red paper)	60.00	30.00

■ Overprinted 'GOVT PARCELS' for use by the Government

1d lilac (1881 issue)	50.00	10.00
1½d lilac (1884 issue)	£250	40.00
1½d purple, green (1887 issue)	65.00	4.00
2d green, red (1887 issue)	£130	14.00
4½d green, red (1887 issue)	£210	£110
6d green (1884 issue)	£1,450	£325
6d purple (1887 issue) (red paper)	£125	18.00
9d green (1884 issue)	£1,250	£325
9d purple, blue (1887 issue)	£175	25.00
1/- brown (1881 issue, plate 13 or 14)	£700	£165
1/- green (1887 issue)	£325	£110
1/- green, red (1887 issue)	£340	£125

■ Overprinted 'BOARD OF EDUCATION'

5d purple, blue (1887 issue)	£1,750	£425
1/- green, red (1887 issue)	£5,500	£3,250

KING EDWARD VII

■ Overprinted 'I.R OFFICIAL' for use by the Inland Revenue

Printed by De La Rue

½d blue-green	20.00	2.00
1d red	15.00	1.25
2½d blue	£600	£140
6d purple	-	-
1/- green, red	£2,000	£350
5/- red	£10,000	£4,500
10/- blue	£55,000	£27,000
£1 green	£36,000	£18,000

■ Overprinted 'O.W OFFICIAL' for use by the Office of Works

Printed by De La Rue

½d blue-green	£400	£110
1d red	£400	£100
2d green, red	£1250	£275
2½d blue	£1600	£400
10d purple, red	£19,000	£3,750

OFFICIAL STAMPS

■ Overprinted 'ARMY OFFICIAL' for use by the Army
Printed by De La Rue

½d blue-green	4.00	1.25
1d red	4.00	1.25
6d purple	£130	45.00

■ Overprinted 'GOVT PARCELS' for use by the Government
Printed by De La Rue

1d red	25.00	10.00
2d green, red	£125	25.00
6d purple	£190	20.00
9d purple, blue	£360	85.00
1/- green, red	£675	£165

■ Overprinted 'BOARD OF EDUCATION'
Printed by De La Rue

½d blue-green	£120	20.00
1d red	£120	20.00
2½d blue	£2,500	£150
5d purple, blue	£15,000	£4,000
1/- green, red	£75,000	-

■ Overprinted 'R.H. HOUSEHOLD' for use by Royal Household
Printed by De La Rue

½d blue-green	£300	£150
1d red	£250	£120

■ Overprinted 'ADMIRALTY OFFICIAL'
Printed by De La Rue

½d blue-green	20.00	10.00
1d red	12.00	4.00
1½d purple, green	£165	70.00
2d green, red	£210	80.00
2½d blue	£300	75.00
3d purple (yellow paper)	£250	70.00

10s blue IR official

5s red IR official

DK Stamps Ltd

For top quality u/m control and cylinder singles, strips and blocks QV to QEII. Wants lists welcome.

Office: 01480 39 39 45
Mobile: 07980 694 784
PO BOX 515,
Huntingdon, PE29 9AB
www.dkstamps.com
E-mail:
info@dkstamps.com

Mint G.B. Stamps

G.B. 1840-1970

Comprehensive stocks of just mint GB material 1840-1970 on our

new website from QE11 commemoratives to QV exhibition pieces.

www.mintgbstamps.co.uk

++44(0)1604 408821

Email -sales@mintgbstamps.co.uk

DAVID SHAW

DEALER IN
GB POSTAL HISTORY
c.1560s-1960s

WRITE, PHONE OR FAX
FOR LISTS
P.O. BOX 27 MALTON, NORTH YORKSHIRE, YO17 7GJ
Tel./Fax: (01653) 694953

E-mail:
david@davidshawpostalhistory.com
Website:
www.davidshawpostalhistory.com

We trade on eBay.co.uk as sutherlandladdie

Visit our eBay shop:
DAVID SHAW'S OLD LETTERS

POSTAGE DUE LABELS

Up to 1936, prices are quoted in three columns: unmounted mint (left), mounted mint (centre) and used (right). After 1936, they are quoted for mint (left) and fine used (right).

Except where stated, all these stamps were printed by Harrison in typography and are perf 14 x 15.

½d to 1/-

2/6 to £1

■ 1914-1923

A) Wmk: Crown and script GVR (Royal Cypher), sideways; crown faces to the right when viewed from front of stamp. Printed by Harrison (all values except 1/-) or at Somerset House (½d, 1d, 5d, 1/-).

½d green	1.25	0.40	0.35
1d red	1.25	0.50	0.25
chalky paper	7.50	4.00	4.00
1½d brown	95.00	35.00	13.00
2d black	1.25	0.80	0.30
3d violet	18.00	4.00	0.60
4d green	90.00	20.00	4.50
5d brown	11.00	4.00	2.00
1/- blue	90.00	19.00	3.00
Set	£300	65.00	22.00

B) Wmk: inverted; crown faces to the left.

½d green	1.50	1.00	1.00
1d red	2.00	1.00	1.00
1½d brown	£120	50.00	15.00
2d black	3.00	1.00	1.00
3d violet	20.00	6.50	2.50
4d green	£110	35.00	5.00
5d brown	32.00	12.00	4.00
1/- blue	90.00	20.00	15.00

■ 1924-1931

A) Wmk: Multiple Crown and block GVR, sideways; crown faces to the left. Printed by Waterlow and (from 1934) Harrison.

½d green	1.25	0.50	0.30

1d red	1.25	0.50	0.10
1½d brown	90.00	27.00	9.00
2d black	6.00	1.25	0.20
3d violet	6.00	1.75	0.20
4d green	40.00	5.00	0.85
5d brown	110.00	35.00	17.00
1/- blue	25.00	4.00	0.25
2/6 purple (yellow paper)	190.00	50.00	0.80
Set	£150	100.00	24.50

B) Wmk: inverted.

½d green	4.50	2.00	1.50
1d red	-	-	8.50
1½d brown	-	-	25.00
2d black	-	-	8.50
3d violet	10.00	5.00	5.00
4d green	80.00	30.00	30.00
1/- blue	-	-	-
2/6 purple (yellow paper)	-	-	-

■ 1936-1937

Wmk: Multiple Crown and E8R (sideways).

½d green	7.00	6.50
1d red	1.00	1.50
2d black	6.00	6.00
3d violet	1.50	1.50
4d green	30.00	22.00
5d brown	25.00	18.00
1/- blue	8.00	6.50
2/6 purple (yellow paper)	£220	10.00
Set	£300	65.00

■ 1937-1938

A) Wmk: Multiple Crown GVIR (sideways).

½d green	8.50	4.50
1d red	2.00	0.20
2d black	1.25	0.30
3d violet	7.00	0.30
4d green	60.00	7.00
5d brown	7.00	0.80
1/- blue	45.00	0.90
2/6 purple (yellow paper)	50.00	2.00
Set	£160	12.00

B) Wmk: inverted.

1d red	£120	-
2d black	10.00	-
3d violet	25.00	-
4d green	£110	-
5d brown	30.00	-
1/- blue	60.00	-

■ 1951-1952

As before but with changed colours.

½d orange	3.50	3.50
1d blue	1.25	0.50
Wmk inverted	-	-
1½d green	1.25	1.50
Wmk inverted	3.00	-
4d blue	30.00	12.00

1/- brown	22.00	4.00
Wmk inverted	£2,000	-
Set	45.00	18.00

■ 1954-1955
Wmk: Multiple tudor Crown E2R (sideways).

½d orange	8.00	8.50
Wmk inverted	12.00	-
2d black	20.00	16.00
3d violet	30.00	30.00
4d blue	16.00	16.00
5d brown	15.00	10.00
2/6 purple (yellow paper)	75.00	8.00
Set	£130	70.00

■ 1955-1957
A) Wmk: Multiple St Edward's Crown E2R (sideways).

½d orange	4.00	4.00
1d blue	3.00	1.25
1½d green	7.00	4.50
2d black	20.00	5.25
3d violet	3.50	1.25
4d blue	16.00	2.00
5d brown	20.00	1.75
1/- brown	40.00	2.00
2/6 purple (yellow paper)	£115	10.00
5/- red (yellow paper)	60.00	18.00
Set	£240	40.00

B) Wmk: inverted.

½d orange	9.00	-
1½d green	12.00	-
3d violet	25.00	-
4d blue	30.00	-
1/- brown	-	-
2/6 purple (yellow paper)	-	-
5/- red (yellow paper)	-	75.00

■ 1959-1963
A) Wmk: Multiple Crowns (sideways).

½d orange	0.15	0.25
1d blue	0.15	0.10
1½d green	1.50	2.00
2d black	1.00	0.30
3d violet	0.35	0.15
4d blue	0.35	0.15
5d brown	0.35	0.30
6d purple	0.50	0.15
1/- brown	1.00	0.15
2/6 purple (yellow paper)	1.50	0.20
5/- red (yellow paper)	4.00	0.50
10/- blue (yellow paper)	10.00	3.00
£1 black (yellow paper)	33.00	4.50
Set	45.00	9.50

B) Wmk: inverted.

½d orange	1.25	-
1d blue	12.00	-
2d black	40.00	-
3d violet	10.00	-

4d blue	30.00	-
5d brown	4.00	-
6d purple	40.00	-
1/- brown	7.00	-
2/6 purple (yellow paper)	6.00	-
5/- red (yellow paper)	10.00	-
10/- blue (yellow paper)	20.00	-

■ 1968-1969
No watermark. Chalky paper.
i) With gum Arabic.

2d black	0.50	0.50
4d blue	0.40	0.20

ii) With PVA gum.

2d black	1.50	1.00
3d violet	0.50	0.50
5d brown	5.00	5.00
6d purple	1.00	1.25
1/- brown	3.00	2.00

■ 1968-1969
Printed in photogravure by Harrison. No watermark.
Chalky paper. PVA gum.

4d blue	4.50	5.00
8d red	0.50	1.00

½p to 7p

10p to £5

■ 1970. Decimal Currency
Des: J. Matthews. Printed in photogravure by Harrison. No watermark. Chalky paper. Perf: 14 x 15.
i) PVA gum. Original coated paper.

½p turquoise	0.10	0.25
1p purple	0.50	0.10
2p green	0.25	0.10
3p blue	0.40	0.10
4p sepia	0.25	0.10
5p violet	0.60	0.10
10p carmine	0.70	0.20
20p deep green	1.00	0.20

50p blue	2.00	0.25
£1 black	4.00	0.25

ii) PVA gum. Fluorescent coated paper.

1p purple	0.50	-
3p blue	1.75	-
5p violet	2.25	-
10p carmine	45.00	-
20p deep green	45.00	-
£5 orange, black	20.00	1.00

iii) PVAD (blue-tinged dextrin gum).

1p purple	0.10	-
2p green	0.10	-
3p blue	0.10	-
4p sepia	0.10	-
5p violet	0.10	-
7p red-brown	0.25	0.25
10p carmine	0.15	-
11p green	0.35	0.35
20p deep green	0.50	-
50p blue	0.90	-
£1 black	1.75	-
£5 orange, black	18.00	1.00
Set (one of each value)	9.00	4.25

iv) PVAD gum. Phosphor coated paper (giving a green phosphor reaction).

10p carmine	0.70	0.50
20p deep green	1.00	0.75

1p to 5p

10p to £5

■ **1982, June 9**
Des: Sedley Place Design Ltd. Printed in photogravure by Harrisons. No wmk. Perf: 14 x 15.

1p crimson	0.10	0.10
2p bright blue	0.10	0.10
3p purple	0.10	0.15
4p blue	0.10	0.10

5p brown	0.10	0.10
10p light brown	0.20	0.10
20p sage green	0.30	0.30
25p blue-grey	0.40	0.60
50p charcoal	1.00	1.50
£1 red	2.00	0.50
£2 turquoise	4.00	2.50
£5 dull orange	8.50	1,25
Set	14.00	5.00
Gutter Pairs	30.00	-

1p, 2p, 5p, 10p, 20p, 25p, £1, £1.20, £5

■ **1994, February 15**
Des: Sedley Place Design Ltd. Printed in lithography by House of Questa. No wmk. Perf: 14 x 15.

Set	27.00	28.00
First day cover		35.00

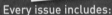

Stamp Magazine is Britain's best for GB collectors

Just cause for celebration

Near perfect?

Every issue includes:
■ Five pages of GB news
■ Full details of latest issues
■ The best first day covers
■ Newly discovered errors
■ Price analysis from dealers and eBay
■ Features on everything from Queen Victoria classics to modern Smilers

Available from newsagents, or visit www.stampmagazine.co.uk

RUSHSTAMPS AT YOUR SERVICE

Just Compare our Prices

PRESTIGE BOOKLETS

ZP1a Cook	£6.50
DX1 wedgewood	£12.95
Do. with good perfs	£32.00
DX2 Wedgewood	£3.30
DX3 S.G.	£4.40
DX4 Royal Mint	£4.40
Dx5 C. Heritage	£12.75
DX6 Times	£8.50
DX7 Br Rail	£11.95
DX8 P&O	£9.50
DX9 Fin Times	£13.95
DX10 Scotts	£9.50
DX11 London Life	£12.00
DX12 Agatha Christie	£8.50
DX13 Wales	£8.50
DX14 J.R.R. Tolkien	£8.50
DX15 Beatrix Potter	£8.95
DX16 N. Ireland	£10.00
DX17 N. Trust	£9.50
DX18 Football	£8.50
DX19 BBC	£8.50
DX20 Dst. Portrait	£9.95
DX21 Speed	£11.50
DX22 Prof. on Print	£13.00
DX23 Changers	£13.00
DX24 Spec, by Design	£15.00
DX25 Queen Mother	£11.50
DX26 Trees	£11.50
DX27 Unseen	£13.95
DX28 Golden Jubilee	£13.50
DX29 Across	£10.25
DX30 Microcosmos	£9.50
DX31 Coronation	£29.00
DX32 Letters	£10.25
DX33 RHS	£13.95
DX34 Jane Eyre	£11.50
DX35 Trafalgar	£10.75
DX36 Brunei	£10.75

FREE NEW 96 page Great Britain Price List on request Rush Express No.60

MINIATURE SHEETS (U/M)

1058 Buildings	£0.55
1089 Rowland Hill	£0.50
1119 London '80	£0.60
1409 Lear	£2.25
1444 Architecture	£1.95
1501 Stamp World	£1.50
2106 Eclipse	£10.50
2123 Timekeepers	£10.95
2123a Do. Opt	£14.50
2146 Mathews	£12.75
2147 Coronation	£6.75
2162 Queen Mother	£3.00
2201 Weather	£7.50
2206 Flags	£3.50
2215 Buses	£4.75
2289 Airliners	£4.75
2292 World Cup	£2.90
2315 Astronomy	£2.20
2326 Wilding I	£3.60
2367 WildingII	£3.80
2402 Transport/Toys	£3.50
2416 Rugby	£2.95
2423 Locomotives	£13.50
2454 Ocean Liners	£5.50
2462 RHS	£4.40
S120 Scottish Parl	£2.60
2501 Christmas	£4.25
2524 Jane Eyre	£4.20
2530 Castles	£3.75
2531 Royal Wedding	£2.80
2546 Trooping	£4.50
2547 WWII	£2.60
2554 London 2012	£2.60
2573 Ashes	£2.75
2580 Trafalgar	£3.95
2588 Christmas	£4.20
2613 Brunel	£3.30
W109 Welsh Ass	£3.10
Set of 37 (ex. 2123a)	£165.00
Set of 38 (inc. 2123a)	£175.00

SMILER SHEETS

LS1 Stamp Show	£24.00
LS6 Cartoons	£30.00
LS7 Occasions	£39.50
LS8 Football	£18.50
LS9 Teddy/Dennis	£19.50
LS10 Christmas'02	£17.50
LS11 Flowers	£18.50
LS12 Occasions	£17.50
LS13 Crossword	£14.50
LS14 Robins	£14.50
LS15-16 Ice Sculptures(2)	£30.00
LS17 Hong Kong	£12.50
LS18 Envelopes	£13.50
LS19 Dahlias (RHS)	£14.50
LS20 Rule Brittania	£12.50
LS21 Christmas '04	£12.50
LS22 Farm Animals	£13.50
LS23 Magic	£15.00
LS24 Australian Expo	£11.50
LS25 White Ensign	£11.50
LS26 Classic ITV	£11.50
LS27 Christmas '05	£10.50
LS28 Paddington Bear	£12.50
LS29 Fruit & Veg	£15.00
LS30 Washington	£12.00
ST1 2003 Autumn Stampex	£15.00
ST2 2004 Spring Stampex	£15.00
ST3 2004 Autumn Stampex	£15.00
PH6 2006 Philatex (2) (Corrected)	£55.00
PH7 2006 Autumn Philatex(1)	£22.95
PH8 2007 Philatex	£29.50
PH9 2007 Philatex	£22.95
BG1 2006 Belgica	£22.50
TO1 2006 Torquay	£24.95
EU1 2006 150th Anniv of 1st Europa stamp	£19.50
EU2 do. with Belgica Opt.	£19.50
EU3 do. with Stampex Opt	£19.50

CAN YOU REFUSE THIS OFFER? Send us £2 (Coins, Stamps, P.O. or Cheque) and we will forward our latest 144 page G.B. RushExpress, together with a special 'Mystery Free Gift', some generous 'Discount Vouchers' and a '£5 Credit Note' to be used against your first order! Too Good to Miss!

YES - WE ALSO BUY -
G.B., British Commonwealth & Foreign.
Top prices - Prompt payment
Send for offer or write with details.

RUSHSTAMPS (RETAIL) LTD.
P.O. BOX 1, LYNDHURST, HAMPSHIRE, ENGLAND SO43 7PP
TEL: (023) 8028 2044, FAX: (023) 8028 2981,
E-MAIL: enquiries@rushstamps.co.uk

REGIONAL ISSUES

Prices in this section are quoted in two columns: mint (left) and fine used (right).

All stamps in this section are printed in photogravure by Harrisons and perf 15 x 14 unless otherwise stated.

The issues of Guernsey, the Isle of Man and Jersey which pre-date the postal independence of the islands are listed here.

ENGLAND

Three Lions (2nd)
Crowned Lion and shield of St George (1st)
Oak tree (E, 40p, 42p)
Tudor Rose (65p, 68p)

2001, April 23
Des: Sedley Place, from sculptures by D. Dathan. Printed in gravure by De La Rue. One phosphor band (2nd), two phosphor bands (others).

2nd slate blue and silver	0.50	0.40
1st red-brown and silver	0.60	0.50
E olive-green and silver	0.80	0.65
65p deep lilac and silver	1.60	1.80
68p deep lilac and silver (July 4, 2002)	1.55	1.75
First day cover (2nd to 65p)		3.00
First day cover (68p)		3.00
Stamp cards	3.00	15.00

(* The 2nd and 1st class also appear printed in gravure by Questa in the Across the Universe prestige stamp book of September 24, 2002.)

2003, October 14. Designs with white borders
Designs as for April 23, 2001 but with a white margin around the stamp design. Printed in gravure by De La Rue (except where stated). One phosphor band (2nd), two phosphor bands (others).

2nd slate blue and silver	0.50	0.40
1st red-brown and silver	0.60	0.50
E olive-green and silver	1.20	0.80
40p olive-green and silver (May 11, 2004)	0.90	0.75
42p olive-green and silver (Apr 5, 2005, printed by Walsall)	0.85	0.85
42p olive-green and silver (May 10, 2005)	1.00	0.75
44p olive-green and silver (May 28, 2006)	0.90	0.85
68p deep lilac and silver	1.40	1.00

72p deep lilac and silver (Mar 28, 2006)	1.00	0.95
First day cover (2nd, 1st, E, 68p)		2.50
First day cover (40p)		2.50
First day cover (44p)		2.50
First day cover (72p)		2.50
First day cover (42p)		3.00
Stamp cards	2.00	10.00

(* The 2nd, 1st and 40p also appear in prestige stamp books, printed by Walsall.)

NORTHERN IRELAND

3d lilac

1958-1968
Des: W. Hollywood (3d, 4d, 5d), L. Philton (6d, 9d), T. Collins (1/3, 1/6)

A) Wmk: Multiple St Edward's Crown. Non phosphor except where stated.

3d lilac (August 18, 1958)	0.15	0.15
one centre band	0.15	0.20
4d blue (February 7, 1966)	0.15	0.15
two phosphor bands	0.15	0.15
6d purple (September 29, 1958)	0.20	0.20
9d green (March 1, 1967)		
two phosphor bands	0.35	0.40
1/3 green (September 29, 1958)	0.35	0.40
1/6 grey-blue (March 1, 1967)		
two phosphor bands	0.40	0.40
First day cover (3d)		25.00
First day cover (6d, 1/3)		30.00
First day cover (4d)		7.50
First day cover (9d, 1/6)		4.00

B) No wmk. Two phosphor bands and PVA gum except where stated.

4d blue (gum Arabic)	0.15	0.15
4d sepia (September 4, 1968)		
one centre band	0.15	0.25
4d red (February 26, 1969)	0.20	0.30
5d blue (September 4, 1968)	0.20	0.20
1/6 grey-blue	1.50	1.40
First day cover (4d sepia, 5d)		2.50
First day cover (4d red)		1.00

(* The 4d blue exists with either gum arabic or PVA gum. The PVA gum version was not placed on sale in Northern Ireland; priced £8.50 mint.)

3p blue

■ 1971, July 7. Decimal Currency
Des: J. Matthews.
The symbol on these stamps was re-drawn and moved less close to the top of the design. Where relevant, the original is noted as 'Type I' and the revised version as 'Type II'.

A) Two phosphor bands except where stated.
i) PVA gum. Original coated paper.

2½p pink (one centre band)	0.90	0.40
3p blue	0.40	0.40
5p violet	1.75	1.25
7½p brown	1.75	1.25

ii) PVA gum. Fluorescent coated paper.

2½p pink (one centre band)	5.25	2.00
3p blue	7.50	2.00
3p blue (one centre band)	0.40	0.20

iii) PVAD gum (blue tinged).

3p blue (one centre band)	1.00	0.40
3½p green (January 23, 1974)	0.30	0.25
one centre band	0.30	0.25
4½p grey-blue (November 6, 1974)	0.30	0.25
5½p deep violet (January 23, 1974)	0.30	0.25
one centre band	0.35	0.25
6½p green-blue (January 14, 1976)		
one centre band	0.30	0.20
7p red-brown (January 18, 1978)		
one centre band	0.35	0.25
8p red (January 23, 1974)	0.35	0.25
8½p green (January 14, 1976)	0.35	0.30
9p violet-blue (January 18, 1978)	0.35	0.30
10p orange (October 20, 1976)	0.35	0.40
one centre band	0.35	0.40
10½p grey-blue (January 18, 1978)	0.40	0.40
11p red (October 20, 1976)	0.40	0.40

B) Phosphor coated paper. PVAD gum (blue tinged).
Issued on July 23, 1980.

12p yellow-green	0.40	0.40
13½p red-brown	0.60	0.60
15p blue	0.50	0.45

C) Printed in litho by Questa. Perf: 13½ x 14. Phosphor coated paper, except 11½p and 12½p (left side band). PVAD gum (11½p, 4p, 18p, 22p), PVAD gum (others).

11½p mushroom (April 8, 1981)	0.70	0.75
12½p light green (February 24, 1982)	0.40	0.40
14p steel-blue (April 8, 1981)	0.50	0.50
15½p pale violet (February 24, 1982)	0.60	0.60

16p light mushroom (April 27, 1983)	0.85	0.85
18p mauve (April 8, 1981)	0.75	0.70
19½p grey-green (February 24, 1982)	1.75	1.60
20½p bright blue (April 27, 1983)	3.00	2.95
22p deep blue (April 8, 1981)	0.80	0.70
26p red, type I (February 24, 1982)	1.00	0.80
28p blue, type I (April 27, 1983)	1.00	90

D) Printed in litho by Questa. Perf: 15 x 14. One side phosphor band (12p, 12½p, 13p); phosphor coated paper (16p, 17p, 31p); advanced coated paper (22p, 26p, 28p), or as indicated. PVAD gum.

12p emerald green (January 7, 1986)	1.00	0.80
12½p light green (February 28, 1984)	4.00	3.50
PVA gum	4.00	-
13p reddish-brown, Type I		
(October 23, 1984)	0.45	0.45
deep brown, Type II	2.00	2.00
deep brown (April 14, 1987)		
printed on paper supplied by Coated Papers Ltd. Type II. PVA gum	0.80	0.80
16p light mushroom		
(February 28, 1984)	6.00	5.00
17p steel blue (October 23, 1984)		
type I	1.00	0.80
advanced coated paper, type I	1.00	0.80
advanced coated paper, type II	100.00	80.00
18p deep green (Janary 6, 1987)	0.65	0.60
18p bright green (December 3, 1991)		
one centre band	0.60	0.45
18p bright green (December 31, 1992)		
perf: 14	1.40	1.40
18p bright green (August 10 3, 1993)		
left band	2.00	1.80
19p orange-red (November 8, 1988)		
phosphor paper	0.65	0.65
20p brownish-black (November 28, 1989)		
phosphor paper	0.65	0.50
22p yellowish-green (Oct 23, 1984)	0.80	0.65
22p orange-red (December 4, 1990)		
phosphor paper	0.85	0.80
23p bright green (November 8, 1988)		
phosphor paper	1.00	0.80
24p deep red (November 28, 1989)		
phosphor paper	1.25	1.15
24p chestnut (August 10, 1993)		
two bands	2.50	2.50
26p red, type II (January 27, 1987)	2.50	1.90
26p drab (December 4, 1990)		
phosphor paper	1.00	1.00
28p blue, type II (January 27, 1987)	1.10	1.00
28p bluish grey (December 3, 1991)		
phosphor paper	1.10	1.10
31p purple, type I (October 23, 1984)	1.00	1.00
type II (April 14, 1987)	2.50	1.50
32p greenish blue (November 8, 1988)		
phosphor paper	1.25	1.25
34p bluish grey (November 28, 1989)		
phosphor paper	1.25	1.15
37p rosine (December 4, 1990)		
phosphor paper	1.50	1.40

39p mauve) (December 3, 1991)

phosphor paper	1.50	1.30

(* The 18p with side phosphor band and 24p chestnut with two phosphor bands come from prestige stamp books.)

E) Stamps with an elliptical perforation along each vertical side, Printed in litho by Questa. One phosphor band (19p and 20p), two phosphor bands (others).

19p bistre (December 7, 1993)	0.60	0.65
19p bistre (band at left)	1.75	1.75
19p bistre (band at right)	1.75	1.50
20p bright green (July 23, 1996)	1.40	1.40
25p red (December 7, 1993)	0.75	0.75
26p red-brown (July 23, 1996)	1.75	1.75
30p olive-grey (December 7, 1993)	1.00	0.85
37p mauve (July 23, 1996)	2.50	2.60
41p grey-brown (December 7, 1993)	1.25	1.00
63p emerald (July 23, 1996)	3.00	2.75

(* Some of these stamps are also found in prestige stamp books, including the 19p with the phosphor band to the left or right.)

F) Stamps with an elliptical perforation along each vertical side. Printed in gravure by Walsall. One phosphor band (19p and 20p), two phosphor bands (others).

19p bistre (June 8, 1999)	1.75	1.75
20p bright green (July 1, 1997)	0.80	0.80
20p bright green (band at right)	1.50	1.00
26p chestnut (July 1, 1997)	1.25	1.30
26p chestnut (perf: 14)	1.75	1.50
26p chestnut (printed by Harrison)	1.50	1.50
37p mauve (July 1, 1887)	1.60	1.60
37p mauve (printed by Harrison)	1.50	1.40
38p ultramarine (June 8, 1999)	5.25	5.25
40p azure (April 25, 2000)	3.00	1.00
63p emerald (July 1, 1997)	3.50	2.65
64p turquoise (June 8, 1999)	5.25	5.25
65p greenish blue (April 25, 2000)	2.50	2.25

(* The 20p with one band at right and 26p with perf: 14 are printed by Harrison. As with the 26p and 37p printed by Harrison, they come from prestige stamp books.)

G) Non value indicator stamp. Printed in gravure by Walsall. One phosphor band.

1st orange-red (February 15, 2000)

perf: 14	1.75	1.75

1st orange-red (April 25, 2000)

perf: 15x14	6.00	6.25

(* The 1st orange-red perf: 14 also appeared in a prestige stamp book.)

First day cover (2½p, 3p, 5p, 7½p)	2.00
First day cover (3½p, 5½p, 8p)	1.25
First day cover (4½p)	1.00
First day cover (6½p, 8½p)	1.00
First day cover (10p, 11p)	1.00
First day cover (7p, 9p, 10½p)	1.75
First day cover (12p, 13½p, 15p)	1.25
First day cover (11½p, 14p, 18p, 22p)	2.00
First day cover (12½p, 15½p, 19½p, 26p)	2.00
First day cover (16p, 20½p, 28p)	1.75

First day cover (13p, 17p, 22p, 31p)	2.00
First day cover (12p)	1.50
First day cover (18p)	1.50
First day cover (14p, 19p, 23p, 32p)	2.00
First day cover (15p, 20p, 24p, 34p)	2.75
First day cover (17p, 22p, 26p, 37p)	2.75
First day cover (18p, 24p, 28p, 39p)	2.75
First day cover (19p, 25p, 30p, 41p)	5.00
First day cover (20p, 26p, 37p, 63p)	5.00
First day cover (38p, 64p)	4.00
First day cover (1st, 40p, 65p)	7.00

Basalt Columns (2nd)
Patchwork fields (1st)
Linen (E, 40p, 42p)
Pattern on vase (65p, 68p)

■ **2001, March 6**
Des: Rodney Miller Associates. Printed in litho by De La Rue (E and 68p), Walsall (2nd, 1st, E, 65p) or Enschedé (2nd, 1st), One phosphor band (2nd), two phosphor bands (others).

2nd multicoloured	0.45	0.50
(Enschedé, Feb 23, 2003)	1.05	1.15
1st multicoloured	0.55	0.40
(Enschedé, Feb 23, 2003)	1.15	1.25
E multicoloured (Walsall)	1.00	1.00
E multicoloured (De La Rue)	1.00	1.00
65p multicoloured	1.50	1.60
68p multicoloured (July 4, 2002)	1.50	1.50
First day cover (2nd to 65p)		3.00
First day cover (68p)		5.00
Stamp cards	3.00	15.00

(* The 2nd and 1st printed by Enschedé come from the £6.99 Microcosmos prestige stamp book.)

■ **2003, October 14. Designs with white borders**
Designs as for April 23, 2001 but with a white margin around the stamp design. Printed in gravure by De La Rue (except where stated). One phosphor band (2nd), two phosphor bands (others).

2nd multicoloured	0.45	0.40
1st multicoloured	0.55	0.50
E multicoloured	1.00	1.05
40p multicoloured (May 11, 2004)	0.80	0.75
42p multicoloured (Walsall, Apr 5, 2005)	0.85	0.85
42p multicoloured (July 26, 2005)	0.95	0.90
44p multicoloured (March 25, 2006)	0.80	0.85
68p multicoloured	1.20	1.00
72p multicoloured (March 28, 2006)	1.30	0.95
First day cover (2nd, 1st, E, 68p)		3.50
First day cover (40p)		2.50

First day cover (42p)		2.50
First day cover (44p, 72p)		2.50
Stamp cards	2.00	10.00

SCOTLAND

3d lilac

1958-1967
Des: G. F. Huntley (3d, 4d, 5d), J. B. Fleming (6d, 9d), A. B. Imrie (1/3, 1/6).

A) Wmk: Multiple St Edward's Crown. Non phosphor except where stated.

3d lilac (August 18, 1958)	0.15	0.15
Two phosphor bands	8.00	2.00
one band at left	0.20	0.35
one band at right	0.20	0.35
se-tenant pair	0.35	0.70
one centre band	0.20	0.30
4d blue (February 7, 1966)	0.15	0.15
Two phosphor bands	0.15	0.15
5d purple (September 29, 1958)	0.15	0.15
two phosphor bands	0.20	0.25
6d green (March 1, 1967)		
Two phosphor bands	0.35	0.40
1/3 green (September 29, 1958)	0.35	0.25
two phosphor bands	0.35	0.40
1/6 grey-blue (March 1, 1967)		
Two phosphor bands	0.40	0.50
First day cover (3d)		10.00
First day cover (6d, 1/3)		20.00
First day cover (3d, 6d, 1/3 phosphor)		£100
First day cover (4d)		7.50
First day cover (9d, 1/6)		2.75

B) No watermark. Two phosphor bands except where stated.
i) Gum Arabic.

3d lilac (one centre band)	0.15	—
4d blue	0.15	—
ii) PVA gum.		
3d lilac (one centre band)	0.15	0.20
4d blue	0.15	0.20
4d sepia (September 4, 1968)		
one centre band	0.15	0.20
4d red (February 26, 1969)		
one centre band	0.20	0.20
5d blue (September 4, 1968)	0.20	0.25

9d green	3.25	3.25
1/6 grey-blue	1.25	1.00
First day cover (4d sepia, 5d)		2.50
First day cover (4d red)		1.00

3½p green

1971, July 7. Decimal Currency
Des: J. Matthews.
The lion symbol on these stamps was re-drawn. On the original version the eye appears as a circle, while the tongue and claws are thin, but on the revised version the eye is solid, while the tongue and claws are thicker; these are noted as type I or type II where relevant.

A) Two phosphor bands except where stated.
i) Gum Arabic.

2½p pink (one centre band)	0.40	—
3p blue	1.00	—
ii) PVA gum. Original coated paper.		
2½p pink (one centre band)	0.35	0.25
3p blue	0.35	0.25
5p violet	1.50	1.00
7½p brown	1.75	1.50
iii) PVA gum. Fluorescent coated paper.		
2½p pink (one centre band)	5.00	0.50
3p blue	11.00	0.25
one centre band	0.35	0.25
3½p green	8.50	—
5p violet	6.00	3.00
7½p brown	70.00	20.00
iv) PVAD gum (blue tinged).		
3p blue (one centre band)	0.75	—
3½p green (January 23, 1974)	0.35	0.25
one centre band	0.35	0.25
4½p grey-blue (November 6, 1974)	0.35	0.25
5½p deep violet (January 23, 1974)	0.30	0.30
one centre band	0.35	0.25
6½p green-blue (January 14, 1976)		
one centre band	0.35	0.25
7p red-brown (January 18, 1974)		
one centre band	0.35	0.25
8p red (January 23, 1974)	0.40	0.30
8½p green (January 14, 1976)	0.35	0.30
9p violet-blue (January 18, 1978)	0.35	0.30
10p orange (October 20, 1976)	0.35	0.35
one centre band	0.40	0.35
10½p grey-blue (January 18, 1978)	0.40	0.40
11p red (October 20, 1976)	0.40	0.40

B) Phosphor coated paper. PVAD gum (blue tinged).
Issued July 23, 1980.

12p yellow-green	0.40	0.40
13½p red-brown	0.60	0.60
15p blue	0.60	0.55

C) Printed in litho by Waddington. Perf 13½ x 14. Phosphor coated paper, except 11½p, 12p, 12½p, 13p, (left side band), 22p (advanced coated paper). PVAD gum (blue tinged) except 11½p and 12½p have PVA gum.

11½p mushroom (April 8, 1981)	0.60	0.45
12p emerald-green (January7, 1986)	1.50	1.50
12½p light green (February 24, 1982)	0.60	0.60
13p light brown, type 1 (Oct 23, 1984)	0.75	0.65
type II	5.00	5.25
15½p pale-violet (February 24, 1982)	0.60	0.60
16p light mushroom (April 27, 1983)	0.75	0.75
printed on Harrison's (November 2, 1983) on advanced coated paper	3.75	3.75
17p steel blue (Oct 23, 1984)		
type I	3.25	3.00
type II	1.10	1.15
type II, PVA gum	1.10	1.15
19½p grey-green (February 24, 1982)	1.60	1.50
20½p bright blue (April 27, 1983)	3.00	3.00
22p deep blue (April 8, 1981)	0.70	0.70
22p yellowish green (Oct 23, 1984)		
type I	2.25	2.25
type II	25.00	20.00
26p red, type I (February 24, 1982)	0.85	0.80
28p blue, type I (April 27, 1983)	1.00	0.90
31p purple (October 23, 1984)		
type I	1.75	1.75
type II	100.00	80.00

D) Printed in litho by Questa. Perf 15 x 14. One phosphor band (12p, 13p), advanced coated paper (22p, 26p, 28p), or as indicated. PVAD gum. All Type II.

12p emerald-green (April 29, 1986)	1.50	1.50
13p light brown (November 4, 1986)	0.90	0.95
printed on paper supplied by Coated Paper Ltd, PVA gum (April 14, 1987)	0.80	0.60
17p steel blue (April 29, 1986)	3.25	3.25
18p deep green (January 6, 1987)	0.80	0.70
18p bright green (December 3, 1991)		
one centre band	0.70	0.50
18p bright green (September 26, 1992)		
perf: 14	0.80	0.80
18p bright green (August 10, 1993)		
left band	1.80	1.80
19p orange-red (November 8, 1988)		
phosphor paper	0.80	0.80
19p orange-red (March 21, 1989)		
two bands	1.25	1.25
20p brownish-black (November 28, 1989)		
phosphor paper	0.65	0.50
22p yellowish-green (January 27, 1987)	0.75	0.80
22p orange-red (December 4, 1990)		
phosphor paper	0.90	0.80
23p bright green (November 8, 1988)		

phosphor paper	0.90	0.85
23p bright green (March 21, 1989)		
two bands	7.50	7.50
24p deep red (November 28, 1989)		
phosphor paper	1.00	1.05
24p chestnut (December 3, 1991)		
phosphor paper	1.00	0.65
24p chestnut (October 19, 1992)		
phosphor paper, perf: 14	2.00	1.60
24p chestnut (August 10, 1993)		
two bands	2.50	2.50
26p red (January 27, 1987)	2.50	2.25
26p drab (December 4, 1990)		
phosphor paper	1.25	1.05
28p blue (January 27, 1987)	1.00	1.00
28p bluish grey (December 3, 1991)		
phosphor paper	1.00	1.10
28p bluish grey (February 18, 1993)		
phosphor paper, perf: 14	3.75	3.50
31p purple (April 29, 1986)	1.60	1.70
32p greenish blue (November 8, 1988)		
phosphor paper	1.25	1.25
34p bluish grey (November 28, 1989)		
phosphor paper	1.25	1.30
37p rosine (December 4, 1990)		
phosphor paper	1.50	1.25
39p mauve (December 3, 1991)		
phosphor paper	1.50	1.25
39p mauve (November 1992)		
phosphor paper, perf: 14	2.25	2.40

(* The 19p and 23p with two bands come from a prestige stamp book.)

E) Stamps with an elliptical perforation along each vertical side. Printed in litho by Questa. One phosphor band (19p and 20p), two phosphor bands (others).

19p bistre (December 7, 1993)	0.60	0.50
19p bistre (right band)	1.75	1.50
20p bright green (July 23, 1996)	0.90	0.90
25p red (December 7, 1993)	0.80	0.85
26p red-brown (July 23, 1996)	1.25	1.40
30p olive-grey (December 7, 1993)	1.00	0.90
37p mauve (July 23, 1996)	2.00	2.25
41p grey-brown (December 7, 1993)	1.25	1.30
63p emerald (July 23, 1996)	3.00	2.40

(* The 19p with phosphor band on the right comes from a prestige stamp book.)

F) Stamps with an elliptical perforation along each vertical side. Printed in gravure by Walsall (except where started). One phosphor band (19p and 20p), two phosphor bands (others).

20p bright green (July 1, 1997)	0.80	0.40
20p bright green (right band)	1.80	2.00
26p chestnut (July 1, 1997)	1.00	1.00
26p chestnut (perf: 14)	1.80	2.00
26p chestnut (printed by Harrison)	1.00	1.00
37p mauve (July 1, 1997)	1.50	1.50
37p mauve (printed by Harrison)	1.50	1.20
63p emerald (July 1, 1997)	2.50	2.10

(* The 20p with one band at right and the 26p perf: 14 come

from prestige stamp books. The 26p and 37p printed by Harrison also come from a prestige stamp book.)

G) Non value indicator stamp. Printed in gravure by Walsall. One phosphor band. Issued on February 15, 2000, in a prestige stamp book.

1st orange-red		1.50	1.50

First day cover		
First day cover (2½p, 3p, 5p, 7½p)	2.00	
First day cover (3½p, 5½p, 8p)	1.25	
First day cover (4½p)	1.00	
First day cover (6½p, 8½p)	1.00	
First day cover (10p, 11p)	1.00	
First day cover (7p, 9p, 10½p)	1.75	
First day cover (12p, 13½p, 15p)	1.25	
First day cover (11½p, 14p, 18p, 22p)	2.00	
First day cover (12½p, 15½p, 19½p, 26p)	2.00	
First day cover (16p, 20½p, 28p)	1.50	
First day cover (13p, 17p, 22p, 31p)	2.00	
First day cover (12p)	1.50	
First day cover (12p, 17p, 31p, Questa)	2.00	
First day cover (13p, Questa)	1.00	
First day cover (18p)	1.50	
First day cover (22p, 26p, 28p, Questa)	3.00	
First day cover (14p, 19p, 23p, 32p)	2.00	
First day cover (15p, 20p, 24p, 34p)	2.75	
First day cover (17p, 22p, 26p, 37p)	2.75	
First day cover (18p, 24p, 28p, 39p)	2.75	
First day cover (19p, 25p, 30p, 41p)	5.00	
First day cover (20p, 26p, 37p, 63p)	5.00	

Scottish flag (*2nd)
Scottish Lion (1st)
Thistle (E, 40p, 42p)
Tartan (64p, 65p, 68p)

1999, June 8
Des: A. Morris (2nd), F. Pottinger and T. Chalk (1st, E, 40p, 42p), and all adapted by Tayburn. Printed in litho by Walsall (2nd, 1st, E, 4p, 65p), De La Rue (2nd, 1st and 68p) or Questa 2nd, 1st, E and 5p). One phosphor band (2nd), two phosphor bands (others).

2nd multicoloured (Walsall)	0.50	0.40
2nd multicoloured (De La Rue)	0.60	0.65
2nd multicoloured (Questa)	0.95	1.00
1st multicoloured (Walsall)	0.55	0.50
1st multicoloured (De La Rue)	0.75	0.80
1st multicoloured (Questa)	1.00	1.05
E multicoloured (Walsall)	0.80	0.80
E multicoloured (Questa)	1.45	1.50

64p multicoloured		4.75	5.00
65p multicoloured (Walsall, Apr 25, 2000)	1.50	1.65
65p multicoloured (Questa)		1.75	1.80
68p multicoloured (July 4, 2002)		1.95	1.80
First day cover (2nd to 64p)			3.00
First day cover (65p)			3.00
First day cover (68p)			3.00
Stamp cards		3.00	12.50

(* The 2nd, 1st, E and 65p printed by Questa come from prestige stamp books.)

2003, October 14. Designs with white borders
Designs as for April 23, 2001, but with a white margin around the stamp design. Printed in gravure by De La Rue (except where stated). One phosphor band (2nd), two phosphor bands (others).

2nd multicoloured	0.45	0.40
1st multicoloured	0.55	0.50
E multicoloured	1.50	1.00
40p multicoloured (May 11, 2004)	0.80	0.85
42p multicoloured (Walsall, Apr 5, 2005)	0.85	0.85
42p multicoloured (May 10, 2005)	0.80	0.75
44p multicoloured (March 28, 2006)	0.85	0.85
68p multicoloured	1.20	1.00
72p multicoloured (March 28, 2006)	1.20	0.95
First day cover (2nd, 1st, E, 68p)		3.50
First day cover (40p)		2.50
First day cover (42p)		2.50
First day cover (44p, 72p)		2.50
Stamp cards	2.00	10.00

WALES

3d lilac

1958-1967
Des: Reynolds Stone.
A) Wmk: Multiple St Edward's Crown. Non phosphor except where stated.

3d lilac (August 18, 1958)	0.15	0.15
one centre band	0.15	0.20
4d blue (February 7, 1966)	0.20	0.15
two phosphor bands	0.15	0.15
6d purple (September 29, 1958)	0.30	0.25
9d green (March 1, 1967)		
two phosphor bands	0.35	0.30
1/3 green (September 29, 1958)	0.45	0.40
1/6 grey-blue (March 1, 1967)		
two phosphor bands	0.40	0.30

First day cover (3d)	10.00	
First day cover (6d, 1/3)	20.00	
First day cover (4d)	7.50	
First day cover (9d, 1/6)	2.75	

B) No watermark, Two phosphor bands except where stated.
i) Gum Arabic.

3d lilac (one centre band)	0.20	0.20
ii) PVA gum		
4d blue	0.20	0.30
4d sepia (September 4, 1968)		
one centre band	0.15	0.15
4d red (February 26, 1969)		
one centre band	0.40	0.15
5d blue (September 4, 1968)	0.30	0.25
1/6 grey-blue	2.00	2.00
First day cover (4d sepia, 5d)	2.50	
First day cover (4d red)	1.00	

3p blue

▢ 1971, July 7. Decimal Currency
Des: J. Matthews.
The dragon symbol on these stamps was re-drawn. On the original version the eye is a circle, while the tongue, claws and tail are thin. On the later version, the eye is solid, while the tongue, claws and tail are thick. These are noted as 'type i' and 'type II' where relevant.

A) Two phosphor bands except where stated.

i) **2½p** pink (one centre band)	0.35	-
3p blue	0.70	-
ii) PVA gum. Original coated paper.		
2½p pink (one centre band)	0.35	0.25
3p blue	0.30	0.20
5p violet	1.25	1.25
7½p brown	1.75	1.75
iii) PVA gum. Fluorescent coated paper.		
2½p pink (one centre band)	1.75	0.75
3p blue	8.00	1.75
3p blue (one centre band)	0.35	0.25
5p violet	18.00	3.75
iv) PVAD gum (blue tinged).		
3½p green (January 23, 1974)	0.30	0.30
one centre band	0.30	0.30
4½p grey-blue (November 6, 1974)	0.30	0.30
5½p deep violet (January 23, 1974)	0.30	0.30
one centre band	0.30	0.30
6½p green-blue (January 14, 1976)		
one centre band	0.30	0.25

7p red-brown (January 18, 1978)		
one centre band	0.30	0.25
8p red (January 23, 1974)	0.35	0.30
8½p green (January 14, 1976)	0.35	0.30
9p violet-blue (January 18, 1978)	0.35	0.35
10p orange (October 20, 1976)	0.35	0.35
one centre band	0.35	0.35
10½p grey-blue (January 18, 1978)	0.40	0.40
11p red (October 20, 1976)	0.40	0.40

B) Phosphor coated paper. PVAD gum (blue tinged). Issued on July 23, 1980.

12p yellow-green	0.40	0.40
13½p red-brown	0.55	0.60
15p blue	0.60	0.55

C) Printed in litho by Questa. Perf 13½ x 14. Phosphor coated paper, except 11½p and 12½p (left side band). PVA gum (11½p, 14p, 18p, 22p). PVAD gum (others).

11½p mushroom (April 8, 1981)	0.60	0.45
12½p light green (February 24, 1982)	0.50	0.40
14p steel-blue (April 8, 1981)	0.50	0.50
15½p pale-violet (February 24, 1982)	0.70	0.65
16p light mushroom (April 27, 1983)	1.25	1.25
18p mauve (April 8, 1981)	0.70	0.70
19½p grey-green (February 24, 1982)	1.50	1.60
20½p bright blue (April 27, 1983)	2.75	2.75
22p deep blue (April 8, 1981)	0.90	0.90
26p red, type I (February 24, 1982	0.80	0.80
28p blue, type I (April 27, 1983)	0.90	0.90

D) Printed in litho by Questa. Perf 15 x 14. One side phosphor band (12p, 12½p, 13p), phosphor coated paper (16p, 17p, 31p), advanced coated paper (22p, 26p, 28p) or as indicated. PVAD gum.

12p emerald-green (January 7, 1986)	1.75	1.75
12½p light green (January 10, 1984)	4.00	4.00
13p reddish-brown (Oct 23, 1984)		
type I	0.50	0.50
deep brown, type II	2.25	2.35
deep brown (April 14, 1987),		
on paper supplied by Coated Papers		
Ltd, PVA gum, type II	1.25	1.30
16p light mushroom (January 10, 1984)	1.25	1.25
17p steel-blue (October 23, 1984)		
type I	0.80	0.85
flourescent brightener omitted, type I	0.80	1.00
advanced coated paper, type I	0.80	0.85
type II	32.50	20.00
18p deep green (January 6, 1987)	0.70	0.70
18p bright green (December 3, 1991)		
one centre band	0.55	0.66
18p bright green (left band)	2.00	2.00
18p bright green (right band)	2.00	2.00
18p bright green (January 12, 1993)		
perf: 14	2.50	2.50
19p orange-red (November 8, 1988)		
phosphor paper	0.75	0.75
20p brownish-black (November 28, 1989)		
phosphor paper	0.65	0.60
22p yellowish-green (Oct 23, 1984)	0.75	0.75

22p orange-red (December 4, 1990)
phosphor paper	0.70	0.65

23p bright green (November 8, 1988)
phosphor paper	1.00	0.80

24p deep red (November 28, 1989)
phosphor paper	1.00	1.00

24p chestnut (December 3, 1991)
phosphor paper	0.75	0.80

24p chestnut (February 25, 1992)
two bands	1.00	1.10

24p chestnut (September 14, 1992)
phosphor paper, perf: 14	2.50	2.50

26p red - Type II (January 27, 1987) | 4.50 | 3.00

26p drab (December 4, 1990)
phosphor paper	1.20	0.95

28p blue, type II (January 27, 1987) | 1.10 | 1.05

28p bluish grey (December 3, 1991)
phosphor paper	1.10	0.95

31p purple (October 23, 1984) | 1.50 | 0.95
advanced coated paper (Jan 27, 1987) | 1.60 | 1.60

32p greenish blue (November 8, 1988)
phosphor paper	1.25	1.20

34p bluish grey (November 28, 1989)
(phosphor paper)	1.25	1.25

37p rosine (December 4, 1990)
(phosphor paper)	1.50	1.25

39p mauve (December 3, 1991)
(phosphor paper)	1.50	1.25

(* The 18p with one band at left or right comes from prestige stamp books. The 18p with a centre band is also found in prestige stamp books.)

E) Stamps with an elliptical perforation along each vertical side. Printed in litho by Questa. One phosphor band (19p and 20p), two phosphor bands (others).

19p bistre (December 7, 1993) | 0.60 | 0.55
19p bistre (right band) | 2.00 | 1.80
20p bright green (July 23, 1996) | 1.25 | 1.30
25p red (December 7, 1993) | 0.75 | 0.75
26p red-brown (July 23, 1996) | 1.25 | 1.25
30p olive-grey (December 7, 1993) | 1.00 | 0.85
37p mauve (July 23, 1996) | 2.50 | 2.60
41p grey-brown (December 7, 1993) | 1.25 | 1.15
63p emerald (July 23, 1996) | 3.00 | 2.75

* The 19p with phosphor band to right comes from a prestige stamp book.)

F) Stamps with an elliptical perforation along each vertical side. Printed in gravure by Walsall. One phosphor band (19p and 20p), two phosphor bands (others). These stamps do not have the 'p' following the denomination.

20p bright green (July 1, 1997) | 0.80 | 0.50
20p bright green (right band) | 2.25 | 2.50
26p chestnut (July 1, 1997) | 1.00 | 0.70
26p chestnut (perf: 14) | 1.40 | 1.40
26p chestnut (Harrison) | 1.25 | 1.00
37p mauve (July 1, 1887) | 1.50 | 1.40
37p mauve (Harrison) | 1.50 | 1.20
63p emerald (July 1, 1997) | 3.50 | 2.25

* The 20p with one band at right and the 26p with perf: 14

come from prestige stamp books. The 26p and 37p printed printed by Harrison come from a prestige stamp book.)

G) Non-value indicator stamp. Printed in gravure by Walsall. One phosphor band. Issued on February 15, 2000, in a prestige stamp book.

1st orange-red | 1.50 | 1.50

First day cover (2½p, 3p, 5p, 7½p) | 2.00
First day cover (3½p, 5½p, 8p) | 1.25
First day cover (4½p) | 1.00
First day cover (6½p, 8½p) | 1.00
First day cover (10p, 11p) | 1.00
First day cover (7p, 9p, 10½p) | 1.75
First day cover (12p 13½p, 15p) | 1.25
First day cover (11½p, 14p, 18p, 22p) | 2.00
First day cover (12½p, 15½p. 19½p, 26p) | 2.00
First day cover (16p, 20½p, 28p) | 1.75
First day cover (12p, 17p, 22p, 31p) | 2.00
First day cover (12p) | 1.50
First day cover (18p) | 1.50
First day cover (14p, 19p, 23p, 32p) | 2.00
First day cover (15p, 20p, 24p, 34p) | 2.75
First day cover (17p, 22p, 26p, 37p) | 2.75
First day cover (18p, 24p, 28p, 39p) | 2.75
First day cover (19p, 25p, 30p, 41p) | 5.00
First day cover (20p, 26p, 37p, 63p) | 5.00

Leek (2nd)
Welsh Dragon (1st)
Daffodil (E, 40p, 42p)
Prince of Wales' feathers (64p, 65p, 68p)

■ 1999, June 8
Des: D. Petersen (2nd), T. and G. Petersen (1st), I. Rees (E, 40p, 42p), R. Evans (64p, 65p, 68p), and all adapted by Tutssels. Printed in litho by Walsall (2nd, 1st, E, 64p, 65p) or De La Rue (68p). One phosphor band (2nd), two phosphor bands (others).

2nd multicoloured | 0.45 | 0.40
2nd multicoloured (right band) | 2.00 | 2.00
1st multicoloured | 0.55 | 0.50
E multicoloured | 1.00 | 1.00
64p multicoloured | 4.75 | 4.75
65p multicoloured (April 25, 2000) | 1.95 | 2.10
68p multicoloured (July 4, 2002) | 1.75 | 1.90
First day cover (2nd to 64p) | | 3.00
First day cover (65p) | | 3.00
First day cover (68p) | | 3.00

(* The 2nd class with band at right comes from the Treasury of Trees prestige stamp book.)

2003, October 14. Designs with white borders

Designs as for April 23, 2001 but with a white margin around the stamp design. Printed in gravure by De La Rue (except where stated). One phosphor band (2nd), two phosphor bands (others).

2nd multicoloured	0.45	0.40
1st multicoloured	0.55	0.50
E multicoloured	150	1.40
40p multicoloured (May 11, 2004)	0.80	0.75
42p multicoloured (Walsall, Apr 5, 2005)	0.85	0.85
42p multicoloured (May 10, 2005)	0.95	0.75
44p multicoloured (March 28, 2006)	0.85	0.85
68p multicoloured	1.20	1.00
72p multicoloured (March 28, 2006)	0.95	0.75
First day cover (2nd, 1st, E, 68p)		3.00
First day cover (40p)		2.50
First day cover (42p)		2.50
First day cover (44p, 72p)		2.50
Stamp cards	2.00	10.00

CHANNEL ISLANDS

Gathering seaweed (1d)
Islanders gathering seaweed (2½d)

1948, May 10. Third Anniversary of Liberation

Des: J.R.R. Stobie (1d), E. Blampied (2½d). Printed in photogravure by Harrison. Multiple GVIR watermark. Perf: 15 x 14.

Set	0.15	0.20
First day cover		17.50

GUERNSEY

2½d, 3d, 4d

1958-68

Des: E.A. Piprell. Printed in photogravure by Harrison. Perf: 15 x 14.

A) Wmk: Multiple St Edward's Crown. Non phosphor (except where stated).

2½d red (June 8, 1964)	0.30	0.35
3d lilac (August 18, 1958)	0.30	0.30
one centre phos band (May 24, 1967)	0.10	0.15
4d ultramarine (February 7, 1966)	0.20	0.25
two phos bands (October 24, 1967)	0.10	0.15
First day cover (2½d)		25.00
First day cover (3d)		20.00
First day cover (4d)		10.00

B) No watermark. Chalky paper. Two phosphor bands (except where stated).

4d ultramarine (April 16, 1968)	0.10	0.15
4d sepia (September 4, 1968)		
one centre phosphor band	0.10	0.15
4d red (February 26, 1969)		
one centre phosphor band	0.10	0.20
5d deep blue (September 4, 1968)	0.10	0.20
First day cover (4d sepia, 5d)		2.00
First day cover (4d red)		1.50

JERSEY

2½d, 3d, 4d

1958-69

Des: E. Blampied (2½d), W.M. Gardner (others). Printed in photogravure by Harrison. Perf: 15 x 14.

A) Wmk: Multiple St. Edward's Crown. Non phosphor (except where stated).

2½d carmine-red (June 8, 1964)	0.20	0.25
3d lilac (August 18, 1958)	0.25	0.25
one centre phos band (June 9, 1967)	0.10	0.15
4d ultramarine (February 7, 1966)	0.20	0.25
two phos bands (September 5, 1967)	0.10	0.15
First day cover (2½d)		25.00
First day cover (3d)		20.00
First day cover (4d)		10.00

B) No watermark. Chalky paper, PVA gum. One centre phosphor band (4d), two phosphor bands (5d).

4d sepia (September 4, 1968)	0.10	0.15
4d red (February 26, 1969)	0.10	0.20
5d deep blue (September 4, 1968)	0.10	0.20
First day cover (4d sepia, 5d)		2.00
First day cover (4d red)		1.50

d, 3d, 4d

1958-69
es: J. Nicholson. Printed in photogravure by Harrison.
rf: 15 x 14.

Wmk: Multiple St Edward's Crown. Non phosphor (except here stated).

d carmine-red (June 8, 1964)	0.20	0.35
lilac (August 18, 1958)	0.15	0.20
alky paper (May 17, 1964)	4.50	4.00
e centre phos band (Jun 27, 1968)	0.10	0.15
ultramarine (February 7, 1966)	0.75	0.75
two phosphor bands (July 5, 1967)	0.10	0.15
rst day cover (2½d)		25.00
rst day cover (3d)		30.00
rst day cover (4d)		10.00

No watermark. Chalky paper. Two phosphor bands xcept where stated).

ultramarine (June 24, 1968)	0.10	0.15
sepia (September 4, 1968)		
e centre phosphor band	0.10	0.15
red (February 26, 1969)		
e centre phosphor band	0.20	0.30
deep blue (September 4, 1968)	0.20	0.30
rst day cover (4d sepia, 5d)		2.00
rst day cover (4d red)		1.50

1971, July 7. Regional Decimal Issue
s: J. Matthews. Printed in photogravure by Harrison.

p magenta	0.20	0.20
ultramarine	0.20	0.20
violet	0.60	0.60
p pale brown	0.75	0.60
st day cover		2.50

The 2½p and 3p exist on either ordinary coated paper or prescent coated paper.)

Stamp Magazine is Britain's best for GB collectors

Every issue includes:

■ Five pages of GB news
■ Full details of latest issues
■ The best first day covers
■ Newly discovered errors
■ Price analysis from dealers and eBay
■ Features on everything from Queen Victoria classics to modern Smilers

Available from newsagents, or visit www.stampmagazine.co.uk

BOOKLETS

In this section, items are priced in mint condition only.

EDWARD VII

■ **2/- booklets**

24 at 1d (sold at 2½d)	£350
12 at 1d, 23 at ½d	£900
18 at 1d, 11 at ½d (printed by De La Rue)	£1,000
18 at 1d, 11 at ½d (printed by Harrison)	£1,400

George V 2/- booklet (Silver Jubilee)

GEORGE V

■ **2/- booklets**

18 x 1d, 12 x ½d, Wmk: Imperial Crown	£600
as above but Wmk: Crown with GRV	£900
as above but stamps of 1911-1913 issue	£700
10 x 1½d, 6 x 1d, 6 x ½d, Wmk: Crown with GV	£1,150
as above but Wmk: Block GVR, printed by Waterlow	£400
as above but Postal Union Congress issue	£475
as above but Wmk: Block GVR, printed by Harrison	£450
as above but printed in photogravure	£1,000
12 x 1½d, 4 x ½d (Silver Jubilee issue)	£80

■ **3/- booklets**

12 x 1½d, 12 x 1d, 12 x ½d, Wmk: Script Cypher	£650
18 x 1½d, 6 x 1d, 6 x ½d, Wmk: Script Cypher	£650
18 x 2d	£700
24 x 1½d	£750
18 x 1½d, 6 x 1d, 6 x ½d, Wmk: Block Cypher, Waterlow	£300
as above but Postal Union Congress issue	£400
as above but printed by Harrison	£375
as above but printed by photogravure	£340
20 x 1½d, 4 x 1d, 4 x ½d (Silver Jubilee issue)	90.00

■ **3/6 booklets**

18 x 2d, 6 x 1d	£850
12 x 2d, 6 x 1½d, 6 x 1d, 6 x ½d	£850

■ **5/- booklets**

34 x 1½d, 6 x 1d, 6 x ½d, printed by Waterlow	£3,500
as above but buff covered	£2,000
as above but printed by Harrison	£950
as above but printed by photogravure	£2,200

EDWARD VIII

■ **6d booklets**

4 x 1½d	30.00

■ **2/- booklets**

10 x 1½d, 6 x 1d, 6 x ½d	75.00

■ **3/- booklets**

18 x 1½d, 6 x 1d, 6 x ½d	70.00

■ **5/- booklets**

34 x 1½d, 6 x 1d, 6 x ½d	£160

GEORGE VI

■ **6d booklets**

4 x 1½d	50.00
2 x 1½d, 2 x 1d, 2 x ½d	£225
4 x 1d, 4 x ½d	£100

■ **1/- booklets**

4 x 1½d, 4 x 1d, 4 x ½d, in pale colours, in panes of two	20.00
as above but in panes at four	£4,500
with changed colours in panes of two	25.00
with changed colours in panes of four	20.00

■ **2/- booklets**

10 x 1½d, 6 x 1d, 6 x ½d, with Royal Cypher on cover	£325
as above but with GPO cypher on cover	£325

■ **2/6 booklets**

6 x 2½d, 6 x 2d, 6 x ½d, with red cover	£750
as above but with blue cover	£750
as above but with green cover	£350
as above but stamps in pale colours	£350
as above but no commercial advertising included	50.00
as above but changed colours	30.00
6 x 2½d, 6 x 1½d, 3 x 1d, 6 x ½d	30.00

■ **3/- booklets**

18 x 1½d, 6 x 1d, 6 x ½d	£600

■ **5/- booklets**

18 x 2½d, 6 x 2d, 6 x ½d	£700
as above but pale colours	£700
as above but no commercial advertising included	85.00
as above but changed colours	45.00
18 x 2½d, 6 x 1½d, 3 x 1d, 6 x ½d	35.00
12 x 2½d, 6 x 2d, 6 x 1½d, 6 x 1d, 6 x ½d	45.00

ELIZABETH II WILDINGS

■ **1/- booklets**

4 x 1½d, 4 x 1d, 4 x ½d, Wmk: Tudor Crown, panes of two	5.00
as above but panes of four	5.00
as above but Wmk: St. Edward's Crown, panes of two	15.00
as above but panes of four	5.00
Wmk: Multiple Crowns	5.00

2/- booklets

x 3d, 4 x 1½d, 4 x 1d, 4 x ½d,	
th Wmk: St. Edward's Crown, pink cover	4.00
above but Wmk: Multiple Crowns (upright)	6.00
above but yellow cover	6.00
above but Wmk: sideways	25.00
above but stamps with phosphor bands	60.00
x 4d, 2 x 1d se-tenant with 2 x 3d	3.00
above but 3d with phos band at left or right)	8.00
above but 3d with two phos bands	4.00
x 2½d, 3 x ½d se-tenant with 1 x 2½d	6.00
x ½d, 8 x 2½d in panes of two of each se-tenant	2.00
x 3d	1.00

2/6 booklets

x 2½d, 6 x 1½d (QE II), 3 x 1d, 6 x ½d (KGVI)	20.00
above but only 1d of KGVI	20.00
above but QEII stamps only, Wmk: Tudor Crown	30.00
above but Wmk: St Edward's Crown	20.00
x 2½d, 6 x 2d, 6 x ½d, Wmk: St Edward's Crown	18.00

3/- booklets

x 3d, 6 x 1½d, 6 x 1d, 6 x ½d, Wmk: St Edward's Crown	14.00
above but Wmk: Multiple Crowns	18.00
above but graphite lined stamps	£150
above phosphor lined stamps	45.00

3/9 booklets

x 2½d, Wmk: Tudor Crown	22.00
above but Wmk: St Edward's Crown	15.00

4/6 booklets

x 3d, Wmk: St Edward's Crown	15.00
above but Wmk: Multiple Crowns	15.00
above but graphite lined stamps	20.00
above but phosphor lined stamps	22.00
x 4d, 6 x 1d, Wmk: Multiple Crowns	14.00
above but phosphor lined stamps	7.00

5/- booklets

x 2½d (QEII), 6 x 2d (KGVI), 6 x 1½d (QEII),	
x 1d (KGVI), 6 at ½d (KGVI)	26.00
above but only 1d and 2d stamps of KGVI	£175
above but only 2d stamps of KGVI	£110
above but QEII stamps only, Wmk: Tudor Crown	30.00
above but 2d deep brown, Wmk: St Edward's Crown	20.00
above but 2d brown	22.00
x 3d, 6 x 2½d, 6 x 1½d, 6 x ½d, Wmk: St Edward's Crown	18.00
above but Wmk: Multiple Crowns	20.00
above but graphite lined stamps	£100
above but phosphor lined stamps, 2½d with two bands	£100
above but 2½d with one band	90.00

6/- booklets

x 4d, Wmk: Multiple Crowns	18.00
above but with phosphor lined stamps	22.00

10/- booklets

x 3d, 6 x 2d, 6 x 1½d, 6 x 1d, 6 x ½d	80.00
x 3d, 6 x 2½d, 6 x 1½d, 6 x 1d	80.00

24 x 4d, 6 x 3d, 6 x 1d	18.00
as above but phosphor lined, 3d with side phos band	8.00
as above but 3d with one centre band	5.00

ELIZABETH II PRE-DECIMAL MACHINS

■ 2/- booklets

Yellow cover, 4 x 4d sepia (two bands), plus	
2 x 1d se-tenant with 2 x 3d (two bands)	0.80
Grey cover, 4 x 4d sepia (two bands), plus	
2 x 4d sepia (centre band) se-tenant with two labels	0.65
Grey cover, 4 x 4d sepia (centre band), plus	
2 x 4d sepia (centre band) se-tenant with two labels	1.50
Grey cover, 4 x 4d red (centre band) plus 2 x 4d red	
(centre band) se-tenant with two labels	2.00

■ 4/6 booklets

Blue plain cover, 6 x 4d sepia, 6 x 4d sepia	
(two bands), 6 x 1d	6.00
as above but blue cover showing Cutty Sark	1.75
as above but blue cover showing Golden Hind	
and 4d with one centre band	1.75
as above but blue cover showing Discovery	1.75
Blue cover showing Queen Elizabeth 2, 6 x 4d red,	
6 x 4d red (centre band), 6 x 1d	1.75
as above but cover showing Sirius	2.00
as above but cover showing Dreadnought	2.50
as above but cover showing Mauretania	3.50
as above but cover showing Victory	3.00
as above but cover showing Sovereign on the Seas	3.00

■ 5/- booklets

Bistre covers showing Ightham Mote, 6 x 5d, 6 x 5d	2.00
as above but cover showing Little Moreton Hall	1.75
as above but cover showing Long Melford Hall	2.50
as above but cover showing Mompesson House	2.50
as above but cover showing Cumberland Terrace	2.00
as above but cover showing The Vineyard, Saffron Walden	2.50
as above but cover showing Mereworth Castle	3.50
as above but cover showing Philympia 1970 London	1.50

■ 6/- booklets

Purple plain cover, 6 x 4d sepia, 6 x 4d sepia,	
6 x 4d sepia (two bands)	£215
Orange cover showing Kingfisher, 6 x 4d sepia,	
6 x 4d sepia, 6 x 4d sepia (two bands)	1.80
as above but cover showing Peregrine Falcon	1.50
Orange cover showing Peregrine Falcon, 6 x 4d sepia,	
6 x 4d sepia, 6 x 4d sepia (centre band)	1.50
as above but cover showing Pied Woodpecker	2.00
as above but cover showing Great Crested Grebe	2.00
as above but cover showing Barn Owl	2.25
Orange cover showing Barn Owl*, 6 x 4d red,	
6 x 4d red, 6 x 4d red (centre band)	2.75
as above but cover showing Jay*	2.75
as above but cover showing Puffin	3.00
as above but cover showing Cormorant	3.00
as above but cover showing Wren	3.00
as above but cover showing Golden Eagle	3.00

Elizabeth II 10/- booklet (Livingstone)

■ **10/- booklets**

Purple cover showing Livingstone,
6 x 4d sepia, 6 x 4d sepia, 6 x 4d sepia,
6 x 4d sepia (two bands), 6 x 3d, 6 x 1d   5.00
Green cover showing Scott,
6 x 5d, 6 x 5d, 6 x 4d sepia, 6 x 4d sepia (one centre band)
plus 4 x 1d se-tenant with 2 x 4d sepia (one band)   4.00
as above but cover showing Kingsley, and 4d red   3.25
as above but cover showing Shackleton, and 4d red   5.00
as above but cover showing Frobisher, and 4d red   6.00
as above but cover showing Cook, and 4d red   6.50

ELIZABETH II DECIMAL MACHINS

■ **10p booklets**

Yellow cover, 2 x ½p, 2 x 1p, 2 x 1½p, 2 x 2p
London's first pillar box   1.50
Pillar box of 1856   1.50
Urban pillar box 1857   1.50
Penfold type 1866   1.50
Double aperture type 1899   1.50
Mellor type 1968   1.75
King Edward VIII type 1936   1.75
Queen Elizabeth II type 1952   2.50
Double aperture type 1973   3.75
Philatelic Posting Box   1.75
General Letter Carrier 1793   1.75
Letter Carrier 1837   1.50
Letter Carrier 1855   0.95

■ **25p booklets**

Violet cover, 5 x ½p, 9 x 2½p
Knifeboard Omnibus   3.00
80 Years of British Stamp Books   3.25
B-type Omnibus   3.50
Showman's Engine   7.50
Royal Mail Van 1913   6.50
Motor Wagonette 1901   4.50
London Taxi Cab 1931   6.00
Norwich Electric Tramway   6.50
Help Children, Save the Children   8.00

■ **30p booklets**

Purple cover (except where stated), 10 x 3p
Curlew   4.00
80 Years of British Stamp Books   4.50

Lapwing   4.00
Robin   4.00
Pied Wagtail   4.00
Kestrel   4.00
Black Grouse   5.00
Skylark   4.00
Oyster-catcher   4.00
Oyster-catcher (bistre cover)   5.00
Help Children, Save the Children (red cover)   8.00
Canada Life Assurance Group (red cover)   4.50

■ **35p booklets**

Blue cover, 10 x 3½p
Cuthred Penny   4.75
Edward I Silver Groat   3.00
Canada Life Assurance Group   2.75

■ **45p booklets**

Brown cover, 10 x 4½p
Elizabeth Gold Crown   4.50

■ **50p booklets**

Blue-green cover, 5 x ½p, 7 x 2½p, 10 x 3p
Large Bindweed   8.00
Primrose   7.75
Honeysuckle   7.75
Hop   8.25
Common Violet   8.25
Lords-and-Ladies   7.50
Wood Anemone   7.50
Deadly Nightshade   6.50
Canada Life Assurance Group   6.50
Deep green cover, 5 x 3p, 10 x 3½p
Canada Life Assurance Group   7.50

■ **85p booklets**

Purple cover, 5 x 3½p, 15 x 4½p
Canada Life Assurance Group   8.00

CARD COVERS WITH STAMPS AFFIXED BY THE MARGIN

■ **10p**

2 x ½p, 3 x 1p, 1 x 6p
Cover design of '10p' made up of red dots   1.25

■ **10p**

2 x ½p, 2 x 1p, 1x 7p
Kent farm buildings   0.70
Northern Ireland farm buildings   0.80
Yorkshire farm buildings   1.00
Wales farm buildings   0.80
Scotland farm buildings   0.75
Sussex farm buildings   0.75

■ **10p**

2 x 1p, 1 x 8p
Post Office stand at London 1980 Stamp Exhibition   0.70
(* This booklet exists with differing postal rates on inner covers

■ 50p
2 x ½p, 2 x 1p, 2 x 6½p, 4 x 8½p
Cover with bold '50p' (6½p with phos band at left)	2.75
Cover with bold '50p' (6½p with phos band at right)	2.75

■ 50p
2 x 1p, 3 x 7p, 3 x 9p
Cover with bold '50p' (7p with phos band at left)	8.00
Cover with bold '50p' (7p with phos band at right)	3.50

■ 50p
2 x 1p, 3 x 7p, 3 x 9p
Clement Talbot Van (7p with phos band on left)	5.00
Clement Talbot Van (7p with phos band on right)	4.00
Austin Cape Taxi (7p with phos band on left)	5.00
Austin Cape Taxi (7p with phos band on right)	4.00
Morris Royal Mail Van (7p with phos band on left)	5.00
Morris Royal Mail Van (7p with phos band on right)	4.00
Guy Electric Dustcart (7p with phos band on left)	5.00
Guy Electric Dustcart (7p with phos band on right)	4.00
Albion Van (7p with phos band on left)	6.50
Albion Van (7p with phos band on right)	5.50
Leyland Fire Engine (7p with phos band on left)	4.00
Leyland Fire Engine (7p with phos band on right)	5.00

■ 50p
x 2p, 2 x 8p, 3 x 10p
Leyland Fire Engine (8p with phos band left or right)	2.50

■ 50p
x 2p, 2 x 8p, 3 x 10p
Rolls Royce Silver Ghost (8p with phos band left or right)	2.50

■ 50p
x 2p, 2 x 10p, 2 x 12p
Grand Prix Austin (10p with phos band left or right)	2.50
1903-1905 Vauxhall car (10p with phos band left or right)	2.25
1900 Daimler (10p with phos band left or right)	2.25

50p
x ½p, 1 x 1p, 1 x 14p, 3 x 11½p
Manchester 1896 (11½p with phos band left or right)	2.25
Bullnose Morris 1913 (11½p with phos band left or right)	2.75
Bugdock Castle (11½p with phos band left or right)	2.25

50p
x 2½p, 2 x 4p, 3 x 11½p
Bugdock Castle (11½p with phos band at left)	3.00
Bugdock Castle (11½p with phos band at right)	4.00
Cow Cop Castle (11½p with phos band at left)	3.50
Cow Cop Castle (11½p with phos band at right)	3.50

50p
x ½p, 4 x 3p pink, 3 x 12½p)
Caxton's Tower (12½p with phos band left or right)	2.00
Temple of the Winds (12½p with phos band left or right)	2.00
Temple of the Sun (12½p with phos band at left or right)	2.00
Water Garden (12½p with phos band left or right)	2.00
Angot Goat (12½p with phos band left or right)	2.50

■ 50p
2 x 1p, 3 x 3½p, 3 x 12½p (all with one centre band)
Gloucester Old Spot Pig	3.25
Toulouse Goose	3.25
Orkney Sheep	3.25

■ 50p
3 x 1p, 2 x 4p, 3 x 13p (all with one centre band)
Orchids, Dendrobium nobile	2.00
Cyripedium calcedolus and ophrys apifera	2.00
Bifienasia and Vandatricolour	2.00
Cymbodium and Arpophyllum	2.00

■ 50p
3 x 17p (two phosphor bands and 'stars' printed on the gummed side)
Pillar box	2.50
Emperor dragonfly	2.00
Common frog	3.00

■ 50p
3 x 17p (two phosphor bands without 'stars' printed on the gummed side)
Common frog	2.00

■ 50p
2 x 1p, 4 x 12p emerald-green (all with one centre band)
Hadrian's Wall	3.50

■ 50p
1 x 1p (right band), 1 x 13p (left band), 2 x 18p (two bands)
Roman Theatre at St Albans	2.50
Portchester Castle, Hampshire	2.50
Weather Vane at Thomas Lord's original cricket ground	2.50
Ashes Urn	2.25
Current Lord's pavilion	2.25
Lord's New Stand	2.25

■ 50p
1 x 1p, 2 x 5p, 3 x 13p (all with one centre band)
Moorhen and Dabchicks	4.00
Great Pond Snail	3.75
Bondnant Gardens, Colwyn Bay	3.00
Botanical Gardens, Edinburgh	3.00
Mount Stuart Gardens (side edges imperforate)	3.00
Mount Stewart	3.00
Kew Gardens	2.50
Common whelk and jellyfish	2.50

■ 50p
1 x 1p, 1 x 13p, 2 x 18p
Pigs	2.50
Birds	2.50
Elephants	2.50

■ 50p
1 x 14p, 2 x 19p
The Yeomen of the Guard	3.00
The Pirates of Penzance	3.50
The Mikado	3.50

Hermit crab, bladder wrack and laver spire shell | 3.00

■ 50p
2 x 15p, 1 x 20p
Armstrong Whitworth Atalanta & De Havilland Dragon | 6.75
Vickers Viscount 806 & De Havilland Comet 4
(contains Penny Black Anniversary definitives) | 4.50
BAC 1-11 & VC10 | 3.00
BAe ATP, BAe 146 & Concorde | 3.00

■ 50p
2 x 1p, 2 x 24p
Sir Arthur Evans at Crete | 2.00
Howard Carter of the tomb of Tutankhamun | 2.00
Sir Austen Layard in Assyria | 1.75
Sir Flinders Petrie at Giza | 2.25
Sheriff's Millennium 1992 | 1.75
Airmail markings | 1.75
Ship mail markings | 1.75
Registered mail | 1.75

■ 50p
2 x 25p
'Paid' marking | 1.75
Swan with Two Necks | 1.75
Bull and Mouth | 1.75
Golden Cross | 1.75
Pheasant Inn | 1.75
John O'Groats | 1.75
Land's End | 1.75
St. David's Head | 3.00
Giant's Causeway | 3.00

■ £1
6 x 17p (advanced coated paper)
Violin | 3.75

■ £1
1 x 13p (right band), 5 x 18p (two bands)
French horn | 5.00
Bass Clarinet | 4.50
A Study in Scarlet | 5.00
The Hound of the Baskervilles | 4.75
Adventure of the Speckled Band (side edges imperforate) | 5.00
Bears | 4.00
Oliver Twist | 4.25
Nicholas Nickleby | 4.50
David Copperfield | 3.50
Great Expectations | 4.00
Sea urchin, starfish and crab | 3.25

■ £1
5 x 20p
Wicken Fen | 4.25
Wicken Fen (glossy cover)
(contains Penny Black Anniversary definitives) | 10.00
Click Mill (contains Penny Black Anniversary definitives) | 3.50
Jack and Jill Mills | 3.25
Howell Mill | 3.50

■ £1
2 x 2p, 4 x 24p
Punch illustrations by Richard Doyle and Hoffnung | 3.00
Punch illustrations by Sir John Tenniel and Eric Burgin | 3.00
Punch illustrations by Sir John Tenniel and Anton | 3.00
Punch illustrations by Sir John Tenniel and Hewison | 3.00
Sheriff's Millennium 1992 | 3.00
University of Wales | 3.75
St. Hilda's College, Oxford | 3.75
Marlborough College | 3.75

■ £1
4 x 25p
Free Church of Scotland College | 4.00
Herbert Asquith | 3.00
David Lloyd-George | 2.75
Winston Churchill | 2.75
Clement Attlee | 2.75
Violette Szabo | 2.75
Dame Vera Lynn | 2.75
R. J. Mitchell | 2.75
Archibald McIndoe | 3.25

■ £1 booklets with red cover and Royal Mail cruciform
4 x 25p | 3.75
2 x 1p, 1 x 20p, 3 x 26p (stamps printed in litho) | 3.00
2 x 1p, 1 x 20p, 3 x 26p (stamps printed in gravure) | 3.00
1 x 1p, 1 x 2p, 1 x 19p, 3 x 26p | 3.00
1 x 2nd, 3 x 1st | 3.50

Panes with a margin to the left or right. Prices are the same for both varieties, except where stated:

■ 65p
10 x 6½p
Cover with bold '65p', right margin | 5.00
Cover with bold '65p', left margin | 12.00

■ 70p
10 x 7p
Cover with bold '70p', either margin | 4.00
With left margin | 4.00

■ 70p
10 x 7p
Horse-shoeing, right margin | 4.00
Horse-shoeing, left margin | 30.00
Thatching, right margin | 4.00
Thatching, left margin | £140
Dry-stone Walling, right margin | 4.00
Dry-stone Walling, left margin | £150
Wheel making, right margin | 4.50
Wheel making, left margin | 5.50
Wattle fence making, right margin | 4.50
Wattle fence making, left margin | 12.50
Basket making, right margin | 4.00
Basket making, left margin | 6.00
Keddlestone Hall, either margin | 6.00

■ 80p
10 x 8p

1915 Vickers, either margin	3.25

■ 85p
10 x 8½p

Cover with bold '85p', right margin	7.00
Cover with bold '85p', left margin	7.50

■ 90p
10 x 9p

Cover with bold '90p', left margin	4.00
Cover with bold '90p', right margin	5.00

■ 90p
10 x 9p

Grand Union Canal, right margin	4.50
Grand Union Canal, left margin	20.00
Llangollen Canal, left margin	3.50
Llangollen Canal, right margin	£275
Kennet & Avon Canal, right margin	7.00
Kennet & Avon Canal, left margin	10.00
Caledonian Canal, left margin	4.50
Caledonian Canal, right margin	6.00
Regent's Canal, right margin	7.00
Regent's Canal, left margin	13.00
Leeds & Liverpool Canal	6.00
Tramway Museum, Crich	6.00

■ £1
10 x 10p (all-over phosphor)

Ironbridge, Telford, Shropshire	3.75

■ £1
10 x 10p (one centre band)

Sopwith Camel and Vickers Vimy	3.50
Hawker Fury and Handley Page Heyford	3.50
Wellington Bomber and Hurricane	3.50

■ £1.15
10 x 11½p (one centre band)

Spitfire and Lancaster	3.75
Lightning and Vulcan	4.00
Natural History Museum, London	3.75
National Museum of Antiquities of Scotland	3.75

■ £1.20
10 x 12p yellow-green

Beetle Mill, Ireland	4.00
Tin mines in Cornwall	4.00
Bottle Kilns, Stoke	4.00

■ £1.20
10 x 12p emerald-green (one centre band)

Pillar box	3.75
National Gallery	3.75
'Maybe'	3.75

£1.25
10 x 12½p (one centre band)

Ashmolean Museum, Oxford	3.75

National Museum of Wales	4.00
Ulster Museum, Belfast	3.75
Castle Museum, York	3.75
GWR Isambard Kingdom Brunel	4.25
LMS Class 4P Passenger Tank Engine	5.00
LNER Mallard	4.25
SR/BR Clan Line	4.25

■ £1.30
10 x 13p (one centre band)

Swansea/Mumbles Railway Car	3.25
The Glasgow Tram	4.00
Blackpool car No. 717	3.75
'D' Class London tram	3.50
The Three Bears starting the day	3.50
Keep in touch	3.50
Garden Scene	3.50
Brighter Writer	3.50
Jolly Postman	3.50
Linnean Society	3.75
Recipes (vegetables)	3.25
Children's Parties (balloons)	3.25

■ £1.30
6 x 14p (two bands), 2 x 11½p (left band), 2 x 11½p (right band)

Penny Black, right margin	4.50
Penny Black, left margin	4.50
King George V ½d and 1d 'Downey Head', left margin	5.00
King George V ½d and 1d 'Downey Head', right margin	17.50

■ £1.40
10 x 14p (phosphor coated paper)

Preston Mill in Scotland	3.75
Talyllyn Railway, Tywyn	4.00
Costumes of 1860-1880	4.00
Costumes of 1815-1830	4.00
Legal Charge	3.75
Fox Talbot photographs	3.75

■ £1.43
6 x 15½p (two bands), 2 x 12½p (left band), 2 x 12½p (right band)

James Chalmers portrait	3.75
Edmund Dulac (KGVI 5/- red)	3.75
Forces Postal Service	3.75
£5 orange of 1882	4.00
Postmark Collecting	4.00
Golden Hinde inscribed 'Holiday Postcard Stamp Book'	4.00

■ £1.45
10 x 16p (phosphor coated paper)

Lyme Regis, Dorset	5.00

(* Sold at a discount of 15p off face value; stamps have a 'D' printed on the gummed side.)

■ £1.46
6 x 16p (two bands), 2 x 12½p (left band), 2 x 12½p (right band)

Seahorse high values	7.50
Parcel Post	7.00
Regional Stamps	7.50

(* Panes have either the four 12½p followed by one 16p on the bottom row, or one 16p followed by four 12½p; prices are the same either way.)

■ £1.50
6 x 17p (two bands), 2 x 12p (left band), 2 x 12p (right band)

Pillar box	4.00
National Gallery	4.00
'No'	4.00

(* Panes have either the four 12p followed by one 17p on the bottom row, or one 17p followed by four 12p; prices are the same either way.)

■ £1.54
6 x 17p (two bands), 2 x 13p (left band), 2 x 13p (right band)

To Pay Labels	3.75
Embossed stamps	3.75
Surface printed stamps	3.75
350th Anniversary of The Post Office	3.75

(* Panes have either the four 13p followed by one 17p on the bottom row, or one 17p followed by four 13p; prices are the same either way.)

■ £1.55
10 x 15½p (phosphor coated paper)

Costumes of 1830-1850	4.25
Costumes of 1850-1860	4.25
Costumes of 1860-1880	4.00
Costumes of 1880-1900	4.00

■ £1.55
10 x 17p (phosphor coated paper)

Paper boat and paper plane	5.00

(* Sold at a discount; stamps have a 'D' printed on the gummed side.)

■ £1.60
10 x 16p (phosphor coated paper)

Birthday Cake	5.00
Weavers Cottages, Bibury	4.25
Write It	4.25

■ £1.70
10 x 17p (phosphor coated paper)

Love Letters	4.00
Hands exchanging letters	4.00
Pillar box	4.25
National Gallery	4.50
'Yes'	4.25

■ £1.80
10 x 18p (phosphor coated paper)

Rag, Tag and Bobtail	5.25
Keep in Touch	7.00
Garden Scene	5.25
Brighter Writer	5.25
Jolly Postman	5.00
Linnean Society	4.75
Recipes (fruits)	5.00
Children's Parties (balloons)	5.00

■ £1.90
10 x 19p

Pocket Planner	5.25
Fox Talbot photographs	5.25

■ £2
8 x 25p

Motorised cycle	3.75
Motor mail van	3.75
Electric mail van	3.75
Sir Rowland Hill (London and Brighton Railway)	3.75
Sir Rowland Hill (Hazlewood School)	3.75
Sir Rowland Hill (Secretary to the Post Office)	4.50
Sir Rowland Hill (Uniform Penny Postage)	4.50

■ £2 booklets with red cover and Royal Mail cruciform

8 x 25p	4.50
1 x 20p, 7 x 26p (stamps printed in litho)	4.00
1 x 20p, 7 x 26p (stamps printed in gravure)	17.50
1 x 19p, 7 x 26p	5.00
2 x 2nd, 6 x 1st	4.50

1978 Christmas booklet

CHRISTMAS STAMP BOOKLETS

■ 1978
£1.60 (10 x 7p, 10 x 9p definitives).

Decoration of holly, 'Greetings Christmas 1978'	4.00

■ 1979
£1.80 (10 x 8p, 10 x 10p definitives).

Christmas cracker, 'Greetings Christmas 1979'	4.25

■ 1980
£2.20 (10 x 10p, 10 x 12p definitives).

Nativity scene, 'Greetings Christmas 1980'	4.50

■ 1981
£2.55 (10 x 14p, 10 x 11½p definitives).

Skating scene, 'Christmas Greetings 1981'	6.25

■ 1982
£2.50 (10 x 15½p, 10 x 12½p definitives).

Christmas mummers	6.50

(* Sold at a discount of 30p off face value; stamps have a blue sta printed on the gummed side)

1983
20 (20 x 12½p definitives).
ntomime scene 6.50
old at a discount of 30p off face value; stamps have a blue star
nted on the gummed side.)

1984, November 20
30 (20 x 13p Christmas stamps)
ver shows a Manger Scene 6.00
mps have a five-pointed star printed on the gummed side)

1985, November 19
40 (20 x 12p Christmas stamps).
ver shows Cinderella's slipper on a cushion 6.00

1986
20 (10 x 13p definitives).
oking Shetland yule cakes 5.50
old at a discount of 10p off face value; stamps have a blue star
nted on the gummed side.)

1990, November 13
x 17p Christmas stamps 7.00

1991, November 12
x 18p Christmas stamps 7.00

1992, November 10
x 18p Christmas stamps 6.25

1993, November 9
x 19p Christmas stamps 7.00

1993, November 9
x 25p Christmas stamps 5.75

1994, November 1
x 19p Christmas stamps 6.75

1994, November 1
x 25p Christmas stamps 5.00

1995, October 30
x 19p Christmas stamps 7.00

1995, October 30
x 25p Christmas stamps 4.50

1995, October 30
60p Christmas stamps 4.50

1996, October 28
x 2nd Christmas stamps 7.00

1996, October 28
x 1st Christmas stamps 6.50

1997, October 27
x 2nd Christmas stamps 7.00

1997, October 27
10 x 1st Christmas stamps 6.50

1998, November 2
20 x 20p Christmas stamps 6.50

1998, November 2
10 x 26p Christmas stamps 6.50

1999, November 2
20 x 19p Christmas stamps 6.75

1999, November 2
10 x 26p Christmas stamps 4.75

2000, November 7
20 x 2nd Christmas stamps 6.25

2000, November 7
10 x 1st Christmas stamps 6.50

2001, November 6
24 x 2nd Christmas stamps 7.50

2001, November 6
12 x 1st Christmas stamps 5.50

2002, November 5
24 x 2nd Christmas stamps 7.50

2002, November 5
12 x 1st Christmas stamps 5.25

2003, November 4
24 x 2nd Christmas stamps 8.50

2003, November 4
12 x 1st Christmas stamps 7.25

2004, November 2
24 x 2nd Christmas stamps 8.50

2004, November 2
12 x 1st Christmas stamps 7.25

2005, November 1
24 x 2nd Christmas stamps 8.50

2005, November 1
12 x 1st Christmas stamps 7.25

2006, November 7
12 x 2nd Christmas stamps 4.50
12 x 1st Christmas stamps 6.00

2007, November 6
12 x 2nd Christmas stamps 4.00
12 x 1st Christmas stamps 5.50

1987 retail stamp book 4 x 13p

RETAIL STAMP BOOKS

In 1987 Royal Mail introduced a new range of stamp booklets that could be sold not only over post office counters, but also through a alternative retail outlets. A distinguishing feature of all these booklets is a bar code on the outside back cover.

At first the front covers included a 'window' through which one of the stamps could be seen (hence they are often referred to as 'window books'), but this was replaced after only about a year by a simple illustration of the contents.

The following booklets have the panes surrounded by a white margin, and a 'window' in the cover

■ **4 x 13p**
August 4, 1987. Printed by Harrison   2.50

■ **10 x 13p**
August 4, 1987. Printed by Harrison   3.75

■ **4 x 14p**
August 23, 1988. Printed by Harrison   4.50
October 11, 1988. Stamps by Harrison; cover by Walsall   5.00

■ **10 x 14p**
August 23, 1988. Printed by Harrison   6.00
October 11, 1988. Printed by Questa   11.00

■ **4 x 18p**
August 4, 1987. Printed by Harrison   2.75

■ **10 x 18p**
August 4, 1987. Printed by Harrison   5.00

■ **4 x 19p**
August 23, 1988. Printed by Harrison   4.00
October 11, 1988. Stamps by Harrison; cover by Walsall   4.50

■ **10 x 19p**
August 23, 1988. Printed by Harrison   9.50
October 11, 1988. Printed by Questa   12.50

■ **4 x 26p**
August 4, 1987. Printed by Harrison   14.00

■ **4 x 27p**
August 23, 1988. Printed by Harrison   8.5

The following booklets no longer have the 'window' in the front cover, and the panes are no longer surround by a white margin. Prior to 1993 the panes have eithe the top and bottom or all three edges imperforate.

■ **4 x 14p**
October 11, 1988. Printed by Harrison   4.5
January 24, 1989. Stamps by Harrison, cover by Walsall   15.0

■ **10 x 14p**
October 11, 1988. Printed by Harrison   8.0
October 11, 1988. Printed by Questa   11.0

■ **4 x 19p**
October 11, 1988. Printed by Harrison   5.0
January 24, 1989. Stamps by Harrison, cover by Walsall   17.5

■ **10 x 19p**
October 11, 1998. Printed by Harrison   8.0
October 11, 1998. Printed by Questa   11.5

■ **4 x 27p**
October 11, 1988. Printed by Harrison   20.0

■ **4 x 29p**
October 2, 1989. Printed by Walsall (two phos bands)   8.0
April 17, 1990. Printed by Walsall (phos paper)   7.0

■ **4 x 31p**
September 17, 1990. Printed by Walsall   4.0

■ **4 x 33p**
September 16, 1991. Printed by Walsall   6.0
September 8, 1992. Printed by Walsall (yellow strip at
right is inscribed 'For Worldwide Postcards')   8.5

■ **2 x 39p**
July 28, 1992. Printed by Harrison   2.5

■ **4 x 39p**
September 16, 1991. Printed by Walsall   2.7

NON VALUE INDICATOR RETAIL STAMP BOOKS

These booklets have either the top and bottom edges all three edges left imperforate.

■ **4 x 2nd bright blue**
August 22, 1989. Printed by Walsall   4.0
November 28, 1989. Stamps by Harrison; cover by Walsall 14.0
August 6, 1991. Printed by Walsall
Cover features Royal Mail cruciform   3.5
January 21, 1992. Printed by Walsall
Cover features logos of Olympic and Paralympic Games   3.5

10 x 2nd bright blue

ıgust 22, 1989. Printed by Harrison	6.00
ɔtember 19, 1989. Printed by Questa	6.50
ıgust 6, 1991. Printed by Walsall	
ɔver features Royal Mail cruciform	4.75
ıgust 6, 1991. Printed by Questa	
ɔver features Royal Mail cruciform	4.75
̄uary 21, 1992. Printed by Walsall	
ɔver features logos of Olympic and Paralympic Games	4.75
̄rch 31, 1992. Printed by Questa	
ɔver features logos of Olympic and Paralympic Games	5.00
ɔtember 22, 1992. Printed by Harrison	
ɔver features Royal Mail cruciform	4.75

4 x 2nd deep blue

ıgust 7, 1990. Printed by Walsall	3.50

10 x 2nd deep blue

ıgust 7, 1990. Printed by Harrison	4.75
ıgust 7, 1990. Printed by Questa	6.00
ıgust 7, 1990. Printed by Walsall	4.75

4 x 1st brownish-black

ıgust 22, 1989. Printed by Walsall	4.50
̆ecember 5, 1989. Stamps by Harrison; cover by Walsall	11.00

10 x 1st brownish-black

ıgust 22, 1989. Printed by Harrison	7.50
̄ptember 19, 1989. Printed by Questa	9.75

4 x 1st orange-red

ıgust 7, 1990. Printed by Walsall	4.00
ıgust 7, 1990. Printed by Walsall. Perf: 13	7.00
̄uary 21, 1992. Printed by Walsall	
ɔver features logos of Olympic and Paralympic Games	3.50

10 x 1st orange-red

ıgust 7, 1990. Printed by Harrison	6.00
ıgust 7, 1990. Printed by Questa	6.00
ıgust 7, 1990. Printed by Walsall	6.00
̄uary 21, 1992. Printed by Harrison	
ɔver features logos of Olympic and Paralympic Games	6.00
̄uary 21, 1992. Printed by Walsall	
ɔver features logos of Olympic and Paralympic Games	6.00
̆bruary 9, 1993. Printed by Walsall	
ɔver features Royal Mail cruciform; back cover has ̆dvertisement for Greetings stamps	6.00

LLIPTICAL PERFORATIONS

̄hese booklets have panes with all four edges ̆erforated.

4 x 30p

̄ay 5, 1998. Printed by Walsall	3.00
̆ugust 3, 1998. Printed by Walsall	
̆over inscribed 'Make their post memorable'	3.00

4 x 35p

̆ovember 1, 1993. Printed by Walsall	

Cover illustrates a single stamp	3.50
May 16, 1995. Printed by Walsall	
Cover shows a block of stamps	3.50
March 19, 1996. Printed by Walsall	
Back cover features Olympic symbols	7.00

■ 4 x 37p

July 8, 1996. Printed by Walsall.	
Back cover features Olympic symbols	4.00
February 4, 1997. Printed by Walsall.	
No Olympic symbols	3.00
August 26, 1997. Printed by Walsall.	
Cover shows street names in London	3.00
August 3, 1998. Printed by Walsall	
Cover inscribed 'Make their post memorable'	3.25

■ 4 x 38p

April 26, 1999. Printed by Walsall	3.25

■ 4 x 40p

April 27, 2000. Printed by Walsall	3.25

■ 4 x 41p

November 1, 1993. Printed by Walsall	
Cover illustrates a single stamp	3.75
May 16, 1995. Printed by Walsall	
Cover shows a block of stamps	3.75
March 19, 1996. Printed by Walsall	
Back cover features Olympic symbols	7.00

■ 4 x 60p

August 9, 1994. Printed by Walsall	
Cover illustrates a single stamp	5.50
October 4, 1994. Printed by Walsall	
As above but 'Worldwide Airmail Stamps' in a scroll design	5.50
May 16, 1995. Printed by Walsall	
Cover shows a block of stamps	4.75
March 19, 1996. Printed by Walsall	
Back cover features Olympic symbols	7.50

■ 4 x 63p

July 8, 1996. Printed by Walsall	
Back cover features Olympic symbols	5.00
February 4, 1997. Printed by Walsall	
No Olympic symbols. Stamps printed in litho	4.00
August 26, 1997. Printed by Walsall	
Stamps printed in gravure	4.00
May 5, 1998. Printed by Walsall	
Cover air mail label below block of stamps	4.00

■ 4 x 64p

April 26, 1999. Printed by Walsall	4.00

■ 4 x 65p

April 27, 2000. Printed by Walsall	4.00

■ 4 x 2nd bright blue

April 6, 1993. Printed by Walsall	3.50
September 7, 1993. Printed by Harrison	3.50
January 10, 1995. Printed by Harrison.	

Cover has white lines through block of stamps	3.50
December 12, 1995. Printed by Walsall.	
Cover shows block of stamps	3.00
February 6, 1996. Printed by Walsall.	
Back cover features Olympic symbols	3.50
February 4, 1997. Printed by Walsall.	
Cover has no line through block of stamps	5.00
August 26, 1997. Printed by Walsall	
Stamps printed in gravure	3.50

■ 10 x 2nd bright blue

April 6, 1993. Printed by Questa	4.75
November 1, 1993. Printed by Walsall	4.75
January 10, 1995. Printed by Questa	
Cover has white lines through block of stamps	4.75
December 12, 1995. Printed by Harrison	
Cover shows block of stamps	4.75
February 6, 1996. Printed by Harrison.	
Back cover features Olympic symbols	4.75
February 6, 1996. Printed by Questa	
Back cover features Olympic symbols	6.00
August 6, 1996. Printed by Harrison	
Cover has no white line through block of stamps	
Back cover features Olympic symbols	4.75
August 6, 1996. Printed by Questa	
Cover has no white line through block of stamps	
Back cover features Olympic symbols	5.00
February 4, 1997. Printed by Harrison	
Cover has no white line through block of stamps	4.75
February 4, 1997. Printed by Questa	
Cover has no white line through block of stamps	6.00
May 5, 1998. Printed by De La Rue	
Cover has no white line through block of stamps	4.75
December 1, 1998. Printed by Questa	
Stamps printed in gravure	5.00

■ 4 x 1st orange-red

April 6, 1993. Printed by Harrison	4.00
August 17, 1993. Printed by Walsall	4.00
January 10, 1995. Printed by Walsall	
Cover has white lines through block of stamps	4.00
February 6, 1996. Printed by Walsall	
Back cover features Olympic symbols	4.00
February 4, 1997. Printed by Walsall	
Cover has no white line through block of stamps	3.50
August 26, 1997. Printed by Walsall	
Stamps printed in gravure	4.50

■ 4 x 1st orange-red with commemorative label

July 27, 1994. Printed by Questa.	
Label marks 300th anniversary of Bank of England	4.00
May 16, 1995. Printed by Walsall	
Label marks the centenary of birth of R. J. Mitchell	4.00
April 16, 1996. Printed by Walsall	
Label marks 70th birthday of Queen Elizabeth II	4.00
February 12, 1997. Printed by Walsall	
Label marks Hong Kong '97 stamp exhibition	3.75
October 21, 1997. Printed by Walsall	
Label marks Commonwealth Heads of Govt Meeting	5.00
November 14, 1998. Printed by Walsall	

Label marks 50th birthday of the Prince of Wales	4.25
May 12, 1999. Printed by Walsall	
Label marks 50th anniversary of the Berlin Airlift	4.75
October 1, 1999. Printed by Walsall.	
Label marks the Rugby World Cup	3.25
(* Panes with commemorative labels, Millennium definitives or	
the self-adhesive definitives are listed in the relevant sections.)	

■ 8 x 1st class orange-red, 2 x Millennium stamps

May 12, 1999. Printed by Walsall	
Containing the Settlers' Tale 26p stamp	6.50
September 21, 1999. Printed by Walsall	
Containing the Farmers' Tale 26p stamp	6.50
May 26, 2000. Printed by Walsall	
Containing the Above & Beyond 26p stamp	6.50
September 5, 2000. Printed by Walsall	
Containing the Stone & Soil 26p stamp	6.50

■ 10 x 1st orange-red

April 6, 1993. Printed by Harrison	6.00
April 6, 1993. Printed by Walsall	6.00
November 1, 1993. Printed by Questa	6.00
November 1, 1993. Printed by Walsall	
Back cover has advertisement for Greetings stamps	6.25
February 22, 1994. Printed by Walsall	
With 'FREE POSTCARDS' on yellow edge at right	5.50
July 1, 1994. Printed by Walsall	
With 'OPEN NOW Chance to win a kite' on yellow strip,	
and 'Better luck next time' on inside back cover	5.75
July 1, 1994. Printed by Walsall	
With 'OPEN NOW Chance to win a kite' on yellow strip, and	
'You've won' on inside back cover	5.75
September 20, 1994. Printed by Walsall	
With 'STAMPERS' and 'DO NOT OPEN UNTIL' on cover	5.75
September 20, 1994. Printed by Walsall	
With 'STAMPERS' and 'KEEP IN TOUCH' on cover	5.75
September 20, 1994. Printed by Walsall	
With 'STAMPERS' and 'HAPPY BIRTHDAY' on cover	5.75
September 20, 1994. Printed by Walsall	
With 'STAMPERS' and 'What's happenin'' on cover	5.75
January 10, 1995. Printed by Harrison	
Cover has white lines through block of stamps	6.00
January 10, 1995. Printed by Questa	
Cover has white lines through block of stamps	6.00
January 10, 1995. Printed by Walsall	
Cover has white lines through block of stamps	6.00
February 14, 1995. Printed by Walsall.	
Cover shows Thornton's chocolates	5.50
April 4, 1995. Printed by Harrison	
Stamps have two phosphor bands	6.00
April 24, 1995. Printed by Walsall	
With 'W.H. Smith Special Offer' on yellow strip	5.50
June 26, 1995. Printed by Questa	
With 'Sainsbury's Promotion' on yellow strip	6.00
September 4, 1995. Printed by Harrison	
Cover shows Benjy Bear and Harry Hedgehog	5.50
February 6, 1996. Printed by Walsall	
Back cover features Olympic symbols	5.25
February 19, 1996. Printed by Harrison	
Cover showing Walt Disney World	5.50

rch 19, 1996. Printed by Harrison
ck cover features Olympic symbols 5.50
y 13, 1996. Printed by Harrison
ver shows lighting the Olympic flame
ck cover shows Shot Put 5.50
y 13, 1996. Printed by Harrison
ver showing lighting the Olympic flame,
ck cover shows Hurdles 5.50
y 13, 1996. Printed by Harrison
ver showing lighting the Olympic flame
ck cover shows Archery 5.50
15, 1996. Printed by Walsall
ith 'W. H. Smith Offer Inside' on yellow strip 5.50
gust 16, 1996. Printed by Harrison
ver has no white line through block of stamps
ck cover features Olympic symbols 6.00
gust 16, 1996. Printed by Walsall
ver has no white line through block of stamps
ck cover features Olympic symbols 6.00
ptember 9, 1996. Printed by Walsall
ver shows iced cakes 5.50
ctober 7, 1996. Printed by Walsall.
ith 'Offer Inside' on yellow strip 5.50
bruary 4, 1997. Printed by Harrison
ver has no white line through block of stamps 6.00
bruary 4, 1997. Printed by Walsall
ver has no white line through block of stamps 6.00
vember 8, 1997. Printed by Walsall
amps printed in gravure 6.00
bruary 2, 1998. Printed by De La Rue
ith 'Win an Adventure holiday to Disney Animal Kingdom' 6.00
ril 27, 1998. Printed by De La Rue
ver shows Peugeot 106. 'Stick one of these on your drive' 5.50
y 5, 1998. Printed by De La Rue 5.50
y 1, 1998. Printed by De La Rue
ver shows JVC Camcorder 5.50
gust 3, 1998. Printed by De La Rue
ver inscribed 'Make their post memorable' 5.50
ptember 7, 1998. Printed by Questa
amps printed in litho 6.00
ecember 1, 1998. Printed by Questa
amps printed in gravure 7.50

10 x 1st gold

ril 21, 1997. Printed by Harrison 6.00
ril 21, 1997. Printed by Walsall 6.00
ptember 15, 1997. Printed by Harrison
ver shows beach, inscribed 'FIRST CLASS TRAVEL' 6.00

993 self-adhesive booklet, 20 x 1st class

SELF ADHESIVE BOOKLETS

Experimental booklets with horizontal format.

■ **20 x 1st orange-red horizontal format**
October 19, 1993. Printed by Walsall 10.00

Booklets with a mainly red cover, and an illustration of the contents.

■ **6 x 2nd bright blue**
January 29, 2001. Printed by Walsall 4.00

■ **10 x 2nd bright blue**
January 29, 2001. Printed by Questa 5.00

■ **12 x 2nd bright blue**
January 29, 2001. Printed by Questa 5.00

■ **4 x 1st orange-red and a commemorative label**
January 29, 2001. Printed by Walsall
Label marks centenary of the death of Queen Victoria 5.00

■ **6 x 1st orange-red**
January 29, 2001. Printed by Walsall 4.50
July 4, 2002. Printed by Questa 4.00

■ **10 x 1st orange-red**
January 29, 2001. Printed by Questa 6.00

■ **12 x 1st orange-red**
January 29, 2001. Printed by Questa 6.50
January 29, 2001. Printed by Questa 6.50
Booklets with a redesigned cover, in the colour of the stamps contained, with the contents given in large type, and with one (1st class), two (2nd class) or no notches (other values) along the right hand edge.

■ **12 x 2nd bright blue**
July 4, 2002. Printed by Questa 5.00
March 27, 2003. Printed by Walsall
Inscription 'The Real Network' under Royal Mail cruciform 5.00
June 15, 2004. Printed by Walsall
No 'The Real Network' inscription 5.50

■ **6 x 1st gold**
June 5, 2002. Printed by Questa 3.75
June 5, 2002. Printed by Walsall 3.75
March 27, 2003. Printed by Walsall
Inscription 'The Real Network' under Royal Mail cruciform 4.00
June 15, 2004. Printed by Walsall
Inscription 'Supporting London 2012' 3.50
March 22, 2005. Printed by Walsall
Advertisement for Smilers on inside front cover 4.00

■ **12 x 1st gold**
June 5, 2002. Printed by Walsall 6.50
March 27, 2003. Printed by Walsall
Inscription 'The Real Network' under Royal Mail cruciform 6.50

■ 6 x E
July 4, 2002. Printed by Walsall   9.00
May 28, 2003. Printed by Walsall
Inscription 'The Real Network' under Royal Mail cruciform 10.00

■ 6 x 42p
July 4, 2002. Printed by Walsall   13.00
May 28, 2003. Printed by Walsall
Inscription 'The Real Network' under Royal Mail cruciform 13.00

■ 6 x 68p
July 4, 2002. Printed by Walsall   14.00
May 28, 2003. Printed by Walsall
Inscription 'The Real Network' under Royal Mail cruciform 15.00

■ 4 x Europe
March 27, 2003. Printed by Walsall
Inscription 'The Real Network' under Royal Mail cruciform 6.00
June 15, 2004. Printed by Walsall
No 'The Real Network' inscription   4.50

■ 4 x Worldwide
March 27, 2003. Printed by Walsall
Inscription 'The Real Network' under Royal Mail cruciform 7.00
June 15, 2004. Printed by Walsall
No 'The Real Network' inscription   6.00

■ 4 x Worldwide Postcard
April 1, 2004. Printed by Walsall   3.75

■ 12 x 2nd bright blue
June 5, 2007. Printed by Walsall
Includes PiP information   4.00

■ 6 x 1st gold
June 5, 2007. Printed by Walsall
Includes PiP information   3.50
June 5, 2007. Printed by Walsall
Facsimile of Arnold Machin's signature on right of pane 3.50

■ 12 x 1st gold
June 5, 2007. Printed by Walsall
Includes PiP information   5.50

2003 Extreme Endeavours booklet

Booklets containing a mixture of 1st class definitives an special issues, with the covers matching the colour of the definitives and (with the exception of Cats & Dogs) illustrating the special stamps inside. The 1st class gold booklets have one notch along the right hand edge.

■ 2 x 1st orange-red, 10 x Cats & Dogs
February 13, 2001. Printed by Walsall   17.5

■ 4 x 1st orange-red, 2 x 1st class Submarines
April 17, 2001. Printed by Questa   70.0

■ 4 x 1st orange-red, 2 x 1st class Punch & Judy
September 4, 2001. Printed by Questa   11.0

■ 4 x 1st orange-red, 2 x 1st class Flags & Ensigns
October 22, 2001. Printed by Questa   11.00

■ 4 x 1st orange-red, 2 x 1st class Airliners
May 2, 2002. Printed by Questa   6.0

■ 4 x 1st orange-red, 2 x 1st class World Cup
May 21, 2002. Printed by Questa   6.25

■ 4 x 1st gold, 2 x 1st class Bridges of London
September 10, 2002. Printed by Questa   6.00

■ 4 x 1st gold, 2 x 1st class Hello!
March 4, 2003. Printed by Questa   6.75

■ 4 x 1st gold, 2 x 1st class Extreme Endeavours
April 29, 2003. Printed by De La Rue   5.00

■ 4 x 1st gold, 2 x 1st class British Journey: Scotland
July 15, 2003. Printed by De La Rue   5.50

■ 4 x 1st gold, 2 x 1st class Toys
September 18, 2003. Printed by De La Rue   6.50

■ 4 x 1st gold, 2 x 1st class British Journey: N Ireland
March 16, 2004. Printed by De La Rue   5.00

■ 4 x 1st gold, 2 x 1st class Ocean Liners
April 13, 2004. Printed by De La Rue   5.00

■ 4 x 1st gold, 2 x 1st class British Journey: Wales
June 15, 2004. Printed by De La Rue   5.75

ROYAL MAIL COMMEMORATIVE BOOKLETS, 1985

■ 1985, July 30. 350th Anniversary of Royal Mail Servic to the Public
£1.53 (10 x 17p 350th Anniversary stamp, with an all-over 'D' pattern printed on the back).
Cover shows a Datapost van, plane, Concorde   4.50

PENNY BLACK COMMEMORATIVE BOOKLETS, 1990

■ 4 x 15p
January 30, 1990. Printed by Walsall ... 3.50

■ 10 x 15p
January 30, 1990. Printed by Harrison ... 6.00
April 17, 1990. Printed by Questa ... 11.50
June 12, 1990. Printed by Walsall ... 6.00

■ 4 x 20p
January 30, 1990. Printed by Walsall ... 4.25
April 17, 1990. Stamps by Harrison; cover by Walsall ... 5.00

■ 5 x 20p
January 30, 1990.
Cover showing Wicken Fen, printed on glossy card ... 10.00
Cover showing Click Mill ... 3.50

■ 10 x 20p
January 30, 1990. Printed by Harrison ... 6.00
April 17, 1990. Printed by Questa ... 11.00
June 12, 1990. Printed by Walsall ... 4.50

■ 2 x 15p, 1 x 20p se-tenant
January 30, 1990.
Cover showing Vickers Viscount and De Haviland Comet ... 3.50

MILLENNIUM DEFINITIVE BOOKLETS, 2000

■ 4 x 1st with a commemorative label
March 21, 2000. Printed by Walsall
Label showing Postman Pat ... 4.25
April 4, 2000. Printed by Walsall
Label for the National Botanic Garden of Wales ... 4.50

■ 10 x 1st
January 6, 2000. Printed by Questa ... 6.00
January 6, 2000. Printed by Walsall ... 6.25

PRICING IN PROPORTION BOOKLETS

■ 4 x 2nd Large
August 15, 2006 ... 3.00

■ 4 x 1st Large
August 15, 2006 ... 3.50

■ 6 x 1st gold
September 12, 2006 ... 3.50

■ 12 x 2nd
September 12, 2006 ... 5.00

■ 12 x 1st
September 12, 2006 ... 5.50

■ 6 x 1st gold
February 1, 2007.
With postcode advertisement inside front cover ... 3.50

BOOKLETS CONTAINING SMILERS DEFINITIVES

■ 6 x Smilers stamps issued on October 4, 2005
October 4, 2005. Printed by Walsall ... 2.75
July 17, 2006. Printed by Walsall. With PiP information. ... 3.50

■ 6 x Smilers stamps issued on October 17, 2006
October 17, 2006. Printed by Walsall ... 3.50

■ 1 x 'Love' stamp, 5 x 1st class definitive
January 16, 2007. Printed by Walsall ... 3.50

PRESTIGE STAMP BOOKS

In this section, prices are quoted for mint condition only.

Stamps for Cooks, 1969

■ 1969, December 1. £1 Stamps for Cooks

Pane of six 1d, three 4d, three 4d, three 5d (recipe label)	10.00
Pane of fifteen 4d (label 'Stuffed Cucumber')	3.00
Pane of fifteen 4d (label 'Method')	3.00
Pane of fifteen 5d (recipe label)	3.00
Complete book	10.00

(* A stapled version of this stitched book exists that is much more rare. It retails at around £300.)

The Story of Wedgwood book, 1972

■ 1972, May 24.
£1 The Story of Wedgwood

Pane of twelve 3p	4.00
Pane of six 2½p, six 3p	6.00
Pane of nine 2½p, one ½p	7.50
Pane of four ½p, two 2½p	45.00
Complete book	45.00

■ 1980, April 16.
£3 The Story of Wedgwood

Pane of six 2p	1.00
Pane of nine 10p	2.50
Pane of nine 12p	2.75
Pane of one 2p, four 10p, four 12p	2.75
Complete book	6.00

■ 1982, May 19. £4 Story of Stanley Gibbons

Pane of six 12½p	2.25
Pane of six 15½p	3.50
Pane of nine15½p	2.50
Pane of one 2p, one 3p, seven 12½p	4.00
Complete book	7.50

■ 1983, September 14.
£4 Story of the Royal Mint

Pane of six 12½p (label 'The Royal Mint & America')	2.25
Pane of six 12½p (label 'Maundy Money')	2.25
Pane of nine 16p	3.00
Pane of one 3p, two 3½p, six 16p	5.00
Complete book	7.50

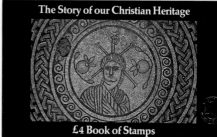

The Story of our Christian Heritage book, 1984

■ 1984, September 4. £4 The Story of Our Christian Heritage

Pane of six 17p	2.75
Pane of six 13p (label 'William Wilberforce')	2.50
Pane of six 13p (label 'Lillian Bayliss')	2.50
Pane of one 10p, one 13p, seven 17p	20.00
Complete book	20.00

The Story of The Times book, 1985

■ 1985, January 8.
£5 The Story of The Times

Pane of six 17p	2.75
Pane of nine 13p	3.25
Pane of nine 17p	3.50
Pane of two 4p, four 13p, two 17p, one 34p	8.50
Complete book	11.00

The Story of British Rail book, 1986

■ 1986, March 18. £5 The Story of British Rail

Pane of six 17p	3.00
Pane of nine 12p	3.75
Pane of nine 17p	4.00
Pane of six 12p, two 17p, one 31p	10.00
Complete book	15.00

■ 1987, March 3. £5 The Story of P&O

Pane of six 13p	2.75
Pane of nine 13p	3.25
Pane of nine 18p	3.50
Pane of one 1p, two 13p, five 18p, one 26p	8.50
Complete book	12.00

■ 1998, March 3. £5 FT100 (Financial Times)

Pane of nine 18p	2.50
Pane of six 13p	2.00
Pane of six 13p, one 18p, one 22p, one 34p	12.00
Pane of six 18p	1.75
Complete book	17.00

■ 1989, March 21. £5 The Scots Connection

Pane of nine 19p Scotland	2.75
Pane of six 14p Scotland	1.50
Pane of five 14p, two 19p, one 23p, all Scotland	11.00
Pane of six 19p Scotland	2.00
Complete book	13.00

■ 1990, March 20. £5 London Life

Pane of four 20p Alexandra Palace	1.50
Pane of six 20p Penny Black Anniversary (label 'Eros')	1.75
Pane of six 20p Penny Black Anniversary (label 'Street Signs')	1.75
Pane of one 15p, one 20p, one 29p all Penny Black Anniversary, plus one 2nd, one 1st, one 15p, one 20p, one 50p	11.00
Complete book	15.00

■ 1991, March 19. £6 Alias Agatha Christie

Pane of six 17p (label 'Styles')	1.50
Pane of six 17p (label "mousetrap')	1.50
Pane of nine 22p	3.00
Pane of six 22p, two 33p	7.00
Complete book	11.00

■ 1992, February 25. £6 Cymru Wales

Pane of four 39p Wintertime	2.50
Pane of six 18p Wales	1.50
Pane of two 18p, two 24p, all Wales, plus one 2nd, one 1st, two 33p	9.50
Pane of six 24p Wales	2.25
Complete book	11.00

Tolkien book, 1992

■ 1992, October 27. £6 Tolkien

Pane of six 24p (label 'Runes')	2.00
Pane of six 24p (label 'Hobbit')	2.00
Pane of six 18p	1.75
Pane of one 2nd, one 1st, two 18p, two 24p, two 39p	7.50
Complete book	11.00

■ 1993, August 10. £5.64 The Story of Beatrix Potter

Pane of four 1st Beatrix Potter	1.50
Pane of one 24p of each of Scotland, Wales and Northern Ireland, one 18p of each of Scotland, Wales and Northern Ireland	4.50
Pane of three 1st, three 2nd	2.50
Pane of two 2nd, two 18p, two 33p, two 39p	6.50
Complete book	12.00

■ 1994, July 26. £6.04 Northern Ireland

Pane of four 30p Prince of Wales Paintings	1.75
Pane of one 6p, one 19p, four 25p	8.00
Pane of two 19p, four 25p, one 30p, one 41p, all Northern Ireland	3.75
Pane of one 19p, one 25p, one 30p, one 41p, all Northern Ireland	3.25
Complete book	14.00

■ 1995, April 25. £6 The National Trust

Pane of six 25p National Trust	1.75
Pane of two 19p, two 25p, one 10p, one 30p, one 35p, one 41p	10.00
Pane of one 19p of each of Scotland, Wales and Northern Ireland, plus one 25p of each of Scotland, Wales and Northern Ireland	4.00
Pane of six 19p	5.50
Complete book	14.00

■ 1996, May 14. £6.48 European Football Championships

Pane of four 19p Football Legends	1.60
Pane of four 25p Football Legends	1.75
Pane of two 35p, two 41p, two 60p Football Legends	5.00
Pane of two 25p, two 25p Scotland, two 25p Wales, two 25p Northern Ireland	3.50
Complete book	11.00

■ 1997, September 23. £6.15 75 Years of the BBC

Pane of one 26p, one 37p Scotland, one 26p, one 37p Wales, one 26p, one 37p Northern Ireland	4.00
Pane of four 26p gold, four 1st gold	4.00
Pane of three 20p, three 26p	3.50
Pane of four 20p Children's Television	4.50
Complete book	12.00

■ 1998, March 10. £7.49 The Wildings Definitive

Pane of nine 26p Wilding	4.00
Pane of six 20p Wilding	2.75
Pane of four 20p, two 26p, two 37p Wilding	5.00
Pane of three 26p, three 37p Wilding	3.75
Complete book	15.00

Breaking Barriers book, 1998

■ 1998, October 13. £6.16 Breaking Barriers

Pane of four 20p Land Speed Records	4.50
Pane of one 20p Scotland, one 20p Wales, one 20p Northern Ireland, three 43p	3.75
Pane of three 2nd, one 26p Scotland, one 26p Wales, one 26p Northern Ireland	3.75
Pane of three 43p, two 10p, three 2nd	8.00
Complete book	17.50

■ 1999, February 16. £7.54 Profile on Print

Pane of eight 1st orange-red	3.25
Pane of four 1st Machin large format embossed	6.00
Pane of four Machin large format intaglio	6.00
Pane of four Machin large format typographed	6.00
Pane of nine 1st orange-red	3.25
Complete book	20.00

■ 1999, September 21. £6.99 World Changers

Pane of four 20p Millennium Jenner's vaccination	1.50
Pane of four 44p Millennium Faraday's electricity	7.00

Pane of four 26p Darwin's theory	5.00
Pane of four 63p Computers in brain	7.50
Pane of four 1p, three 19p, one 26p	4.00
Complete book	19.00

Special by Design book, 2000

■ 2000, February 15. £7.50 Special by Design

Pane of eight 1st Millennium definitive	4.50
Pane of three 1st Scotland, three 1st Wales, three 1st Northern Ireland	8.00
Pane of four 19p, olive-green, two 38p	8.00
Pane of six 1st Penny Black Anniversary	5.50
Complete book	25.00

■ 2000, August 4. £7.03 HM Queen Elizabeth The Queen Mother

Pane of six 2nd Scotland, two 65p Scotland	5.00
Pane of nine 1st Millennium definitives	4.50
Queen Mother's Century miniature sheet	6.00
Pane of four 27p Queen Mother	5.50
Complete book	18.00

■ 2000, September 18. £7 A Treasury of Trees

Pane of two 65p Millennium Doire Dach, Forest for Scotland	2.50
Pane of four 45p Millennium Sycamore Seeds, Seed Bank, Ardingly	4.00
Pane of two 65p Millennium Bluebell Wood Groundwork's Changing Places	2.50
Pane of four 1st Millennium definitives, four 2nd Northern Ireland	10.00
Pane of four 2nd Millennium Yews	2.00
Complete book	18.00

■ 2001, October 21. £6.76 Unseen and Unheard

Pane of two 1st, two 65p Submarines	6.00
Pane of two 2nd, two 45p Submarines	5.00
Pane of four Flags and Ensigns	3.50
Pane of four 1st Scotland, four E Scotland	5.00
Complete book	18.00

2002, February 6. £7.29 A Gracious Accession

ane of four 2nd, four E	4.00
ane of one 2nd, one 1st, one E,	
ne 45p Golden Jubilee	3.00
ane of one 1st, one E, one 45p,	
ne 65p Golden Jubilee	2.75
ane of four 1st Wilding, five 2nd Wilding	
ne of the 2nd is tilted)	5.00
omplete book	15.00

2002, September 24. £6.83 Across the Universe

ane of four 1st England, four 2nd England,	
ne 1st Scotland	4.00
ane of four 1st Millennium National Space Centre	10.00
ane of four 1st gold, four E	5.00
stonomy miniature sheet	4.00
omplete book	18.00

2003, February 25. £6.99 Microcosmos

ane of four 1st Northern Ireland,	
ve 2nd Northern Ireland	3.25
ane of four 1st gold, four E	4.00
ane of two 1st and two 2nd Discovery of DNA	1.50
ane of four E Discovery of DNA	2.50
omplete book	12.00

2003, June 2. £7.46 A Perfect Coronation

ane of four 1st gold, four 2nd	4.25
ane of four 1st 50th Anniversary of Coronation	3.25
ane of four (different)	
st Anniversary of Coronation	3.25
ane of two 47p Wilding, two 68p Wilding,	
ne £1 1953 Coronation	32.50
omplete book	40.00

This book is rare as over half its print run was bought by a ublisher to mail out a Coronation book. It also contains a £1 emake' of the 1953 1/3 Coronation stamp that is unavailable sewhere.)

2004, March 16. £7.44 Letters by Night

ane of three 2nd Scotland, three 68p Scotland	4.75
ane of one 28p, one E,	
ne 42p Classic Locomotives	2.00
ane of four 1st Pub Signs	2.00
ane of four 1st gold, four 37p	4.25
omplete book	12.00

THE GLORY OF THE GARDEN
A CELEBRATION OF THE RHS

he Glory of the Garden book, 2004

■ 2004, May 25. £7.23 The Glory of the Garden

Pane of four 1st gold, two 42p, two 47p	7.00
Pane of one 2nd, one E, one 68p, one 42p RHS	5.00
Pane of one 1st Iris latifolia, two 1st Tulipa,	
one 1st Gentiana acaulis	6.00
Pane of one 1st, two 47p RHS	4.50
Complete book	20.00

■ 2005, February 24. £7.43 The Brontë Sisters

Pane of four 2nd, two 39p, two 42p	4.50
Pane of two 2nd England, two 40p England	2.50
Pane of two 1st Brontë, two 1st Bronté	2.00
Pane of one 40p, one 57p, one 68p,	
one £1.12 Brontë	4.50
Complete book	13.00

■ 2005, October 4. £7.26 Battle of Trafalgar

Pane of four 1st, two 50p, two 68p	6.00
Pane of two 1st White Ensign	1.75
Pane of one 1st, one 42p, one 68p first Trafalgar	3.00
Pane of one 1st, one 42p, one 68p second Trafalgar	3.00
Complete book	12.50

■ 2006, February 23. £7.40 Brunel

Pane of one 40p, one 60p, one 47p all Brunel	3.50
Pane of one 1st, one 42p, one 68p all Brunel	3.50
Pane of four 1st, two 35p, two 40p	3.50
Pane of two 68p Ocean Liners, one 47p Brunel	4.00
Complete book	13.00

■ 2006, September 21. £7.41 Victoria Cross

Pane of first 1st, 64p and 72p Victoria Cross	2.50
Pane of second 1st, 64p and 72p Victoria Cross	2.50
Pane of four 20p Gallantry Awards	1.50
Pane of four 1st, four 50p	4.50
Complete book	10.00

■ 2007, March 1. £7.68 World of Invention

Pane of three 2nd Scotland and three 44p Wales	2.50
Pane of four 1st revised style and four 5p definitives	3.00
Pane of two 1st and two 64p World of Invention	3.50
Pane of two 1st and two 72p World of Invention	3.50
Complete book	11.00

■ 2007, June 5. £7.66 40th Anniversary of the Machin

Pane of four 2p, two 46p, two 48p definitives	3.00
Pane of two £1 ruby definitives	3.00
Pane of two 1st Arnold Machin and two 1st 4d	
deep olive-sepia designs	2.00
Pane of one 2nd and one 1st revised style, and	
two 2nd and two 1st Large definitives	3.50
Complete book	11.00

■ 2007, September 20. £7.49 British Army Uniforms

Pane of one each of 1st definitives of England,	
Northern Ireland, Scotland and Wales	2.50
Pane of three 1st British Army Uniforms	2.00
Pane of three 78p British Army Uniforms	3.50
Pane of two 1p, four 46p and two 54p definitives	3.50
Complete book	11.00

GREETINGS BOOKS

GREETINGS BOOKS

In this section, prices are quoted for mint condition only.

These booklets contain the **GB Greetings stamps**, which are listed individually in the Decimal QEII section. Normally the panes comprise one of each of the designs, often with additional greetings labels.

Greetings book, 1989

■ **1989, January 31. Various designs**
Cover shows elements from the stamp designs. Pane comprises two of each of the five designs
The stamps are all of 19p 30.00

'Smiles' greetings book, 1990

■ **1990, February 6. Smiles**
Cover shows the stamps within smiling lips.
The stamps are all of 20p 17.50

'Good luck' greetings book, 1991

■ **1991, February 5. Good luck**
Cover shows good luck charms
The stamps are all of 1st class NVIs 7.00

■ **1991, March 26. Smiles**
Cover shows a happy pillar box. Designs as for February 6, 1990, but inscribed 1st 6.00

■ **1992, January 28. Memories**
Cover shows a label inscribed Memories and pressed flowers 7.00

■ **1993, February 12. Gift Giving**
Cover shows Rupert the Bear 6.50

■ **1994, February 1. Messages**
Cover shows Rupert the Bear 7.00

'Art' greetings book, 1995

■ **1995, March 21. Art**
Cover shows a clown (the yellow strip has either the inscription 'Pull Here' or no inscription) 6.00

www.stampmagazine.co.u

'Cartoons' greetings book, 1996

■ **1996, February 26. Cartoons**
Cover shows asking for more, with bowl marked
'Love'. Stamps are on phosphor paper   6.00

■ **1996, November 11. Cartoons**
As booklet of February 26, 1996, but stamps
have two phosphor bands   20.00

'Flower Paintings' greetings book, 1996

■ **1997, January 6. Flower Paintings**
Cover shows a flower   6.00

■ **1997, February 3. Flower Paintings**
Cover as for January 6, 1997, but with the
additional inscription 'WIN A BEAUTIFUL
BOUQUET INSTANTLY'   7.00

■ **1998, January 5. Flower Paintings**
Cover shows a box of chocolates.   7.00

■ **1998, August 3. Flower Paintings**
Cover inscribed 'Make their post memorable'   7.00

Stamp Magazine is Britain's best for GB collectors

Every issue includes:

■ Five pages of GB news
■ Full details of latest issues
■ The best first day covers
■ Newly discovered errors
■ Price analysis from
dealers and eBay
■ Features on everything
from Queen Victoria
classics to modern Smilers

Available from newsagents, or
visit www.stampmagazine.co.uk

SMILERS GENERIC SHEETS

In 2000 Royal Mail introduced customised stamps by which a personal photograph could be printed on a label alongside a conventional stamp (known as Smilers), and sheets of stamps on which decorative labels replace the photographs (known as Generic sheets).

2000 Stamp Show

■ **2000, May 22. The Stamp Show 2000.**
Sheet of ten Smiles 27.50

■ **2000, October 3. Christmas.**
Sheet of 20 Robin looking through slit in pillar box.
Copyright 'Post Office 2000' 150.00
Sheet of 10 Father Christmas with Cracker.
Copyright 'Post Office 2000' 150.00

■ **2001, June 5. Occasions: Hallmarks**
Sheets of 20 comprising four of each designs 150.00

■ **2001, July 3. Smiles**
Sheet of ten Smiles stamps as May 22, 2000, but with revised labels and border 200.00

■ **2001, October 9. Christmas**
Sheet of 20 Robin looking through slit in pillar box.
Copyright 'Consignia 2001' 500.00
Sheet of 10 Father Christmas with Cracker.
Copyright 'Consignia 2001' 500.00

■ **2001, December 18. Cartoons.**
Sheet of 10 with labels of humorous quotes 35.00

■ **2002, April 23. Occasions: Pictorial messages**
Sheet of 20 comprising four of each of the five designs 50.00

■ **2002, May 21. Football World Cup**
Sheet of 20 of the lower right hand corner flag design 25.00

■ **2002, October 1. Smiles**
Sheet of 10 of the Teddy Bear design and ten of the Dennis the Menace design 22.50

■ **2002, October 1. Christmas**
Sheet of 20 of the Father Christmas with Cracker design 20.00

■ **2003, January 21. Flower paintings**
Sheet of 20 comprising two of each of the ten designs 20.00

■ **2003, February 4. Occasions**
Sheet of 20 comprising a multiple of the six designs 20.00

■ **2003, July 29. Cartoons Crossword**
Sheet of 20 comprising two of each of the ten designs, with the labels forming a crossword 16.00

■ **2003, September 30. Christmas: Winter Robins**
Sheet of 20 of the 1st class Winter Robins design.
Self-adhesive 16.00

■ **2003, November 4. Christmas: Ice Sculptures**
Sheet of 20 of the 2nd class Ice Sculptures design.
Self-adhesive 20.00
Sheet of 20 of the 1st class Ice Sculptures design.
Self-adhesive 15.00

■ **2004, January 30. Hong Kong stamp exhibition**
Sheet of 20 of the Hello greetings stamp design 15.00

■ **2004, February 3. Occasions: Envelopes**
Sheet of 20 comprising four of each of the five designs 15.00

■ **2004, May 25. Royal Horticultural Society**
Sheet of 20 of the 1st class design 17.50

■ **2004, July 27. Rule Britannia**
Sheet of 20 of the 1st class Union Flag design 15.00

■ **2004, November 2. Christmas: Father Christmas**
Sheet of 20 comprising 10 2nd and ten 1st designs 15.00

■ **2005, January 11. Farm Animals**
Sheet of 20 comprising two of each of the ten designs 15.00

■ **2005, March 1. Magic**
Sheet of 20 of the 1st class design 17.50

■ **2005, April 21. Pacific Explorer stamp exhibition**
Sheet of 20 of the 1st class Hello design 12.50

■ **2005, June 21. White Ensign**
Sheet of 20 of the 1st class White Ensign design 15.00

■ **2005, September 15. ITV**
Sheet of 20 of the 1st class Emmerdale design 12.50

■ **2005, November 1. Christmas**
Sheet of 20 comprising 10 of the 1st class and ten of the 2nd class Winter Robins designs 12.50

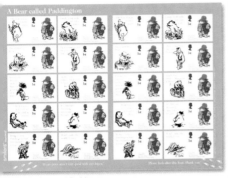

2006 A Bear Called Paddington

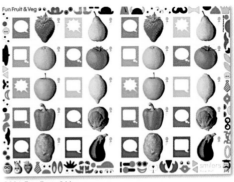

2006 Fun Fruit & Veg

■ **2006, January 10. A Bear Called Paddington**
Sheet of 20 of the Paddington Bear stamp
from the Animal Tales set — 12.50

■ **2006, March 7. Fun Fruit and Veg**
Sheet of 20 of the Fruit and Veg stamps — 11.00

■ **2006, May 25. Washington Stamp Exhibition 2006**
Sheet of 20 of the large size 'Hello' stamp — 11.00

■ **2006, June 6. World Cup Winners**
Sheets of 20 of the 1st World Cup Winners stamp — 11.00

■ **2006, July 4. For Life's Special Moments**
Sheet of 20 of the small size pictorial definitives — 11.00

■ **2006, November 7. Christmas**
Sheet of ten 1st and ten 2nd of the Christmas designs — 11.00

■ **2006, October 17. For Life's Extra Special Moments**
Sheet of 20 of the pictorial definitives of October 2006 — 11.00

■ **2006, November 9. We Will Remember Them**
Sheet of 20 of the 1st Poppies design — 11.00

■ **2006, November 14. Belgica stamp exhibition**
Sheet of 20 of the 1st large size Hello design — 11.00

■ **2007, March 1. Glorious Wales**
Sheet of 20 of the 1st Wales design, self-adhesive — 11.00

■ **2007, April 23. Glorious England**
Sheet of 20 of the 1st England design, self-adhesive — 11.00

■ **2007, May 17. Wembley Stadium**
Sheet of 20 of the 1st Lion & Shield of St George design — 11.00

■ **2007, June 5. 40th Anniversary of the Machin Definitive**
Sheet of 20 of the 1st Arnold Machin design — 11.00

■ **2007, July 17. Harry Potter**
Sheet of 20 of the 1st Crest designs — 11.00

■ **2007, November 6. Christmas**
Sheet of 20 of the 2nd, 1st and 78p designs — 15.00

■ **2007, November 8. We Will Remember Them**
Sheet of 20 of the 1st Lest We Forget design — 11.00

Stamp Magazine is Britain's best for GB collectors

Every issue includes:

■ Five pages of GB news
■ Full details of latest issues
■ The best first day covers
■ Newly discovered errors
■ Price analysis from dealers and eBay

Available from newsagents, or visit
www.stampmagazine.co.uk

Subscribe to Stamp Magazine
and save over 30% on the standard rate

Stamp Magazine is essential reading for every GB collector, with all the latest information on new issues, first day covers, printing dates, error discoveries and market and auction prices.

Every issue also offers special GB, Commonwealth and all-world features, details of exhibitions, auctions and fairs, and the chance to have your questions answered by a panel of experts.

To subscribe, call 0845 676 7778
quoting code 34U

Or visit www.stampmagazine.co.uk (offers may vary online)

DID YOU MISS THE BOAT
OR DID YOU TAKE OUR ADVICE?

In 1973 we recommended and sold the British definitive 1/2p (SG X842) with one phosphor band on side. We told our customers to buy them at 25p each. WE WERE RIGHT!!! Today this stamp is catalogued at £55.00 each. If you had taken our advice, for an outlay of only £50.00 in 1973, the current catalogue value of your investment would be a staggering total of £11,000.00.

In 1999 we recommended our customers to buy the Princess Diana Welsh Language Presentation Packs. The catalogue value was only £2.50 each, but we were telling our customers to buy them for up to double catalogue value £5.00 each. Within only 6 years they had increased in catalogue value by 5,900%.

In 2003 we recommended our customers to buy the Coronation £1 Green (SG 2380) it was catalogued by Stanley Gibbons at £1.50 per stamp. Within one year the catalogue value had increased to £50 per stamp, an increase of over 3,200%.

As recently as 2004 we told our customers to buy the Fruit & Veg Presentation Pack - it was catalogued at £4.50. We said ignore the catalogue value, it's cheap even at treble catalogue value - this pack increased in Stanley Gibbons Catalogue to £65.00 within three years. An increase of well over 1,200%.

We hope that you took our advice recently. We recommended you to buy the Locomotives Miniature Sheet (SG.MS.2423). The Stanley Gibbons Catalogue value was £3.75 each. Now only two years later the Stanley Gibbons Catalogue value has increased to £35 each. An increase of over 700% in only two years.

As recently as 1 year ago we recommended the English Entente Cordiale presentation pack. It was catalogued by Stanley Gibbons at £4.25 1 year ago. Now the catalogue value in the latest 2007 Stanley Gibbons concise catalogue is £35, a massive increase of over 600% in only one year.

As everyone knows, investments can go down as well as up and the past is not necessarily a guide to the future. However, being selective and taking sound advice is the best way to make your hobby pay for itself.

PLEASE LISTEN TO US NOW
we most strongly advise our customers to buy the

GB 2003
Rugby World Cup
Presentation Pack (number M9B)

Catalogue value in the Stanley Gibbons 2007 edition of Collect British Stamps is £16.00.

We recommend you buy it at the cheapest price from any dealer willing to sell...

BUY IT NOW!

12 Prince Albert Street, Brighton, Sussex, BN1 1HE
Tel: 01273 326994   FAX: 01273 321318

PRESENTATION PACKS

In this section, prices are quoted for packs in mint condition only.

Many collectors regard the first GB presentation packs (the 'forerunners') as the pre-packaged definitives sold in 1960 to mark the international stamp exhibition in London (with a sales tour undertaken by the Post Office in the USA). Low value Wildings, Castle high values, phosphor/graphite definitives and the regional stamps were each made available in these packs, which can be found priced in sterling or in US dollars.

In 1964 the Post Office introduced the presentation pack to accompany the Shakespeare Festival special issue, and since then they have regularly been issued for GB special stamps, as well as for new definitives.

Some have been issued in foreign language and other special versions.

SPECIAL ISSUES

■ 1964

Shakespeare	16.00
Geographical Congress	90.00
Botanical Congress	90.00
Forth Road Bridge	£425

■ 1965

Churchill	45.00
Parliament	65.00
Battle of Britain	50.00
Post Office Tower	5.00

■ 1966

Robert Burns	45.00
Westminster Abbey	45.00
World Cup	11.00
Birds	11.00
Technology	9.00
Battle of Hastings	4.00
Christmas	4.00

■ 1967

EFTA	3.00
British Flowers	4.00

British Paintings	4.00
Discoveries	2.50

■ 1968

British Bridges	2.50
Anniversaries	2.00
Paintings	2.00
Paintings (German version)	10.00
Christmas	2.00
Christmas (German version)	7.00

■ 1969

British Ships	3.00
British Ships (German version)	20.00
British Ships (Cunard version)	22.00
Concorde	7.50
Concorde (German version)	30.00
Anniversaries	3.00
Anniversaries (German version)	50.00
Cathedrals	2.00
Cathedrals (German version)	18.00
Prince of Wales Investiture	2.25
Prince of Wales (German version)	18.00
Prince of Wales (Welsh version)	25.00
Post Office Technology	2.00
Christmas	2.00

■ 1970

Cottages	3.50
Anniversaries	2.00
Literary Anniversaries	2.75
Commonwealth Games	2.00
Philympia	2.00
Christmas	2.00

■ 1971

Ulster Paintings	3.50
Literary Anniversaries	3.50
Anniversaries	3.50
Universities	4.50
Christmas	3.25
Christmas (Heinz version)	25.00

(* A Heinz soup promotion allowed the labels from eight different Heinz soups to be exchanged for six 2½d Christmas stamps that were sent in a presentation pack format.)

Christmas pack, 1967

Anniversaries (German language version), 1969

Christmas pack, 1969

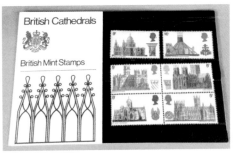

British Cathedrals pack, 1969

1972

Explorers	2.75
Anniversaries	2.50
Churches	5.00
Churches (Belgica pack)	5.00
BBC	2.50
BBC (staff version)	15.00
Christmas	2.50
Royal Silver Wedding	2.50
Royal Silver Wedding (Japanese version)	5.00

* To mark the 50th anniversary of the BBC a special version of the BBC pack was sent to all staff.)

1973

EC	1.75
Oak	1.50
Explorers	1.75
Cricket	3.50
Paintings	1.85
Inigo Jones	1.85
Parliament	1.85
Royal Wedding	1.50
Christmas	1.85

BBC presentation pack (staff version), 1972

1974

Chestnut	1.50
Fire Service	2.00
UPU	2.00
Great Britons	2.00
Churchill	2.00
Christmas	2.00

1975

Turner	2.00
Architecture	2.00
Sailing	1.50
Railways	3.00
Parliament	1.25
Jane Austen	2.00
Christmas	2.50

1976

Telephones	3.00
Social Pioneers	2.00
USA Bicentennial	1.00
Cultural Traditions	2.50
Roses	2.00
Caxton	2.00
Christmas	2.50

1977

Racket Sports	2.00
Chemistry	2.00
Silver Jubilee	1.25

Heinz promotional Christmas pack, 1971

Energy pack, 1978

Charles Darwin pack, 1982

Heads of Government	0.75
Wildlife	1.00
Christmas	2.00

■ 1978

Energy	1.75
Buildings	2.00
25th anniversary of Coronation	1.25
Horses	1.25
Cycling	1.25
Christmas	1.25

■ 1979

Dogs	1.25
Spring Flowers	1.25
Elections	1.25
Derby	1.25
Year of the Child	2.00
Rowland Hill	1.25
Police	1.25
Christmas	1.25

■ 1980

Birds	1.25
Liverpool & Manchester Railway	1.25
London 1980	1.25
Landmarks	1.25

Authors	1.75
Conductors	1.25
Sport	1.25
Christmas	1.25

■ 1981

Folklore	2.25
Year of the Disabled	1.35
Butterflies	1.35
National Trust	1.50
Royal Wedding	1.50
Royal Wedding (Japanese version)	4.50
Duke of Edinburgh Award	1.50
Fishing	1.50
Christmas	1.50

■ 1982

Darwin	1.50
Youth Organisations	1.75
Theatre	3.00
Maritime	2.50
Textiles	1.50
Information Technology	1.00
Cars	1.50
Christmas	1.50

(* The Charles Darwin issue was the first of a new style of presentataion pack. The essential style has changed little since.)

■ 1983

Fish	1.50
Commonwealth Day	1.50
Engineering Achievements	2.25
British Army	2.00
Gardens	1.60
Fairs	1.60
Christmas	1.75

■ 1984

Heraldry	1.75
Cattle	2.00
Urban Renewal	1.60
Europa	2.75
Greenwich Meridian	1.75
Mail Coaches	1.60
British Council	1.60
Christmas	1.75

Royal Wedding pack (souvenir book version), 1981

1985

amous Trains	3.75
nsects	2.25
Composers	3.00
afety at Sea	1.75
Royal Mail	1.75
Arthurian Legends	1.75
British Film Year	2.75
Christmas	2.00

1986

ndustry	2.00
Halley's Comet	2.00
The Queen's 60th birthday	2.75
Conservation	2.50
Medieval	2.00
port	2.50
Royal Wedding	1.25
RAF	2.50
Christmas	2.25
Christmas folder	8.50

* The Christmas stamps were also made available in a special
older that contained 36 of the 13p Glastonbury Thorn design.)

1987

lowers	2.25
Newton	2.25
Architects	2.75
t John Ambulance	2.25
Heraldry	2.25
Victorian Life	2.25
Pottery	2.25
Christmas	2.25

1988

Linnean Society	2.25
Welsh Bible	2.25
port	2.25
Transport	2.75
Australian Bicentennial	2.25
panish Armada	2.25
dward Lear	2.25
Christmas	2.25

Christmas folder, 1986

1989

Birds	2.25
Food and Farming	2.25
Anniversaries	2.50
Toys	2.75
Industry	2.25
Microscopes	2.25
Lord Mayor's Show	2.25
Christmas	2.00

1990

Penny Black	4.25
RSPCA	2.50
Buildings	3.25
Queen's Awards	2.50
Kew Gardens	2.25
Thomas Hardy	1.25
Queen Mother	3.50
Gallantry	2.25
Astronomy	2.50
Christmas	2.40

1991

Dogs	2.50
Science	2.40
Europe in Space	2.75
Sport	2.40
Roses	2.40
Dinosaurs	3.00
Ordnance Survey	2.40
Christmas	2.40

1992

Wintertime	2.40
Happy and Glorious	3.50
Tennyson	2.50
International	3.25
Civil War	2.40
Gilbert and Sullivan	2.50
Greener Environment	2.40
Europe	1.25
Christmas	2.25

1993

Abbotsbury Swannery	4.00
Harrison Timekeepers	3.00
Orchids	2.50
Art	3.25
Roman Britain	2.40
Waterways	2.40
Autumn	2.40
Sherlock Holmes	2.50
Christmas	2.75

1994

Steam Locomotives	3.25
Prince of Wales Paintings	2.50
Picture Postcards	2.50
Channel Tunnel	2.50
D-Day	3.50

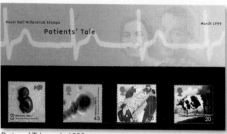

Patients' Tale pack, 1999

Inventors' Tale pack, 1999

Golf	2.60
Summertime	2.50
Medical	2.75
Christmas	2.50

■ 1995
Cats	3.25
Springtime	2.50
National Trust	2.50
Peace and Freedom	3.00
Science Fiction	2.60
Shakespeare	2.60
Communications	2.60
Rugby	3.00
Christmas	3.00

■ 1996
Robert Burns	2.50
Wildfowl Trust	2.50
Cinema	2.50
Football	3.50
Olympics	2.40
Women	2.50
Children's Television	3.00
Classic Cars	3.50
Christmas	3.00

■ 1997
King Henry VIII	5.00
Missions of Faith	2.75
Legends	2.50
Architects of the Air	4.25
The Queen's Horses	3.00
Sub Post Offices	3.00
Enid Blyton	3.00
Christmas	3.00
Royal Golden Wedding Anniversary	5.00

■ 1998
Endangered Species	3.50
Princess of Wales Memorial	4.50
Princess of Wales (Welsh version)	60.00
The Queen's Beasts	2.50
Lighthouses	3.25
Comedians	3.25
National Health Service	3.00
Fantasy Novels	3.25

Carnival	3.00
Speed	3.50
Christmas	3.25

(* The Princess of Wales pack's limited edition Welsh language version was made available only at post office counters in Wales.)

■ 1999
Inventors' Tale	3.75
Travellers' Tale	3.75
Patients' Tale	3.75
Settlers' Tale	3.75
Workers' Tale	3.75
Entertainers' Tale	3.75
Royal Wedding	2.00
Citizens' Tale	3.75
Scientists' Tale	3.75
Farmers' Tale	3.75
Soldiers' Tale	3.75
Christians' Tale	3.75
Artists' Tale	3.75
Millennium Timekeeper	16.00

■ 2000
Above and Beyond	3.75
Fire and Light	3.75
Water and Coast	3.75
Life and Earth	3.75
Art and Craft	3.75
Her Majesty's Stamps	60.00
Penny Black	35.00
People and Place	3.75
Stone and Soil	3.75
Tree and Leaf	3.75

Princess of Wales Memorial pack, 1998 (Werlsh version)

Penny Black pack, 2000

Her Majesty's Stamps pack, 2000

Queen Mother's 100th birthday pack, 2000

Football World Cup	4.50
Commonwealth Games	3.50
Peter Pan	3.50
London Bridges	3.50
Astronomy	3.25
Pillar Boxes	4.50
Wildings I, 50th anniversary	47.50
Christmas	3.50

(* A Wildings I pack was issued on December 5, 2002 to mark the 50th anniversary of the Wildings designs, but most of the print run was destroyed by Royal Mail as the packs contained printing errors. Only 8,500 were ever in circulation.)

2003

Birds of Prey	4.75
Occasions	3.25
The Secret of Life DNA	3.50
Fruit and Veg	40.00
Extreme Endeavours	4.25
Wildings II, 50th anniversary	4.25
Coronation Anniversary	20.00
Prince William	20.00
British Journey: Scotland	4.25
Pub Signs	6.50
Toys	3.80
British Museum	6.50
Christmas	5.50
Rugby World Cup	35.00

(* The Fruit and Veg pack was a self-adhesive issue brought out with accompanying stickers to add facial features to the stamps. Many packs are thought to have been used rather than being collected in mint condition.)

2004

Classic Locomotives	30.00
Occasions	3.25
Lord of the Rings	11.00
British Journey: Northern Ireland	4.25
Entente Cordiale	17.50
Ocean Liners	4.75
Royal Horticultural Society	4.50
British Journey: Wales	4.50

Queen Mother's 100th birthday	12.50
Mind and Matter	3.75
Body and Bone	3.75
Spirit and Faith	3.75
Sound and Vision	3.75

(* The Her Majesty's Stamps and Penny Black packs were produced specifically for Stamp Show 2000.)

2001

Hopes for the Future	3.75
Occasions	5.00
Cats and Dogs	11.00
Weather	6.50
Submarines	5.50
Double deck buses	5.50
Hats	4.00
Pond Life	4.50
Punch and Judy	3.25
Nobel Prizes	11.00
Flags and Ensigns	12.00
Christmas	3.75

2002

Just So Stories	11.00
Golden Jubilee	4.00
Occasions	2.75
Coastlines	4.50
Queen Mother Memorial	3.25
Circus	3.50
Aircraft	3.50

Royal Society of Arts	4.80
Woodland Animals	4.80
Crimean War	5.50
Christmas	5.50

(* The Classic Locomotives pack was meant to herald a redesign of GB presentation packs to make the stamp 'mounts' integral to the whole pack. A few early prints of this were produced before the redesign was scrapped due to 'technical problems', but none has yet come onto the market.)

▪ 2005

Farm Animals	4.80
British Journey: South-West England	4.50
Jane Eyre	5.50
Magic!	5.25
Royal Wedding	4.50
World Heritage Sites	5.75
Trooping the Colour	5.75
Motorcycles	5.50
London 2012	5.50
Changing Tastes	5.50
Classic ITV	5.50
The Ashes (miniature sheet)	4.00
Battle of Trafalgar	5.50
Christmas	5.50

▪ 2006

Animal Tales	5.75
British Journey: England	5.25
Brunel	5.25
Ice Age Animals	5.25
The Queen's 80th birthday	6.00
World Cup Winners	5.25
Building Modern Britain	5.25
National Portrait Gallery	5.50
Victoria Cross	6.00

Beside The Seaside pack, 2007

Sounds of Britain	5.50
Smilers	3.75
Christmas	5.75:
Lest We Forget	5.75
Celebrating Scotland	4.25

▪ 2007

The Beatles	7.50
Sea Life	5.75
Sky at Night	5.50
World of Invention	6.00
Abolition of Slavery	5.50
Celebrating England	4/50
Beside the Seaside	5.75
Machin Anniversary	4.50
Grand Prix	6.00
Harry Potter	6.00
Scouts	5.50
Birds	6.00
Army Uniforms	5.50
Golden Wedding	5.50
Christmas	6.00
Lest We Forget	5.50

Stamp Magazine is Britain's best for GB collectors

Every issue includes:

▪ Five pages of GB news
▪ Full details of latest issues
▪ The best first day covers
▪ Newly discovered errors
▪ Price analysis from dealers and eBay
▪ Features on everything from Queen Victoria classics to modern Smilers

Available from newsagents, or visit www.stampmagazine.co.uk

DEFINITIVES

■ Forerunners

1960	Wilding definitives: priced in Sterling	£175
1960	Wilding definitives: priced in Dollars	£275
1960	Phosphor-graphite: priced in Sterling	£175
1960	Phosphor-graphite: priced in Dollars	£275
1960	Regionals: priced in Sterling	£175
1960	Regionals: priced in Dollars	£275
1960	Castle high values: priced in Sterling	£1,100
1960	Castle high values: priced in Dollars	£1,600

■ Low value Machins

1967	½d to 1/9	2.50
1967	(German version)	80.00
1971	½p to 9p	2.25
1971	Scandinavia Tour	12.50
1971	NABA stamp exhibition	85.00
1971	½p to 10p	12.00
1977	To 50p	2.75
1981	To 75p (pack no. 129a)	12.50
1983	To 75p (pack no. 1)	26.00
1984	½p to 75p	21.00
1987	1p to 75p	27.00
1988	14p to 35p	6.00
1989	15p to 37p	5.00
1990	Penny Black Anniversary	4.00
1990	10p to 33p	5.00
1991	1p to 75p	27.00
1991	6p to 39p	5.00
1993	Self-adhesive booklet	8.50
1993	19p to 41p	4.50
1995	1p to £1	25.00
1996	20p to 63p	6.00
1997	2nd and 1st	4.50
1997	26p and 1st	4.50
1998	2nd, 1st, 1p to £1	11.00
1999	7p to 64p	5.25
2000	Millennium 1st	3.00
2000	Jeffery Matthews Palette	70.00
2000	8p to 65p	5.50
2002	2nd, 1st, 1p to £1	7.50

Britain's first decimal stamps pack, 1971

Self-adhesive definitives pack, 1993

2002	37p to 68p	3.75
2002	Wildings (part 1)	35.00
2003	Worldwide and Europe	3.25
2003	Wildings (part 2)	10.00
2004	1st, Worldwide Postcard, 7p to 43p	4.25
2005	Re-issued Wilding Castle definitives	5.00
2005	9p, 35p, 46p	1.50
2005	1p, 2p, 5p, 9p, 10p, 20p, 35p, 40p, 42p, 46p, 47p, 50p, 68p, £1, plus self-adhesive 2nd, 1st, Europe, Worldwide and postcard	10.00
2005	Definitive Collection folder, containing the low value definitive pack (2005), high values pack (2003), Country stamps packs (2003), Country 42p stamps pack (2005)	32.00
2006	Tariff Charge	3.50
2006	Pricing in Proportion	3.25
2007	16p to 78p	4.50
2007	1d to £1 ruby	11.00

■ High value Machins

1969	2/6 to £1	6.50
1969	(German version)	50.00
1970	10p to 50p	4.50
1971	20p to £1	7.00
1977	£1 to £5 (pack no. 91)	13.50
1987	£1 to £5 (pack no. 13)	£145
1987	£1.60	20.00
1988	Castles £1 to £5	16.00
1992	Castles £1 to £5	20.00
1993	£10	35.00
1995	£3	14.00
1997	Castles £1.50 to £5	85.00
1999	£1.50 to £5 (Enschedé)	35.00
1999	£1.50 to £5 (De La Rue)	18.00
1999	£1.50 to £5 (gravure)	17.50

POSTAGE DUES

1971	½p to 5p, 10p, 20p, 50p, £1	17.00
1977	½p to £1	8.50
1982	1p to £5	27.00
1994	1p to £5	35.00

GREETINGS STAMPS

1992	Memories	7.50
1993	Gift giving	9.50
1994	Messages	9.50
1995	Art	9.50
1996	Cartoons	12.50
1997	Flowers	10.50

COUNTRY DEFINITIVES

■ England
2001	2nd, 1st, E, 65p	4.00
2003	2nd, 1st, E, 68p	2.75

■ Northern Ireland
1970	3d, 4d sepia, 4d red, 5d, 9d, 1/3, 1/6	2.00
1971	2½p, 3p, 5p, 7½p	1.75
1974	3p, 3½p, 5½p, 8p	1.40
1974	3p, 3½p, 4½p, 5½p, 8p	1.65
1976	6½p, 8½p, 10p, 11p	1.40
1981	7p, 9p, 10½p, 11½p, 12p, 13½p, 14p, 15p, 18p, 22p	4.50
1983	10p, 12½p, 16p, 20½p, 26p, 28p	12.50
1984	10p, 13p, 16p, 17p, 22p, 26p, 28p, 31p	10.00
1987	12p, 13p, 17p, 18p, 22p, 26p, 28p, 31p	13.00
1999	19p, 25p, 30p, 41p	7.50
2000	1st, 40p, 65p	12.00
2001	2nd, 1st, E, 65p	4.50
2003	2nd, 1st, E, 68p	2.75

■ Scotland
1970	3d, 4d sepia, 4d red, 5d, 6d, 9d, 1/3, 1/6	4.00
1971	2½p, 3p, 5p, 7½p	1.75
1974	3p, 3½p, 5½p, 8p	1.40
1974	3p, 3½p, 4½p, 5½p, 8p	1.65
1976	6½p, 8½p, 10p, 11p	1.40
1981	7p, 9p, 10½p, 11½p, 12p, 13½p, 14p, 15p, 18p, 22p	4.50
1983	10p, 12½p, 16p, 20½p, 26p, 28p	12.50
1984	10p, 13p, 16p, 17p, 22p, 26p, 28p, 31p	10.00
1987	12p, 13p, 17p, 18p, 22p, 26p, 28p, 31p	13.00
1999	2nd, 1st, E, 64p	7.50
2000	65p	5.25
2002	2nd, 1st, E, 65p	3.00
2003	2nd, 1st, E, 68p	2.75

Scotland pre-decimal definitives pack, 1970

Greetings stamps pack, 1993

■ Wales
1970	3d, 4d sepia, 4d red, 5d, 9d, 1/6	3.00
1971	2½p, 3p, 5p, 7½p	1.75
1974	3p, 3½p, 5½p, 8p	1.40
	3p, 3½p, 4½p, 5½p, 8p	1.65
1976	6½p, 8½p, 10p, 11p	1.40
1981	7p, 9p, 10½p, 11½p, 12p, 13½p, 14p, 15p, 18p, 22p	4.50
1983	10p, 12½p, 16p, 20½p, 26p, 28p	12.50
1984	10p, 13p, 16p, 17p, 22p, 26p, 28p, 31p	10.00
1987	12p, 13p, 17p, 18p, 22p, 26p, 28p, 31p	13.00
1997	20p, 26p, 37p, 63p	10.50
1999	2nd, 1st, E, 64p	7.50
2000	65p	5.25
2002	2nd, 1st, E, 65p	3.00
2003	2nd, 1st, E, 68p	2.75

■ All Countries
These packs contain the stamps of Northern Ireland, Scotland and Wales (shown as 'x 3') or also including England (shown as 'x 4').

1988	14p, 19p, 23p, 32p (x 3)	9.50
1989	15p, 20p, 24p, 34p (x 3)	9.50
1990	17p, 22p, 26p, 37p (x 3)	9.50
1991	18p, 24p, 28p, 39p (x 3)	9.50
1993	19p, 25p, 30p, 41p (x 3)	9.50
1996	20p, 26p, 37p, 63p (x 3)	15.00
1998	20p (centre band), 26p, 37p, 63p (x 3)	10.50
2002	68p (x 4)	5.00
2004	40p (x 4)	3.50
2005	42p (x 4)	3.00
2006	44p, 72p (x 4)	7.50
2007	48p, 78p (x 4)	8.00

SOUVENIR PACKS

1972	Royal Silver Wedding	1.00
1973	Cricket	3.50
1973	Parliament	3.00
1974	Churchill	2.00
1975	Railways	2.25
1977	Silver Jubilee	1.25
1978	25th aAnniversary of Coronation	1.50
1981	Royal Wedding	2.00
1984	Mail coaches	3.75
1985	British Film Year	5.75

1986	The Queen's birthday	4.00
1988	Australian Bicentennial	8.50
1990	Penny Black Anniversary	10.50
1997	Golden Wedding	25.00

SPECIAL PACKS

1971	Decimal low values from ½p to 9p (plus an additional 2p and 2½p)	5.00
1994	Channel Tunnel	37.00
1995	National Trust	12.50
2000	Penny Black reproduction	35.00
2000	Stamp Show 2000 pack of three prestige stamp books	75.00
2001	Occasions: Hallmarks (five packs each containing a block of ten of one of the stamps)	100.00
2003	Across the Universe and Microcosmos prestige stamp books	40.00

YEAR PACKS

1967	1.50
1968 (blue cover)	3.50
1968 (red cover)	2.25
1968 (German version)	25.00
1969	10.00
1970	20.00
1971	26.00
1972	17.50
1973	12.50
1974	5.00
1975	4.50
1976	5.50
1977	4.00
1978	4.00
1979	5.00
1980	5.50
1981	7.50
1982	12.50
1983	12.50
1984	15.00
1985	15.00
1986	15.00
1987	15.00

1988	15.00
1989	15.00
1990	17.00
1991	17.00
1992	17.00
1993	17.00
1994	22.00
1995	22.00
1996	27.00
1997	30.00
1998	42.00
1999	55.00
2000	55.00
2001	55.00
2002	42.00
2003	43.00
2004	43.00
2005	50.00
2006	60.00

YEAR BOOKS

1984	45.00
1985	40.00
1986	40.00
1987	17.50
1988	17.50
1989	18.50
1990	20.00
1991	20.00
1992	22.00
1993	27.00
1994	22.00
1995	22.00
1996	25.00
1997	30.00
1998	42.00
1999	55.00
2000	55.00
2001	55.00
2002	47.00
2003	55.00
2004	55.00
2005	55.00
2006	60.00

ar Book, 2000

Year Pack, 1998

USE THIS PAGE TO RECORD YOUR WANTS LIST

Key contacts

To help you find your way around the hobby, here are contact details for the major players in the world of British stamps

ROYAL MAIL

Philatelic Bureau
Tallents House, 21 South Gyle Crescent,
Edinburgh EH12 9PB.
Tel: 08457 641641 (orders)
www.royalmail.com/stamps

London Special Handstamp Centre
Mount Pleasant, Farringdon Road,
London EC1A 1BB.

**Northern England Special
Handstamp Centre**
South Shields DO, Keppell Street,
South Shields, Tyne & Wear NE33 1AA.

Midland Special Handstamp Centre
Birmingham Mail Centre, St Stephen's Street,
Birmingham B6 4AA.

**Wales & The West Special
Handstamp Centre**
220-228 Penarth Road,
Cardiff CF11 8TA.

**Scotland & Northern Ireland Special
Handstamp Centre**
Rutherglen DO, Duchess Place, Rutherglen,
Glasgow G73 1BT.

FAMOUS COLLECTIONS

British Library
96 Euston Road, London NW1 2DB.
Tel: 020 7412 7635
www.collectbritain.co.uk

British Postal Museum & Archive
Freeling House, Phoenix Place,
London WC1X 0DL.
Tel: 020 7239 2570
www.postalheritage.org.uk

Royal Philatelic Collection
www.royal.gov.uk

SOCIETIES

Royal Philatelic Society
41 Devonshire Place, London W1N 1PE.
Tel: 020 7486 1044
www.rpsl.org.uk

National Philatelic Society
c/o BPMA, Freeling House,
Phoenix Place, London WC1X 0DL.
Tel: 020 7239 2571
www.ukphilately.org.uk/nps

**Association of British
Philatelic Societies**
www.ukphilately.org.uk/abps

Modern British Philatelic Circle
www.mbp-circle.co.uk

Machin Collectors Club
www.machins.org

British Thematic Association
www.stampdomain.com/thematic

Philatelic Traders Society
PO Box 371, Fleet, Hampshire GU52 6ZX.
Tel: 01252 628006
www.philatelic-traders-society.co.uk

British Philatelic Trust
Suite 101, Business Design Centre,
52 Upper Street, London N1 0QH.
Tel: 020 7688 8423
www.ukphilately.org.uk/bpt

STAMP SHOWS

Stampex
www.stampex.ltd.uk

Philatex
www.stampshows.net

STAMP MAGAZINE

www.stampmagazine.co.uk

ENJOY A WONDERFULLY UNIQUE EXPERIENCE IN SALISBURY

Photo by Jon Stone

If you cannot visit Salisbury, why not visit **DAUWALDERS'** website at www.worldstamps.co.uk Comprehensive Albums, Accessories and Stamps.

Photo by Jon Stone

COME AND VISIT **DAUWALDERS'**

NEW, COMPLETELY REFURBISHED STAMP STORE

THE LARGEST AND BEST OF ITS KIND IN THE WORLD FULLY AIRCONDITIONED

OPEN 6 FULL DAYS A WEEK

VISIT **DAUWALDERS'** INCREDIBLE STAMP STORE

NEW TO STAMPS? CAN'T DECIDE ON AN ALBUM?

We have a huge range of *OFF THE SHELF* Albums, Pages and Catalogues.
Want to see hingeless Albums before buying?
We stock Davo, Lighthouse, Safe, Kabe' & Lindner hingeless albums of GB and many countries. *Full range of Stanley Gibbons products.*

Our RENOWNED stock of GB STAMPS is available for inspection. Virtually any stamp of Great Britain can be purchased individually or in sets.

Why not spend a day or a weekend away in Salisbury. We can offer advice on accommodation. Dauwalders are 4 minutes from Salisbury Railway Station. Make a great stamp collecting experience into a super mini-break. Join one of the many keen collectors who travel hundreds of miles to visit **DAUWALDERS** Stamp Store.

COLLECTIONS FOR SALE

Always a large number of collections available of many countries.

WE STOCK THE WORLD

This is our Price Brochure. Ring
01722 412100
DAUWALDERS
for your copy

How to find us:

...... or if you cannot find us

By road or by rail, we are close to Salisbury Railway Station

Book of British Stamps 2007 from Salisbury

Britain's largest Provincial Stamp Shop
T: 01722 412100
F: 01722 410074
Email: sales@worldstamps.co.uk
www.worldstamps.co.uk
42 Fisherton Street, Salisbury, Wiltshire SP2 7RB

42 Fisherton Street, Salisbury SP2 7RB   Tel: 01722 412100 Fax: 01722 410074
www.worldstamps.co.uk   Email: sales@worldstamps.co.uk

GB YEAR COLLECTIONS

COMMEMORATIVE SETS

Year		U/M	F/U	G/U	FDC	PP
*2006	11 sets + 6m/s	87.50	90.00	-	-	-
*2005	11 sets + 9m/s	75.00	77.00	-	-	-
**2004	12 sets + 4m/s	75.00	75.00	-	80.00	-
*2003	11 sets + 2m/s	70.00	70.00	-	70.00	-
*2002	13 sets + 3m/s	47.00	48.00	-	52.00	-
*2001	11 sets + 3m/s	46.00	46.50	-	42.00	-
*2000	13 sets + 1m/s	38.00	38.50	-	39.50	-
1999	13 sets + 2m/s	46.00	46.00	-	49.50	-
1998	10 sets	22.00	22.00	16.00	22.00	-
1997	9 sets	20.00	21.00	15.00	22.00	-
1996	9 sets	19.00	20.50	14.00	22.00	22.00
1995	9 sets	17.00	18.00	14.00	21.00	22.00
1994	9 sets	17.00	17.50	14.00	21.00	22.00
1993	9 sets	16.50	17.50	14.00	21.00	22.00
1992	9 sets	15.50	15.50	13.50	19.00	20.50
1991	8 sets	14.00	14.20	14.50	16.00	20.00
1990	10 sets + 1m/s	18.00	18.00	16.50	21.00	24.00
1989	8 sets + 1m/s	14.50	14.50	17.50	19.00	20.50
1988	8 sets + 1m/s	14.20	14.50	13.30	18.00	19.50
1987	8 sets	11.90	13.00	12.30	19.00	19.50
1986	10 sets	14.00	14.00	11.00	18.00	23.00
1985	8 sets	12.00	12.50	11.00	14.50	22.50
1984	9 sets	10.30	10.85	8.00	11.50	17.00
1983	7 sets	8.00	8.25	4.80	11.00	15.00
1982	8 sets	8.70	8.50	5.40	10.00	14.50
1981	8 sets	6.75	7.00	4.35	8.00	11.00
1980	9 sets + 1m/s	5.55	6.70	4.30	7.75	9.50
1979	8 sets + 1m/s	4.60	5.15	4.10	5.60	7.00
1978	6 sets + 1m/s	3.40	3.60	3.35	4.80	6.00
1977	6 sets	2.80	3.40	2.25	4.30	6.75
1976	7 sets	2.95	3.50	2.55	4.50	8.50
1975	8 sets	2.75	3.50	2.55	4.50	8.50
1974	6 sets	2.25	3.15	2.00	4.00	8.50
1973	9 sets	3.95	6.00	4.60	5.50	16.50
1972	6 sets	2.25	2.90	2.30	4.50	14.00
1971	5 sets	1.70	3.00	2.25	6.00	13.50
Decimal Commemoratives complete 1971 to end 2006		727.00	745.00	430.00	615.00	

SMILER SHEETS

CODE	YEAR		Price £
LS1	2000	Stamp Show	25.00
LS2	2000	Christmas 19p Robin	
LS3		Christmas 1st cracker pair	240.00
LS2a	2001	Christmas 19p Robin	
LS3a		Christmas 1st cracker pair	1050
LS4		Occasions - Ingots	140.00
LS5		Smilers	165.00
LS6		Cartoons	37.00
LS7	2002	Occasions	42.00
LS8		World Cup	20.00
LS9		Knock knock	18.00
LS10		Christmas crackerx20	18.00
LS11	2003	Flowers	18.00
LS12		Occasions	17.00
LS13		Crosswords/cartoons	17.00
LS14		Winter Robins	17.00
LS15		Christmas 2ndx20	12.00
LS16		Christmas 1stx20	28.00
LS17	2004	Hong Kong	11.00
LS18		Occasions	12.00
LS19		RHS - Dahlias	16.00
LS20		Rule Britannia	11.75
LS21		Christmas	12.00
LS22	2005	Farm Animals	12.00
LS23		Magic	11.00
LS24		Pacific Explorers	10.50
LS25		White Ensign	10.50
LS26		Classic TV	10.50
LS27		Christmas	10.50
LS28	2006	Paddington Bear	10.50
LS29		Fruit & Veg	9.75
LS30		Hello Washington	10.50
LS31		Football	10.50
LS32		Life's Special Moments	10.70
LS33		Extra Special Moments	10.50
LS34		Christmas	10.50
LS35		We will remember them	10.50
LS36		Belgica	10.00
LS37		Glorious Wales	10.00

STAMPEX SMILERS

YEAR			Price £
1. 2003 Spring	50th Anniv		15.00
2. Autumn 2003	Teddy Bears		15.00
3. Spring 2004	Br.Gibraltar		15.50
4. Autumn 2004	Br.Phil Comp		13.50
5. Spring 2005	Cent. of Rotary Int		13.50
6. Autumn 2005	Nelson		11.50
7. Spring 2006			11.50
8. Autumn 2006			11.50
9. Spring 2007			11.50

SPECIAL GROUP COLLECTIONS

Year	SETS	U/M	F/U	G/U
1967		4.70	7.00	-
1966-67	11	3.75	5.10	-
1965	9	6.60	7.70	-
1964	4	5.50	5.70	-
1962-63	7	6.50	6.50	-
1953-61	9	19.00	14.50	-
1924-51	12	89.00	57.00	45.00
1961-67	Phosphor Sets 132	105	-	

SPECIAL
1953 Coronation Complete to Christmas 1970
U/M £42.50 VFU £42.95

DAUWALDERS
42 Fisherton Street,
Salisbury SP2 7RB
Tel: 01722 412100
Fax: 01722 410074
www.worldstamps.co.uk
Email: sales@worldstamps.co.uk

NB: * Year Sets include miniature sheets where issued, but excludes "Greetings" books and 'a' number issues. *** Includes Greetings stamps from sheets, excludes perforation varieties.

Advertisers Index